WRIT MEDICO-LEGAL REPORTS IN CIVIL CLAIMS

an essential guide

Giles Eyre and Lynden Alexander

Published by Professional Solutions Publications

This edition published in 2011 by Professional Solutions Publications
Atlas Chambers, 3 Field Court, London WC1R 5EP

Professional Solutions Publications is an imprint of: Professional Solutions Learning and
Development (www.prosols.uk.com)

Typeset in Minion Pro and Century Gothic by
Karen Arnott, Graphic Designer, 14a High Street, West Wratting, Cambridge. CB21 5LU.
(www.karenarnott.co.uk)

EDITORS' NOTE: The views set out in this text are those of the authors alone. Whilst
great care has been taken in connection with the preparation of this work, no liability
whatsoever can be accepted in respect of the material contained herein by the authors or
publishers. The reader is directed to the legislation, case law and other primary materials
referred to in the text. Medical opinion used in this book is provided only for the purpose
of illustrating medico-legal principles and the authors do not put forward the medical
opinions expressed as definitive of medical opinion.

ISBN 978-0-9569341-0-9

A Cataloguing-in-Publication record is available for this book from the British Library.

Authors

Giles Eyre

Giles Eyre is a barrister practising from 9 Gough Square, London (www.9goughsquare.co.uk). Giles has extensive experience in conducting and advising in personal injury, industrial disease and clinical negligence claims. He is a Recorder and a mediator on the CEDR Solve Lead Mediators Panel.

Giles regularly presents seminars for lawyers on a wide variety of topics, and for medical practitioners on effective report writing and giving evidence. He is a contributing editor of Asbestos Claims: Law, Practice and Procedure, published by 9 Gough Square (2nd edition April 2011) and Clinical Negligence Claims - A Practical Guide, published by 9 Gough Square (2nd edition April 2011)

Lynden Alexander

Lynden Alexander is a communication skills consultant who specialises in forensic communication. He leads the expert witness programme at Professional Solutions Learning and Development (www.prosols.uk.com).

He began offering training to medical experts in 1996 and has since trained more than 5000 expert witnesses in forensic writing and courtroom presentation skills. He also presents workshops on expert witness skills for the Expert Witness Institute and other professional bodies. Before working in the field of forensic communication, he was a Eurobond and Equity Derivatives trader in the City of London.

Acknowledgements

We would like to thank James Badenoch QC for his careful reading and insightful comments and suggestions that have added immensely to the text. We also thank him for his willingness to invest the considerable reputation of the Expert Witness Institute in this work by contributing to the foreword.

We would also like to thank Sir Roger Vickers for adding some much needed medical perspective on this book with his own contribution to the foreword.

We are grateful to Dr Kenneth Gulleford and Dr Dominic Heaney for their careful reading and detailed criticism of the text, which has been much improved by their efforts. It perhaps goes without saying that any mistakes that remain in the text remain entirely the fault of the authors.

Contents

			Authors	
			Acknowledgements	
			Contents	
			Foreword	i
			Authors' Note	iii
			Picture of Kuthodaw Pagoda, Mandalay, Burma	iii
			Introduction to the Text	**v**
1			**Essential Qualities of Medical Experts**	**1**
	1.1		'Medico-Legal Mind'	2
	1.2		Role of the Expert Witness	3
	1.3		Medical Expert Reports	5
		1.3.1	Functions of Expert Reports	5
		1.3.2	Writing the Report	6
		1.3.3	Comparison of Medical Reports and Medical Expert Reports	7
	1.4		Dissatisfaction with Medical Expert Reports	8
		1.4.1	Consequences Arising from Sub-Standard Reporting	8
		1.4.2	Common Problems with Medical Expert Reports	9
	1.5		Commercial Realities of Litigation	11
		1.5.1	Imperative for Developing Evidential Skills	11
2			**Legal Context of a Civil Claim for Damages for Personal Injury**	**15**
	2.1		Purpose of a Civil Claim for Damages	16
	2.2		Legal Basis of a Claim	17
		2.2.1	Breach of Duty	18
		2.2.2	Injury, Loss or Damage	19
		2.2.3	Causation	19
		2.2.4	Contributory Negligence	20
	2.3		Adversarial Litigation Process	20
	2.4		Proof	21
	2.5		Damages: Underlying Principle	21
	2.6		Types of Claim for Damages	22
		2.6.1	Non-Pecuniary Loss	23
		2.6.2	Pecuniary Loss	23
		2.6.3	Death	24
		2.6.4	Possible Future Complications and Provisional Damages	25
	2.7		Valuation of the Claim	26
		2.7.1	Non-Pecuniary Loss	26
		2.7.2	Pecuniary Loss	27
		2.7.3	Future Pecuniary Loss	27
	2.8		Costs of Litigation – Why Winning Matters	29
		2.8.1	Conditional Fee Agreements	30
		2.8.2	Part 36 – Offers to Settle	31

3			**Progression of a Claim**	**35**
	3.1		Civil Procedure Rules 1998	36
		3.1.1	Court Managed Litigation	37
	3.2		Structure of the CPR	38
		3.2.1	Overriding Objective	38
		3.2.2	Court Management	39
	3.3		Pre-Action Protocols	40
		3.3.1	Pre-Action Protocol for the Resolution of Clinical Disputes	42
		3.3.2	Pre-Action Protocol for Personal Injury Claims	44
		3.3.3	Pre-Action Protocol for Disease and Illness Claims	47
	3.4		Low Value Personal Injury Claims in Road Traffic Accidents	48
	3.5		Commencement of Proceedings	49
		3.5.1	Tracks	50
	3.6		Court Directions	52
	3.7		Court Control of Expert Evidence	52
		3.7.1	Purpose of Expert Evidence	53
		3.7.2	The Court's Powers	53
		3.7.3	Limiting Experts' Fees	54
	3.8		Legal Professionals Involved in a Case	54
		3.8.1	Role of the Solicitor	55
		3.8.2	Role of the Barrister	55
		3.8.3	Role of the Judge	56
	3.9		Judge's Approach to Conflicting Expert Evidence	57
4			**Roles and Duties of the Expert Witness**	**61**
	4.1		Duties of Experts	62
		4.1.1	The Expert as Fact Finder	62
		4.1.2	GMC Guidance	63
		4.1.3	CPR Part 35	64
		4.1.4	Narrowing the Area of Dispute	65
		4.1.5	Independence	65
		4.1.6	Duty to Co-Operate with the Court Process	69
		4.1.7	Investigating Claims	70
		4.1.8	Restriction on Expert Evidence	70
		4.1.9	Form of Expert Evidence	71
	4.2		Content of Expert Reports	71
		4.2.1	Instructions	74
		4.2.2	Details of Qualifications	76
		4.2.3	Literature	78
		4.2.4	Factual Basis of the Evidence	79
		4.2.5	Incident/Accident Details and Subsequent Events	81
		4.2.6	Examination Findings	82
		4.2.7	Factual Disputes	83

	4.2.8	Disputes between Medical Records and the Claimant's Account	84
	4.2.9	Opinion Evidence	86
	4.2.10	Fact and Opinion	86
	4.2.11	Qualified Opinion	86
	4.2.12	Range of Opinion	87
	4.2.13	Summary of Conclusions	89
	4.2.14	Expert's Declaration	90
	4.2.15	Statement of Truth	90
4.3		Amendments to Reports	91
4.4		Written Questions to Experts	94
	4.4.1	Format for the Response	96
4.5		Single Joint Experts	96
	4.5.1	Comparison of a Single Joint Expert and a Jointly Selected Expert	98
	4.5.2	Status of a Single Joint Expert's Report	99
4.6		Court Orders	99
	4.6.1	Notice of Court Orders	100
	4.6.2	Seeking Directions from the Court	100
4.7		The Joint Discussion (or Meeting of Experts)	101
	4.7.1	Object of the Discussion and the Expert's Role	102
	4.7.2	Agenda for the Discussion	103
	4.7.3	People Present at the Meeting of Experts	105
	4.7.4	The Joint Statement	105
	4.7.5	Status of the Discussion and Agreement at Trial	106
5		**Proof**	109
5.1		Civil Standard of Proof	110
	5.1.1	Applying the Standard of Proof	112
	5.1.2	Differential Decisions	114
5.2		Decision-Making in Civil Litigation	114
5.3		Applying 'On the Balance of Probabilities'	115
5.4		Establishing Proof	117
6		**Opinion Evidence**	121
6.1		Causation of Damage	122
	6.1.1	Competing Causes of Injury	125
	6.1.2	Material Contribution	126
6.2		Giving Opinions on Causation	126
	6.2.1	Causation Graphs	127
	6.2.2	'Egg-Shell Skull' Principle and Causation	130
	6.2.3	Use of Percentages	130
	6.2.4	Questions about Percentages	133
6.3		Industrial Disease Claims and 'Material Contribution'	134
	6.3.1	Application of Material Contribution Test to Complex Factual Situations	135
	6.3.2	Apportionment of Damages	138
	6.3.3	Approach to the Evidence	140

6.4		'Acceleration' and 'Exacerbation'	141
	6.4.1	Differences in Valuation	146
6.5		Prognosis and Future Risk	148
	6.5.1	Use of Percentages	149
	6.5.2	Use of Dates	150
	6.5.3	Clinician's Approach to the Future	151
	6.5.4	Using Percentages in Opinions on Prognosis	152
	6.5.5	Life Expectancy	154
6.6		Consequences of Injuries	155
	6.6.1	Addressing Consequential Loss	155
	6.6.2	Consequences to Assess	157
	6.6.3	Pain and Suffering, and Loss of Amenity	157
	6.6.4	Medical or Therapeutic Treatment	158
	6.6.5	Care and Assistance	158
	6.6.6	Current Employment	159
	6.6.7	Future Employment and 'Ogden 6'	161
	6.6.8	Life Expectancy	163
	6.6.9	Additional Housing, Mobility or Transportation Needs	163
	6.6.10	Restrictions on Activities of Daily Living	164
	6.6.11	Restrictions on Domestic, Recreational, Social or Sporting Activities	164
7		**Opinion Evidence in Complex Claims**	**171**
7.1		Difficulties in Diagnosis	172
	7.1.1	Approach to the Evidence	173
7.2		Linking the Injury to its Cause	175
	7.2.1	Approach to the Evidence	175
7.3		Competing Factual Scenarios	178
	7.3.1	Approach to the Evidence	179
7.4		Exaggeration and Malingering	180
	7.4.1	Exaggeration	180
	7.4.2	Malingering	180
	7.4.3	Approach to the Evidence	181
	7.4.4	Observations Outside the Medical Examination	182
	7.4.5	Observations Within the Medical Examination	183
7.5		Surveillance Evidence	186
7.6		Seat Belts and Contributory Negligence	188
7.7		Multi-Accident Claims	190
	7.7.1	Applying Causation Graphs	191
	7.7.2	Approach to the Evidence	194
	7.7.3	Cumulative Effects Cases	198
7.8		Breaking the Chain of Causation	199
	7.8.1	Approach to the Evidence	200
7.9		Criticism of Medical Treatment in a Personal Injury Claim	201
	7.9.1	Approach to the Evidence	202
7.10		Cases that Rely on Expertise	204

		7.10.1	Structure for a 'Difficult' Opinion	205
8			**Clinical Negligence – Legal Principles**	**211**
	8.1		Legal Principles in Clinical Negligence Claims	212
		8.1.1	The 'Bolam Test'	212
		8.1.2	Approach to the Evidence – Applying the Bolam Test	214
		8.1.3	Use of the Terms 'Negligent' or 'Negligence'	217
	8.2		Level of Skill Required – Novices and Specialists	217
		8.2.1	Novices	217
		8.2.2	Specialists	219
	8.3		Consent and Failure to Warn	219
		8.3.1	Failure to Warn	220
	8.4		Failure to Treat	222
	8.5		Conflicting Opinion on Factual Issues	222
	8.6		Conflicting Opinion on Standard of Care	223
	8.7		Causation and 'Material Contribution'	225
9			**Reporting in Clinical Negligence Claims**	**231**
	9.1		Clinical Negligence Marketplace	232
	9.2		Purpose of Expert Reports in Clinical Negligence Cases	233
	9.3		Areas of Potential Difficulty in Clinical Negligence	234
		9.3.1	Hindsight and Focus Bias	235
		9.3.2	Establishing the Factual Basis of the Claim	237
		9.3.3	Factual Disputes in the Evidence	238
		9.3.4	Series of Events	240
		9.3.5	Complex Medical Issues	244
10			**Writing the Report**	**251**
	10.1		Presentation of the Report	252
	10.2		Expert Report Structures	253
		10.2.1	Linear Report Structure	253
		10.2.2	Modular Report Structure	255
		10.2.3	Report Templates	257
		10.2.4	Presenting Evidence in a Logical Order	258
	10.3		Writing Skills	260
		10.3.1	Writing for the Court	261
		10.3.2	Providing Technical Explanations	261
		10.3.3	Using Descriptive Language	267
		10.3.4	Using Modal Auxiliary Verbs	269
		10.3.5	Addressing the Standard of Proof and Relevant Legal Tests	271
	10.4		Writing Opinion	273
		10.4.1	Long-Form Opinion	275
		10.4.2	Short-Form Opinion	276
			Appendices	**281**
1 (a)			Personal Injury Report Template – Physical Injuries	282
1 (b)			Personal Injury Report Template – Psychological/	

	Psychiatric Injuries	283
1 (c)	Personal Injury Report Template – Industrial Disease	284
1 (d)	Clinical Negligence Report Template	292
2	Report Checklist	296
3	CPR Part 35	299
4	Practice Direction to Part 35	306
5	Protocol for the Instruction of Experts to give Evidence in Civil Claims	313
6	GMC Guidance – Acting as an Expert Witness	326
7	Example of a Schedule of Loss	330

Foreword

This is an important and admirable book. It is thorough, lucid and extremely practical and is a manual of all that medical expert witnesses need to know about their proper role in the justice system, and about the law and practice in civil litigation.

The overwhelming majority of medical experts are aware of their duty to the court and many regard their understanding as sufficient for the role of expert witness. In this guide, the authors ask experts to go further, by understanding the expert's duty to the court in the context of both the wider processes of the civil justice system, as codified by the Civil Procedure Rules (CPR), and the legal principles upon which the civil law is founded. They argue that such an understanding enables experts to offer opinions that are more pertinent and more precise in dealing with the issues in dispute and are therefore more helpful to the court and the overriding objective of the CPR, 'to deal with cases justly'.

There is little doubt that medical experts are often faced with very difficult medico-legal issues to address and do their honest best to deal with these issues in a manner that complies with their duty to the court. However, many experts feel that there is a paucity of detailed guidance that they can refer to when dealing with such cases. This book offers an impressive level of detailed and practical guidance on how to deal with cases properly, from applying basic principles such as proof, breach of duty and causation through to extremely complex cases that involve both evidential and legal difficulty - cases in which medical experts need to possess a high level of technical skill in medico-legal practice. Throughout the text there are practical examples of helpful and unhelpful expert evidence when addressing such matters and these will no doubt prove to be an extremely useful starting point when considering the best way to report to the court.

The authors' purpose, brilliantly achieved, is to create a user-friendly guide to the perils and pitfalls of expert witness work, and to the ways and the means of making expert evidence most useful and most effective. It will I believe become the standard reference, and should be compulsory reading for all medical expert witnesses, and also for all lawyers who enlist, instruct and call them – in short it will be an invaluable resource for all who are concerned with medico-legal work.

James Badenoch Q.C.
Chairman of the Expert Witness Institute
1 Crown Office Row, Temple, London EC4Y 7HH

Giles Eyre and Lynden Alexander have written this excellent book with the aim of helping medical practitioners to write better medico-legal reports, in the form and with the clarity that lawyers and judges need.

It is not only a very practical guide to best practice in report writing, but it also sets out the law and the procedure which apply to personal injury, industrial disease and clinical negligence cases. The text is always expressed in clear and accessible terms and offers useful practical guidance on many of the difficult issues that arise in medico-legal practice.

Having just written my last medico-legal report, some thirty five years after the first - for the form of which I had to rely on advice from my then consultant's secretary - I welcome this book for the invaluable help it gives. How helpful it would have been at the start of my 'career' as an 'expert' to have been able to read and refer to it.

Sir Roger Vickers, KCVO, FRCS.
Previously, Consultant Orthopaedic Surgeon to St George's Hospital, London.
Council Member, Medical Defence Union.

Authors' Note

The Origin of "Foot-Wearing"

A holiday snap taken many years ago by Giles while in Mandalay, Burma, is the source for an informal technical term, 'Foot-Wearing'. This term we have come to use when discussing extracts from medical expert reports that defy a proper legal interpretation.

Kuthodaw Pagoda, Mandalay, Burma

Whilst most visitors to this particular temple complex are generally in awe of the sacred architecture, Giles found himself distracted by the sign at the entrance to the site. Intended to make clear to visitors unacceptable forms of behaviour, the sign became the subject of detailed lawyerly scrutiny and especially:

"Strictly Prohibited: Foot-Wearing"

Giles found this prohibition a little worrying. Glancing down to his feet, he found, sure enough, definite signs of Foot-Wearing. Unsure as to the proper interpretation of the prohibition and wary of local sensibilities, he decided to tread carefully and to remove his shoes (though not his feet). The visit passed without incident, not least because he had neither bicycle nor umbrella.

At this point, an analysis of the context for this attempt at communication is valuable. What to Giles appeared to be a succession of bubbles, would, to a Burmese, have made clear the writer's interdict. To the translator, bridging the expanse between the language of Burma and the language of the native English speaker, the prohibition was also clear. However, for Giles, comfortable only in his native English, guesses or assumptions had to be made as he sought to avoid causing offence.

Time passes and Giles is now to be found in chambers reading his daily dose of medico-legal reports:

> 'He should make a reasonable recovery from the effects of his injury over the next few years.'

> 'Although it is likely that there was some congenital weakness, the hernia was most probably the result of the heavy lifting in which he was involved.'

> '30% of his current symptoms are the result of his underlying condition and would have been present in any event, while 70% are attributable to the injury sustained in the accident'

> 'The accident has made symptomatic previously asymptomatic degenerative disease. The period of acceleration is about 3 to 5 years. As a result of these symptoms he has been unable to work.'

> 'His heavy cigarette smoking may be aggravating the extent and severity of his episodic finger whitening. I cannot rule out the possibility that this may be contributing to the neurological symptoms that he describes.'

Giles, in his role as a personal injury lawyer, finds these paragraphs as meaningful as 'No Foot-Wearing' when he was a tourist in Burma. These medico-legal paragraphs communicate to a lawyer that there is an issue to be considered, but beyond this, the interpretation relies heavily on guesswork. Yet, medical experts produce evidence of this quality on a daily basis without seeming to have any idea as to how defective this evidence actually is in medico-legal terms.

This poor standard of evidence has led to the frequent exhortation being made to medical experts (at least by Giles!) that in evidence, there should be "No Foot-Wearing!"

NO FOOT-WEARING!

The medical expert must ensure that the medical evidence is expressed in language that a lawyer can understand, without the need to make guesses or assumptions as to its meaning or its application to the case.

Introduction to the Text

The recent Supreme Court decision in *Jones v Kaney*[1] has placed the quality of medical expert reports firmly in the judicial spotlight. This landmark decision overturned the previous rule of law that gave experts immunity from being sued for negligence in the provision of expert evidence for the purposes of a civil claim for damages.

In his judgment, Lord Brown suggested that the removal of immunity would tend to ensure a greater degree of care in the preparation of the initial report and the joint report, as it is almost certain to be one of those reports rather than evidence in the witness box that will be the focus of any attack.[2] It is perhaps self-evident when we conclude that the quality of the expert report is now an issue that should be of the greatest concern to every expert throughout his/her involvement in a claim.

In the coming weeks and months, we will no doubt see the impact of this decision on the commissioning and provision of expert evidence and on the insurance premiums that professionals will ultimately have to pay to act as expert witnesses. However, it is clear that the low standard of practice of expert witnesses that has become common in the civil justice system can now be remedied by litigants by way of professional negligence claims.

---

1   [2011] UKSC 13

2   We consider this ruling further at Section 4.1.5 below.

Lawyers' Dissatisfaction with Medical Expert Reports

So, let us begin with the bad news: only a minority of those doctors who produce expert evidence in the civil courts actually understands how to produce the evidence in a manner that meets the requirements of the civil litigation process. The lawyers who use expert evidence on a daily basis often express deep concern at the present standard of such evidence, but fall into dissatisfied silence when asked how matters could be improved. It is undoubtedly true that most lawyers are unable to suggest any workable solution to the present problems they face with medical expert evidence.

At the root of the lawyers' dissatisfaction is an issue of the professional competence of medical experts. Producing medical expert evidence requires professional skills that lie beyond the boundaries of ordinary medical skill. Alas, a lack of the proper professional skills does not seem to inhibit doctors from accepting instructions to perform the role of expert witness or indeed instructing lawyers from accepting the sub-standard expert evidence that usually results.

In civil litigation, the parties in an action are encouraged to bring a claim to an expeditious settlement, or to a trial, without any undue delay or unnecessary costs being incurred. As expert evidence is often central to proving (or disproving) and quantifying a claim, it is of fundamental importance that all expert evidence – presented in the form of written reports – is clear, concise and reliable in all respects.

In such an environment, the quality of expert evidence – and for our purposes, *medical expert reports (a.k.a. medico-legal reports)* - would seem to be of such critical importance that no expert would take on the role without first developing the appropriate skills. However, the vast majority of doctors who produce expert evidence are not adequately skilled to properly fulfil the role. Most do so without first learning their duties and responsibilities as experts or the basic disciplines of writing expert reports. This general lack of appropriate skill has begun to reveal itself in an increasing number of high-profile cases, where highly regarded doctors have fallen short when performing the role of expert witness. Common to all of these cases is an underlying lack of forensic competence.

The Challenge of Medico-Legal Reporting

Amongst the many professionals who are instructed to provide expert evidence in civil claims, the role of the medical expert is particularly challenging: every injured person responds differently to a trauma; every person heals and recovers in a different way; and the consequences of a trauma are unique to each person. Where clinical negligence is claimed, the complexity of medical practice is combined with the difficulty of predicting what the outcome would have been had the clinical care been exemplary. In all such cases, the lawyers look to medical experts for answers, even when answers that are soundly based on medical proof are difficult or even impossible to establish.

The Civil Procedure Rules 1998 (CPR) - the rules that govern the conduct of litigation in the civil courts - place specific requirements on the form and content of expert reports. Each requirement is intended to help experts to deal with the difficult and complex issues that arise in disputes and to do so in a manner comprehensible to the lawyers and to the courts. However, the CPR cannot and never sought to address the legal concepts and practical issues that an expert has to encounter or confront when producing an expert report. Gaining such insight is the sole responsibility of the expert.

It is perhaps a little unfair to hold doctors solely responsible for the difficulties they have in understanding what lawyers actually require of their evidence. A communication void has undoubtedly developed between the medical and legal professions - even as each profession recognises that it does not understand the other, neither seems able to grasp quite why this is so. The present standard of medical expert evidence seems to indicate that somewhere in the midst of professional life two socio-economically equivalent groups, with similar standards of education, have lost the ability to communicate meaningfully with each other.

Improving Medico-Legal Communication

Now, let us move on to the good news: this guide is written to bridge this communication void and to provide medical experts with the practical help they need to deal with what can often be very difficult evidential issues.

Writing Medico-Legal Reports in Civil Claims: An Essential Guide will seek to achieve four aims:

1.   to help medical experts to understand the legal context and principles that should inform and guide the evidence they produce;

2.   to introduce the technical discipline of writing medical expert reports, offering skills and techniques to ensure that these reports are produced to the highest standards;

3.   to provide detailed medical expert report templates for personal injury, industrial disease and clinical negligence reports; and

4.   to provide examples of both good and inadequate medical expert report writing with explanatory notes on each.

In the past ten years, we have delivered workshops on writing medical expert reports to over two thousand expert witnesses – a majority being in the early stages of their medico-legal careers, with a significant minority being highly experienced.

Following these workshops, we have been approached on numerous occasions by highly experienced experts who have told us that, even after many years of writing medico-legal reports, they had not realised how much more they had still to learn. We have then faced the inevitable request for a good book on the subject and have simply been unable to recommend one.

In the end, we decided to write a guide that would deal with both the introductory and advanced needs of medical experts. The knowledge, skills and techniques detailed in this guide will provide both a robust theoretical framework and detailed practical guidance on how to write high-quality medical expert reports. It will also be valuable when reporting on many of the difficult issues that arise in civil cases.

It can be read from beginning to end, providing a step-by-step approach to the process of producing evidence, or can be used for reference whenever an expert is faced with a difficult issue and needs guidance on the best way to report on the matter. We have also provided end-of-chapter exercises to give the reader the opportunity to integrate the learning, with online resources to provide help and guidance where needed (available at www.prosols.uk.com/medico-legal).

We live in changing times

In this the first edition, we have attempted to state accurately the law as it is at 31 March 2011. However, the legal process, like the National Health Service, is forever changing. The stated driving force for change is, as always, the search for greater efficiency and the creation of a more user-friendly service provider.

The latest Government proposals in *'Reforming Civil Litigation Funding and Costs in England and Wales – Implementation of Lord Justice Jackson's Recommendations'* (March 2011) if carried out will result in:

1. a major overhaul of conditional fee agreements (see Section 2.8.1);

2. an increase in general damages of 10% (as some compensation for the proposed non-recoverability of success fees);

3. 'Qualified One Way Costs Shifting' so that a claimant would not normally be at risk of paying a defendant's costs in the event of losing (compare the present situation in Section 2.8);

4. changes in the CPR Part 36 procedure to increase the incentive for defendant's to settle claims (see Section 2.8.2);

5. the introduction of contingency fee agreements where a lawyer is paid out of the successful claimant's damages; and

6. further controls on the level of legal costs recoverable at the end of a claim.

Meanwhile, the relatively few cases in which a claimant is supported by public funding (Legal Aid), principally in clinical negligence, are likely shortly to disappear.

Alongside these proposals, the Government consultation paper *'Solving disputes in the county court – creating a simpler, quicker and more proportionate system – a consultation on reforming civil justice in England and Wales'* (March 2011) proposes the extension of the new procedure for low value personal injury claims in road traffic accidents (see Section 3.4) to all personal injury claims and the introduction of a scheme of fixed recoverable costs for claims under £25,000 (and possibly a higher level, and to include clinical negligence claims) with substantial increases in the maximum value of claims assigned to each track (see Section 3.5.1).

The time-scale for such changes, and their final form, is not yet known. We can only therefore offer two crumbs of comfort for the medical expert attempting to keep up-to-date with these changes. First, that change is an inherent quality of the civil justice system, so there will continue to be an ongoing drive to change the way civil claims are conducted. Secondly, you will be able to keep up-to-date with such changes through our online resources at www.prosols.uk.com/medico-legal.

We very much hope that you find this guide useful and that it will help you to avoid the many evidential pitfalls that lead to the charge of Foot-Wearing!

Giles Eyre and Lynden Alexander
1 June 2011

1

Essential Qualities of Medical Experts

1.1   'Medico-Legal Mind'
1.2   Role of the Expert Witness
1.3   Medical Expert Reports
1.4   Dissatisfaction with Medical Expert Reports
1.5   Commercial Realities of Litigation

Introduction

The skills needed to produce clear, concise and reliable medical expert evidence are fundamentally different from the skills needed to be successful in medical practice. When producing medical expert evidence, doctors must apply specific legal standards and tests to the opinions they express and must produce evidence that fulfils the requirements of the litigation process. They must also write for an audience with no medical expertise and only limited medical knowledge. The vast majority of medical experts in practice today do not fully understand what the lawyers and the court require of their evidence and so consistently produce evidence that does not meet the requirements of the litigation process.

Chapter Outline

In this chapter, we will provide an overview of the key issues that medical experts have to understand before they begin to write medical reports. We will introduce the concept of the 'medico-legal mind' and explore the specific abilities that developing this mind enables. We will introduce the role of medical experts within the litigation process and the status of their evidence. We will then discuss medical expert reports and how these differ from pure medical reports before moving on to explain the dissatisfaction that lawyers have with the quality of medical expert reports. Finally, we will explain the commercial realities that underpin the litigation process and the consequences that result for medical experts and the reports they produce.

1.1 'Medico-Legal Mind'

Medical experts give medical opinions within a legal context. It is, therefore, essential that medical experts understand the legal principles and precedents that show how the court will assess and evaluate their evidence. They must also learn the analytical and evidential writing skills necessary to communicate effectively with both their instructing lawyers and with the court. A medical expert will only achieve a sufficient level of professional competence as an expert when this knowledge and these skills have been properly developed.

To achieve professional competence as a medical expert, a doctor has to develop ways of thinking that are beyond the purely medical – to develop what we term a 'medico-legal mind'.[1]

There are seven key-qualities that distinguish experts who have developed a medico-legal mind. These experts are able to:

1. understand the duties of an expert witness and the specific requirements of expert evidence within the litigation process;

2. adopt an appropriate methodology to provide reliable evidence dealing with the medico-legal issues in dispute;

3. identify the factual matters relevant to a dispute and apply medical expertise to these facts in a logical and medically supportable way;

4. address all relevant medical issues that arise by providing opinions and conclusions that a lawyer can understand and engage with;

5. understand and apply, in every case, the civil standard of proof and the appropriate legal tests to the evidence;

---

1   A *Google* search, limited to the UK, for "medico-legal mind" produces 0 results – this expression is unique to this book and is not in common usage.

6.   understand how to assess and report on the consequences of an injury; and

7.   recognise that the fundamental purpose of medical expert evidence is to help the court to assess the validity of a compensation claim and the level of damages to be awarded.

In essence, competent medical experts are able to assess each medico-legal issue in a case, first applying their medical expertise or 'medical mind' to each issue and then placing their medical findings within a legal context by applying their medico-legal expertise or 'medico-legal mind'. This helps the court to more easily resolve a compensation claim.

Experts who have developed a medico-legal mind know that the strong medical emphasis on an evidence-based approach is important[2], but also understand that conclusive medical evidence is only useful and relevant if it can be gathered without incurring disproportionate cost and without the demand of invasive tests and procedures. The expert must also be able to work effectively knowing that in many cases no conclusive medical evidence or medical certainty will ever be established and must understand that medical certainty is never required for a civil case to be proved and for damages to be recovered.

Experts who have developed a medico-legal mind also know that in performing the role of an expert, they are required to express a clear and firm opinion on any issue where the evidence is capable of being assessed to the civil standard of proof, 'on the balance of probabilities'. This requirement holds even when no conclusive medical evidence is available to decide issues to a medical or scientific standard of certainty.

1.2   Role of the Expert Witness

The role of an expert witness is to help the court to decide issues that are beyond its technical knowledge or expertise. An expert has an overriding duty to the court to be independent and objective, no matter what pressure he/she may face from any party in the litigation.

The prevailing level of medical knowledge amongst lawyers and judges is at best rudimentary. Even in high-value and complex personal injury and clinical negligence claims, judges hearing cases are extremely unlikely to have any formal medical training or knowledge. The most carefully constructed and erudite medical expert evidence from a leading expert in his/her field will be of little practical use in the litigation process, unless it can be readily understood by an educated adult with a legal rather than a medical background. The ability to communicate complex medical matters in a clear manner to a lay audience is an essential skill for an expert to develop.

---

2   Any conclusive evidence that a medical-expert is able to present is likely to lead to a rapid settlement of a case.

Medical expert evidence has an elevated status when compared with the evidence of factual witnesses. Once a doctor has established his/her right to give expert evidence – by placing before the court details of his/her qualifications and relevant experience in respect of the medical issues in dispute – he/she can then give opinion evidence. Other witnesses, who are not experts, are not permitted to give opinion evidence and the court will stop any such witness who attempts to do so. With the elevated status an expert witness has in the litigation process and because the lawyers and the court have only a rudimentary knowledge of medical matters, lawyers and judges alike frequently surrender crucial elements of their decisions to the evidence of medical experts. In general, what is said by a medical expert (whether in an expert report or in oral evidence) will be accepted by a court - and everyone involved in the litigation process knows it.

It is essential, therefore, that medical experts remain within their specific area of expertise as doctors and that they should never adopt the attitude of a 'quasi-lawyer'. Medical experts can be assured that there will be enough qualified lawyers already involved in the litigation without their trying to join in as well.

The fundamental reason for instructing a medical expert is to bring medical expertise to the case, so it is essential that the medical expert always seeks guidance from the lawyers on any legal question or issue that may arise. This important distinction is perhaps most easily seen at the pre-trial meeting of experts, where the medical experts' role is not to achieve an acceptable compromise of the claim – this being the lawyers' role - but rather to identify whether any agreement on any of the medical aspects of the claim can be reached. Where this is not possible, the medical experts need to explain as clearly as possible the differences in opinion and, most importantly from the point of view of the lawyers, the reasons for these differences.[3]

A fundamental issue for medical experts to fully understand and engage with is that a claimant should never be regarded as being a patient. A medical expert does not owe a medical duty of care to a claimant, and is not meeting the claimant in order to treat him/her or to recommend appropriate treatment. The medical expert does not have the same professional relationship with a claimant as he/she has with a patient. In a doctor-patient relationship, the doctor owes an express duty of care to the patient. However, when reporting to the court the expert owes an overriding duty to assist the court beyond any contractual duty to the claimant or to the lawyers who have instructed the expert.

---

3   See Section 4.7 'The Joint Discussion'

1.3   Medical Expert Reports

Medical expert evidence is provided to the court in the form of a written report, known as an 'expert report'. Expert reports are an essential component of claims for personal injury, industrial disease, and clinical negligence and have a unique status within civil litigation. The maker of the expert report is assumed by the court, whether justifiably or not, to be giving objective unbiased opinion evidence. The court will also assume that the expert has assessed all material facts and has complied with the duties and responsibilities set out in the *Civil Procedure Rules 1998 (CPR)*.

Medical expert reports are fundamental in enabling the court to assess:

1. the injury, damage and loss caused by an accident, injury or other adverse event;

2. the damages claimed for pain and suffering and loss of amenity;

3. the damages for financial loss, both past and future; and

4. in clinical negligence cases, the duty of care owed to a patient by the medical practitioners involved in his/her care.

1.3.1   Functions of Expert Reports

In personal injury cases, medical expert reports dealing with condition and prognosis serve four functions:

1. to identify the factual basis relevant to the medical aspects of the claim;

2. to identify the nature of the injury;

3. to provide expert opinion on the causation of the claimant's injuries; and

4. to provide expert opinion on the consequences arising from the claimant's injuries.

In industrial disease cases, in addition to the functions of a personal injury report, the expert may also be required to address whether the injury was 'reasonably foreseeable' or whether exposure to a substance made a 'material contribution' to the injuries or condition that is the subject of the claim.[4]

---

4   See Section 6.3

In clinical negligence cases, the parties need to obtain medical expert reports on breach of duty and causation to establish whether there is a basis for a claim for damages. Medical expert reports dealing with breach of duty and causation serve three functions:

1. to identify the factual basis relevant to the medical aspects of the claim;

2. to establish the duty of care owed by the defendant to the claimant and whether this duty of care has been breached; and

3. to establish the causation of the medical injuries sustained.[5]

Medical expert reports need to fulfil these functions in a clear, concise and reliable manner. Only then can the lawyers involved in the case make high-quality decisions about pursuing or settling the case and, should the case reach court, allow the judge to weigh up the evidence appropriately.

1.3.2 Writing the Report

It is essential that the expert understands how the report will be used by the lawyers and the court, and what specific issues the report needs to address. The expert must also be clear on the standard of proof and the legal test that the court will apply to each opinion, so that the expert can express his/her opinion in language that the lawyers and the court can accurately interpret and assess. The expert report needs therefore to:

1. establish the facts relevant to the medical aspects of the claim;

2. give clear opinions on all relevant issues;

3. support these opinions with clear and informed reasoning; and

4. apply to each opinion the civil standard of proof and the appropriate legal test.

Most experts are aware of their responsibilities in respect of identifying the medical aspects of a claim, but continue to have problems with the medico-legal aspects that the report needs to address. In personal injury reports, difficulties commonly arise when dealing with causation, prognosis and the consequences of the injuries, while in clinical negligence reports, issues arise with causation, breach of duty and factual conflicts in the evidence. In industrial disease claims, causation and the legal tests to be applied create most difficulty.

---

5   Clinical negligence reports dealing with causation are often obtained by the parties first, as this is where most clinical negligence actions founder. Reports on condition and prognosis are usually obtained at a later stage in the litigation process.

1.3.3 Comparison of Medical Reports and Medical Expert Reports

The duties of an expert are fundamentally different to those of a treating clinician and the differences between the medical expert report and the medical report reflect this difference in duties.

A medical expert report is not a medical report about a patient, addressing the health of a patient and appropriate treatment. A medical expert report about a claimant is prepared for the purposes of litigation to address whether or not the claimant is entitled to recover damages and if so, how much. It is also a report that may be subjected to close analysis and criticism – rarely the case with a medical report – and which must comply with and show understanding of numerous legal rules.

Let us summarise the differences between a medical report and a medical expert report:

	MEDICAL REPORTS	MEDICAL EXPERT REPORTS
1	Written about a patient	Written about a claimant
2	Written for a medically qualified readership	Written for a non-medically qualified readership
3	Used in medical treatment	Used in litigation to assess the validity of a compensation claim
4	Deals with clinical issues	Deals with medico-legal issues
5	Supportive of a patient	Independent assessment of a claimant
6	Emphasises positive or potentially positive outcomes	Assesses likely outcomes objectively
7	Supportive of clinical colleagues	Willing to criticise clinicians (if required to do so)

A high-quality medical expert report that deals fully with all of the relevant issues is easier and quicker to write than an inadequate report. Struggling to deal properly with the relevant medico-legal issues takes far more time than dealing with them accurately, clearly and concisely - a well-written report is often half the length of an inadequate report.

The vast majority of civil cases are settled based on the written evidence of one or more medical experts. The accuracy and clarity of the expert report are critical to the litigation process. The quality of the communication – "the words on the page" – really matters.

1.4   Dissatisfaction with Medical Expert Reports

Lawyers express a high-degree of dissatisfaction with the quality of medical expert reports. Amongst lawyers, medical experts and the medical expert reports they produce are frequently criticised for their lack of forensic understanding. It is a common occurrence for a lawyer to be asked by a colleague to recommend a "good expert" in a particular field and to be unable to provide even one name. Even seeking an expert who can deliver an acceptable standard of report elicits the names of a very few.

Based on 30 years of professional practice, reading medical expert reports on a daily basis, we assess that 90% of these reports are not written to an acceptable professional standard. The vast majority of medical expert reports do not deal accurately or clearly with the matters that the lawyers need to have addressed and that the legal process requires to be addressed. This includes reports written by medical experts who believe themselves to be familiar with the process and who have much experience of writing expert reports.

1.4.1   Consequences Arising from Sub-Standard Reporting

The consequence for the parties to the litigation of inadequate medical evidence is that a claim will ultimately be settled or decided at an incorrect value, whether it is the claimant who gets less than a fair level of compensation or the insurance company or health care provider that has to pay out too much. A failure by an expert to comply with the CPR may also result in the instructing party being penalised in costs, and in extreme cases, may result in the court refusing to allow the medical evidence to be given in evidence at all – with disastrous results for the instructing party.

The consequence for the medical experts of inadequate reports is that their expectations of repeat instructions may fail to be realised. Questions of clarification may also arrive many months or even years after they have examined claimants and filed case papers and reports away. With little memory of the case, experts are then required to address issues they had not previously considered to be relevant, or are asked to re-address issues in a manner they had not previously thought to be necessary or even appropriate.

The professional consequences for medical experts of providing inadequate medical evidence are also potentially serious. Apart from failing to provide a proper professional standard of service to their clients, experts may face possible complaints before their professional bodies.[6] The expert is at risk of being sued by the instructing party for damages resulting from an unacceptable standard of practice[7] or of being made liable for wasted costs.[8] Where an expert has provided an inadequate report to an unsuccessful party in litigation, that party may be required to pay additional costs to the winning side if the expert has been severely criticised for failing to address his/her responsibilities or to conduct him/herself properly as an expert witness.[9] If an inadequate report is provided to a successful party in litigation, then that party may be denied recovery of all or some of its costs. In both these situations, there would be a consequent potential claim against the medical expert for the resulting loss.

It takes only one instance of judicial criticism of an expert's performance in court or of an expert's failure to comply with his/her duty as a medico-legal expert to destroy a reputation and therefore a medico-legal practice. Judgments are frequently available on the internet and those that are not are often shared between lawyers through various professionally directed websites or more informally through their own databases. Several examples of such judgments are referred to in the course of this book.

> If a medical expert is unwilling to go to court to defend his/her opinion under cross-examination, then he/she should not be performing the role of expert witness at all. Having expert evidence tested in court is a fundamental part of the litigation process.

1.4.2 Common Problems with Medical Expert Reports

A medical expert report must address those matters that the law and the legal process require to be addressed, applying those legal tests that the law requires to be applied and directed towards the legal principles relevant to the issues in the case.

---

6   *GMC v Meadow* [2006] EWCA Civ 1390

7   See Section 4.1.5 below

8   See *Phillips v Symes* [2004] EWHC 2330 in which an expert who caused significant expense to be incurred in 'flagrant and reckless disregard' of his duties to the court was penalised by paying costs so wasted.

9   *Williams v Jervis* [2009] EWHC 1837

Let us now identify the issues that commonly cause difficulties for medical experts, and ultimately for the lawyers who instruct them, when writing expert reports:

1. applying clearly, unambiguously and comfortably the civil standard of proof and appropriate legal tests to the evidence;

2. identifying and explaining the nature of the injury sustained and, where appropriate and necessary, explaining the interrelation between physical and psychological symptoms or causes;

3. identifying what injuries have been suffered or caused by the accident and explaining what difference this accident or injury has made to the claimant (i.e. causation);

4. describing and explaining complex progression or recovery from injuries following an accident and the symptoms and effects[10] experienced by the claimant during each stage of the progression or recovery;

5. dealing with the range of expert opinion on a matter;

6. dealing with a claimant's inconsistent, non-organic or exaggerated symptoms;

7. addressing the 'restrictions on activities' consequent on the injury - since the accident, at present and for the future;

8. addressing prognosis and future risks and relating these to potential future consequences;

9. distinguishing appropriately between the consequences of more than one accident or incident;

10. providing a measured balance between explaining the medicine and overwhelming the lawyer with medical terminology;

11. (in clinical negligence) explaining clearly, in terms that a lawyer can understand, what constitutes an appropriate standard of medical care; and

12. using the English language in a way that enables the lawyers to understand a clear and precise message – No Foot-Wearing![11]

In the chapters that follow, we will address the knowledge and writing skills needed to resolve each of these issues.

---

10   We discuss the medico-legal use of the terms 'injuries', 'symptoms', 'effects' and 'consequences' in Section 6.1 below.

11   For an explanation of "Foot-Wearing" see the Authors' Note and the Introduction to the Text above

1.5 Commercial Realities of Litigation

The vast majority of personal injury claims in which medical reports are obtained are settled by negotiation before they arrive at court – perhaps 98% of all claims that are intimated. 50% of litigated claims in the County Court (where the majority of proceedings are issued) are for damages under £5,000 and 80% are for under £15,000.[12] Fewer than 4% of issued claims are stated to be for over £50,000.

Most personal injury claims settle on the basis of the untested written word of one or more medical experts. This may be because there is only one expert dealing with a particular area of expertise or because the parties compromise in relation to the differences between two similar experts. Medical evidence will be necessary in all such claims in order to assess their value, but in a majority of cases, the time that can economically be justified by the lawyers for careful analysis of these reports will be minimal. Most personal injury claims are therefore processed quickly in something akin to a production line. The financial pressures on solicitors mean that this production line is often manned by trained but legally unqualified staff. With most claims settling prior to trial, it is rare for a medical expert in a personal injury claim to have a report scrutinised under cross-examination.

Similarly, most clinical negligence claims are settled without a court hearing.[13] Many such claims resolve around the issue of whether it can be proved that any claimed negligence has made a difference to outcome. Although by the nature and value of these claims there is an increased opportunity to give close attention to the expert reports (compared with most personal injury claims), it is still unusual for the evidence of the medical experts to be tested in court.

1.5.1 Imperative for Developing Evidential Skills

Medical expert reports are written in a communication void in which it can be readily – but wrongly – assumed that the lack of comment from the lawyers arises from their satisfaction with the report. Medical experts rarely receive comments on difficulties with their reports, such as a difficulty with understanding the content of the report or a difficulty applying the report to the required legal principles relevant to the claim. Rarely will medical experts receive notification from the lawyers on the settlement of a claim and the role in that settlement that their evidence played. As with any process that exists without feedback, mistakes will be repeated and dysfunctional aspects of professional practice soon become 'the way it is done'.

An unforeseen consequence of solicitors' economic imperatives and the court's desire that parties settle rather than come to court is that the medical expert – even an expert who is not achieving an appropriate level of professional practice – has been given what is frequently an unassailable and pivotal role in the legal process.

---

12   Judicial and Court Statistics 2009

13   The experience of the National Health Service Litigation Authority (NHSLA) is that typically less than 4% of claims where a formal letter of claim is received "go to court" – NHSLA Annual report and Accounts 2009/10

The legal profession has unwittingly surrendered much of the task of assessing the strength and the value of a claim to medical experts who often have little understanding of what is actually required. Currently, much of the responsibility for achieving a just settlement in medical cases has been placed upon the medical expert and it is an urgent imperative that medical experts develop their forensic skills in order to ensure a professional approach to meeting that responsibility.

Conclusion

A medical expert has to express his/her medical expertise within the context of the litigation process. This involves developing knowledge and skills beyond ordinary medical practice in order to engage with the medico-legal aspects of a claim for compensation. It is also essential that the expert understands his/her role and duties as an expert witness and the specific requirements of expert evidence. Being able to produce high-quality expert reports is fundamental to the expert's role in the litigation process, as the commercial realities of litigation have placed greater importance on the role of the medical expert.

Key-Point Summary

1. Medical experts need to develop (medico-legal) knowledge and skills beyond those that are required in medical practice.

2. The overriding duty of a medical expert is to the court, not to the instructing party.

3. Medical experts must produce objective and unbiased evidence and must act as professionals who are independent of the parties.

4. There is great dissatisfaction amongst lawyers at the quality of medical expert evidence - an absence of feedback is not the same as client satisfaction.

5. The lawyers and the court give great weight to the evidence of medical expert witnesses.

Next Steps

In the next chapter, we will explore the essential legal principles that underlie a compensation claim for damages.

Developing Your Medico-Legal Mind (1)

1. Have you defined your business goals for building a medico-legal practice? Specifically, have you addressed the following questions:

    *   How many reports would you like to write each week/month?
    *   What types and complexity of cases do you want to report upon?
    *   Do you wish to report on clinical negligence cases?
    *   What will you charge per hour (or per report)?
    *   Have you set out clearly your terms of business?
    *   Have you got the correct insurance to practice as a medico-legal expert?
    *   Have you decided on a marketing strategy to develop your profile in the medico-legal arena?

2. Have you accepted, in your own mind, the limitations of the civil litigation process and the fundamentally different role a medical expert has to perform when producing reports on compensation claims?

3. Are you willing to commit time and energy to developing your skills as an expert witness, including gaining membership of relevant professional bodies and attending medico-legal training and CPD events?

4. Have you defined your professional goals in seeking to build a medico-legal practice? Specifically, have you addressed the following questions:

    *   How will your medico-legal practice integrate with your work as a clinician?
    *   Are you considering doing any research or to publish any papers to raise your profile in your area of expertise?
    *   What skills beyond the purely clinical would you like to develop as part of your medico-legal practice?

2

Legal Context of a Civil Claim for Damages for Personal Injury

2.1   Purpose of a Civil Claim for Damages
2.2   Legal Basis of a Claim
2.3   Adversarial Litigation Process
2.4   Proof
2.5   Damages: Underlying Principle
2.6   Types of Claim for Damages
2.7   Valuation of the Claim
2.8   Costs of Litigation – Why Winning Matters

Introduction

The foundations of the medico-legal mind are constructed from the relevant legal rules and procedures applicable to the claim. Yet medical experts often admit to having only a vague understanding of the legal rules and procedures that are essential to bringing a civil claim for damages for personal injury. These legal rules and procedures not only affect the instructions that medical experts receive from their instructing solicitors, but also the nature of the evidence that experts need to provide to the court. It is essential when performing the role of medical expert that the expert understands the fundamental issues facing the lawyers in bringing or defending a claim and ensures that the expert report deals fully with all relevant issues.

Chapter Outline

In this chapter, we will place the role of the medical expert within the context of a civil claim for damages for personal injury, which includes claims in clinical negligence and for industrial disease.[1] We will see how such claims are made, what the claim consists of and the issues that are of concern to the parties and their lawyers. We will also explore how medical expert evidence plays an essential role in the litigation process.

2.1   Purpose of a Civil Claim for Damages

The purpose of a civil claim arising out of personal injury suffered as a result of an accident, clinical negligence or from industrial disease is to achieve financial compensation – known as 'damages'. Claimants use civil litigation as a method of recovering damages, while defendants actively seek to absolve themselves of responsibility or to limit the level of damages they may be required to pay.

Sometimes, there are non-financial issues at stake, particularly from a claimant's viewpoint, such as seeking:

- an apology or acceptance of responsibility by a defendant;
- a change of working practice in businesses or hospitals (or wherever) to ensure that no one else suffers in the same way;
- an acknowledgement that the claimant's injuries and physical complaints are real;
- the re-education or retraining of the person seen as at fault; or even
- retribution and revenge.

Although these non-financial issues may be a key to what fires the litigation for the claimant, and may make achieving a settlement more difficult, these issues will never be resolved in court or by the direct act of legal proceedings. The only instrument of civil justice is the award of money. In most cases, the claimant is interested in what money can be recovered and the more the claimant recovers, the more satisfied with the system the claimant tends to be.

The defendant is normally an insurer, or in a clinical negligence claim, an NHS Trust or medical defence organisation. For sound commercial and ethical reasons, defendants are concerned to ensure that the award of damages is the lowest that can reasonably be made, so as to protect their own interests. Defendants may also occasionally have an ulterior motive, perhaps where the view is taken at an early

---

1   The term 'personal injury' is widely used in two different ways. Technically, every compensation claim that arises from an injury to a person gives rise to 'a personal injury claim' – there is no differentiation of injuries arising from an industrial disease, an act of clinical negligence or even a 'slip and trip'. However, lawyers and doctors also commonly refer to 'a personal injury claim' to specify a claim that deals with an accident, rather than industrial disease or an injury arising from clinical negligence. We use the term in both of these ways throughout this book and offer explanation where the sense we intend is unclear.

stage that the claim is fabricated or exaggerated or that it is necessary to discourage the particular type of claim that is being made. In such circumstances, commercial reasoning (the balance of risk against cost) may take a backseat to a desire to expose a fraud or to send a clear message to other potential claimants.

The parties' lawyers will have interests similar to those of the parties themselves, although in the case of the claimant's lawyers, with less emphasis on the non-financial issues (i.e. apology, acceptance of responsibility, change in systems for the future etc). Generally, the party seen as the loser at the conclusion of the claim has to pay the costs incurred in the claim by both parties. Given the very considerable sums likely to be incurred in costs – court fees, the costs of the lawyers, the costs of the medical experts, and all of the ancillary costs in making a claim – winning is vital.

Winning means that a party recovers its own costs and is not liable for the costs of the other side. However, it is possible to recover damages, but in particular circumstances still be regarded as the loser because the liability for costs outweighs the damages recovered.[2]

2.2   Legal Basis of a Claim

Suffering an injury does not provide an automatic right to recover compensation. Damages will only be awarded to compensate for provable loss caused by a breach of duty of care - a legally imposed duty of care or a statutory duty – owed to the claimant by the defendant. To succeed in a claim for damages for personal injury, it is necessary for the claimant to prove:

1.   that the defendant is in breach of a duty owed to the claimant;

2.   that injury, loss or damage has been caused to the claimant (sufficient to form the basis of a claim in law) as a result of the breach of duty; and

3.   the nature and extent of the injury, loss or damage sustained.

---

2   See the discussion of Part 36 offers at Section 2.8.2 below

In response, the defendant may deny:

1. the existence of a legal duty;

2. the duty has been breached;

3. any breach has caused injury, loss or damage; and

4. the damage sustained is as great as that claimed.

The defendant may assert any one or more or even all of these points. In addition, the defendant may allege that the claimant is partly to blame for the injury as a result of his/her acts or defaults (contributory negligence) or that the claimant has failed to take reasonable steps to minimise his/her loss or damage (or both).

2.2.1   Breach of Duty

In the areas of personal injury, clinical negligence and industrial disease claims, a breach of duty will normally arise because of:

1. negligence or a breach of statutory duty (or both); or

2. a breach of a term of a contract.

Negligence is the failure to take reasonable care to prevent foreseeable injury to a person whom the law regards as being within a category of persons to whom such a legal duty is owed. For example, the motorist owes such a duty to other road users; the employer owes such a duty to employees or others over whose work he/she has sufficient control; a medical practitioner owes such a duty to patients.

Statutory duties exist in many areas. They are created by primary legislation (Acts of Parliament) and secondary legislation (Statutory Instruments). For example, occupiers of land owe a duty to take reasonable care of visitors under the Occupiers' Liability Act 1957 and a more limited duty to trespassers under the Occupiers' Liability Act 1984.

Employers are required to take measures to prevent injury to employees and others under the Health and Safety at Work (Etc.) Act 1974 and a wide range of statutory instruments. A breach of statutory duty that results from a failure to comply with the requirements of a statutory instrument may give rise to criminal proceedings as well as to a civil claim in damages.

A term of a contract, the breach of which may give rise to a claim, may be a written term of a contractual agreement or may be a term implied by law, such as is the case in an employer/employee relationship or in a doctor/patient relationship when receiving private medical care.

In most personal injury claims – typically, car accidents, slip and trips or workplace accidents - the issue of breach of duty is not a matter for expert medical evidence. However, breach of duty is a matter central to the role of medical experts in clinical negligence claims, where patients are owed a duty of care by the clinicians who treat them. Medical expert evidence is essential in helping the court to decide what the particular duty is and whether it has been breached by the clinicians involved.[3]

There are also situations in the area of workplace or industrial disease claims, where medical evidence may contribute to considerations of the relevant standard of care and the foreseeability of injury in exposing employees to potentially hazardous agents. These would include chemicals, vibration, dust or noise, or exposure to unusual or repetitive activities. Psychologists or psychiatrists may be asked to address the 'reasonable foreseeability' of psychiatric illness arising from exposure of the claimant to particular situations or stressors.

2.2.2   Injury, Loss or Damage

The injury (the term to include a medical condition or disease), loss or damage suffered by the claimant must be 'more than minimal' for the claimant to be able to claim damages. However, damage must be extremely trivial before the court will conclude that there has been no damage sufficient to establish a claim. A small cut resulting in a very minor scar or a blow resulting in a black eye is regarded as enough of an injury to enable a claim for damages to be made, although somewhat paradoxically, asymptomatic pleural plaques resulting from exposure to asbestos (and indicative of a risk of developing terminal disease but not visible to another person) are not at this point considered by the court to be sufficient to bring a personal injury claim.[4] Medical evidence may therefore be required to establish whether or not an injury caused by a breach of duty is asymptomatic and therefore should be regarded as minimal.

2.2.3   Causation

In every claim, the claimant has to establish that the injury, loss and damage in relation to which damages are claimed were caused by the breach of duty of the defendant and compensation will not be awarded for any such injury or loss that would have occurred in any event. Medical evidence is often crucial in establishing causation – the issue being whether or not the claimed breach of duty by the defendant actually caused the injury to the claimant.

---

3   We will discuss Clinical Negligence claims in detail in Chapters 8 and 9

4   *Johnston v NEI International Composition* [2007] UKHL 39 although in relation to claims under Scottish law by recent statute law it is now again possible to recover damages for pleural plaques (as was the case prior to 2007).

2.2.4   Contributory Negligence

Where the claimant proves that there has been a breach of a duty owed by the defendant to the claimant, the defendant may allege that the claimant's damages should be reduced to reflect his/her own contribution of negligence or blame-worthiness for the accident or injury. Such allegations of contributory negligence commonly arise in road traffic accidents (the failure to wear a seat belt may result in such a finding) as well as in workplace accidents. It would be unusual for such an allegation to be made in the context of a clinical negligence claim, although it could be asserted in a case where it is said that the claimant failed for no good reason to follow a recommended course of treatment that would have improved the eventual outcome.

2.3   Adversarial Litigation Process

Legal proceedings are adversarial and not inquisitorial. The judge is not an inquisitor who attempts through his own investigation of the evidence to uncover the truth of the matters before the court, but rather hears the case of each party and makes a decision based on the evidence placed before the court. Each side will seek to put its case in the best light possible with a view to obtaining a favourable decision from the court and will also seek to discredit the evidence of the other side by cross-examination of its witnesses.

Whilst the claimant must prove his/her claim to the satisfaction of the court, the defendant often seeks only to challenge or undermine the evidence brought forward by the claimant rather than attempting to prove its own case on the facts available. After each party has presented its evidence and cross-examination has taken place, the judge is left to conclude what has or has not been proved to a sufficient standard. If the defendant undermines the claimant's case sufficiently, the claimant will be unable to prove his/her case and no damages will be awarded.

Since the introduction of the *Civil Procedure Rules 1998* (CPR), a more co-operative approach to the conduct of litigation has been codified in order to make the litigation process more efficient. However, the process itself remains adversarial.

> The testing of evidence requires that the expert sets out clearly in the report the reasons (or the reasoning process) that supports each opinion expressed. There is no place for unsupported opinion in an expert report.

2.4   Proof

In a civil case, the claimant must prove his/her case to the civil standard of proof, 'on the balance of probabilities'. This means that the claimant must satisfy the judge that it is more likely than not that his/her injuries and the consequential loss for which damages are claimed were caused by the defendant's breach of duty. Similarly, the claimed loss must also be established on the balance of probabilities.

Once a fact is proved to the judge's satisfaction on the balance of probabilities (i.e. as being more likely than not), then this fact is established for all purposes in the case. Similarly, once the judge decides that one expert opinion - for example as to the nature of the injury sustained - is to be preferred on the balance of probabilities, then this will be the expert opinion on which the claim will be resolved.[5]

2.5   Damages: Underlying Principle

Once it is established that there has been a breach of duty that has caused injury or damage to the claimant, the legal principle underlying the assessment of an award of damages is known as the '100% Recovery Principle':[6]

> 'In settling the sum of money to be given for reparation of damages you should as nearly as possible get at that sum of money which will put the party who has been injured, or who has suffered, in the same position as he would have been in if he had not sustained the wrong for which he is now getting his compensation or reparation.'[7]

This principle may be applied without great difficulty to past loss, where for example loss of earnings can be based on the earnings received immediately before the accident or on the earnings of a comparable employee and where expenses reasonably incurred can be proved with receipts. For future loss of earnings, in a straightforward case, the court can assess damages on the basis of the likely level of earnings along a probable career path. However, valuing damages for non-financial loss, such as a physical or psychological injury or the loss of ability to enjoy certain aspects of the claimant's pre-injury lifestyle, defies a truly logical approach.

---

5   Proof is considered in more detail in Chapter 5

6   *Wells v Wells* [1999] 1 AC 345 at 382H, *Thompstone v Tameside & Glossop Acute Services* [2008] EWCA Civ 5

7   Lord Blackburn in *Livingstone v Rawyards Coal Company* (1880) 5 App Cas 25 at 39

Assessing the compensation necessary to achieve full and fair recovery in relation to losses that have not yet been incurred is often fraught with difficulty and may enter the realm of educated guesswork:

> 'The object of the award of damages for future expenditure is to place the injured party as nearly as possible in the same financial position as he or she would have been in but for the accident. The aim is to award such a sum of money as will amount to no more, and at the same time no less, than the net loss.'[8]

As a result, the parties will need to adduce evidence addressing not only what the consequences of an injury on the claimant's capabilities are and probably will be, but also what would probably have occurred in the claimant's life in the absence of the injury sustained. Both aspects will probably be full of uncertainty, but the court will have to establish the probable scenarios and will almost certainly rely on expert opinion to achieve this.

In reality, a full recovery of a loss sustained may not in fact be achievable in relation to many aspects of claim. It is not really possible for the court to fully compensate a claimant for loss of an active sex life or for loss of a place in a county tennis team or for the risk of developing post traumatic arthritis. However, subject to the practical difficulties of making assessments based on a degree of speculation and uncertainty, 100% recovery is what the court will expressly aim to achieve.

2.6   Types of Claim for Damages

Damages fall into two basic categories: non-pecuniary (non-financial) and pecuniary (financial) loss. Non-pecuniary damages are often referred to by lawyers as 'general damages' or 'generals' and pecuniary damages are referred to as 'special damages' or 'specials'. General damages are related to the impact of the injury on the claimant, while special damages are specific to the particular circumstances of the claimant and therefore the financial loss he/she has suffered. Special damages are based on a mathematical calculation of the financial cost or loss actually incurred or to be incurred. Sometimes lawyers will use 'specials' as shorthand for past losses only.

There is no limit to the types of claim or 'heads of claim' that can be included in a claim for damages. Heads of claim are the categories or types of loss for which compensation is claimed. What can be claimed will depend on the particular circumstances of the claimant and the case, and on the imagination of the claimant's lawyers.

---

8   Lord Hope in *Wells v Wells* [1999] 1 AC 345 at 390A

2.6.1   Non-Pecuniary Loss

Damages for non-pecuniary loss consist mainly of pain, suffering and loss of amenity. The terms pain and suffering are self-explanatory - though how these are valued is not without difficulty. The assessment of damages will depend on the type and level of impact upon the particular claimant of the pain and suffering that has been caused by the injury. Loss of amenity covers any impact that reduces the claimant's enjoyment of life or impairs his/her physical senses. Damages may also be awarded for loss of the enjoyment of a congenial occupation as a result of an injury.

2.6.2   Pecuniary Loss

Anything that can be seen as financial loss that is consequential upon the injury sustained can be compensated for in damages. The claimant may have been planning a career as a professional footballer or may have been unemployed and living on produce grown from his own allotment: the provable financial impact on these activities, both in the past and for the future, can form a basis for the assessment of damages.

Examples of potential items of claim for pecuniary loss include:

1.   any items damaged in the accident;

2.   loss of earnings to date and for the future;

3.   a disadvantage in the employment market, which may result in the employed claimant having greater difficulty finding employment in the future;

4.   the loss of a specific and congenial career (generally public service occupations);

5.   loss of pension resulting from reduced or lost earnings until the age at which without the injury the claimant had planned to retire or loss of employment benefitting from a non-contributory pension scheme;

6.   the cost of medical and therapeutic treatment reasonably incurred and reasonably to be incurred in the future;

7.   the cost of care and assistance that has reasonably been provided;

8.   the cost of care and assistance reasonably to be incurred in the future (which in the case of a serious injury is likely to be by far the largest head of claim);

9.   the reasonable cost of employing others to perform tasks which have previously been carried out by the claimant and can no longer reasonably be carried out;

10. the value of the care and assistance or the help with other tasks provided gratuitously by others including family members;

11. any equipment purchased or now reasonably needed as a result of any disability resulting from the accident;

12. any additional transport costs arising from the injury including costs of travelling for treatment and costs of adaptations to vehicles or changes in the means of transportation resulting in additional costs;

13. any additional accommodation costs resulting from any disability – from handrails and raised toilet seats to stair lifts, bungalows or additional rooms for carers;

14. any additional holiday costs resulting from disability; and

15. where life expectancy has been reduced, a proportion of the net income that would have been earned during the period of 'lost years'.[9]

Although this list contains the majority of items that can be claimed, the medical expert should always ask a claimant about how an injury has affected his/her activities of daily living and what limitations the claimant attributes to the injuries sustained.

2.6.3   Death

Where the claimant dies, whether or not as a result of the injury sustained, his/her personal representatives can claim for the benefit of the deceased's estate all the losses that the deceased could have claimed up to the moment of death – such as, damages for the injury itself, care and assistance, loss of earnings, and expenses incurred up to death. Lawyers refer to this type of claim as a 'Law Reform Act claim'.[10]

If the injury that is the subject of the claim caused the death, then in addition to a Law Reform Act claim, the deceased's dependant(s) can make a 'Fatal Accidents Act claim'.[11] Where the dependants are children, the claim will be made on their behalf. The potential heads of claim in a Fatal Accidents Act claim are different to those made by an injured claimant. The dependants can claim for the financial loss

---

9   Although if the claimant dies before the claim is completed, this head of claim does not pass to his/her Estate

10   The claim is made under the Law Reform (Miscellaneous Provisions) Act 1934

11   Under the Fatal Accidents Act 1976

they have suffered, being the loss in a share of the deceased's income from which they would have benefited but for the death or the loss of what the deceased would have done for them for nothing, but which must now either be done by others or purchased as a service. Certain dependants can also recover a statutory sum by way of bereavement damages. Funeral costs are also recoverable.

2.6.4   Possible Future Complications and Provisional Damages

A claimant can recover damages for the possible future complications of his/her injuries. The law states that a claim can be made for a provisional award of damages:

> '[…in] an action for damages for personal injuries in which there is proved or admitted to be a chance that at some definite or indefinite time in the future the injured person will, as a result of the act or omission which gave rise to the cause of action, develop some serious disease or suffer some serious deterioration in his physical or mental condition.' [12]

As a result, the court can reserve the position when awarding damages so as to enable further damages to be awarded in the future for something that has not yet occurred. A provisional award of damages is an assessment of damages made on the basis that a serious disease or a serious deterioration in the claimant's condition will not occur, but allowing the claimant to return to court for a further award of damages should it occur. Such future complications need to be expressly identified and addressed by the medical expert, so that the lawyers can advise whether to make a claim now for damages to cover the possibility that the complication will occur or instead seek a provisional award of damages which does not include compensation for that risk, with the option to make a further claim should the complication actually occur.

The claimant or the court itself may decide to deal with this risk by an award of immediate damages reflecting the degree of risk that the complication will occur. These are extremely important decisions and any decision as to how appropriately to compensate the claimant for the risk must be made in the light of a clear medical opinion as to the degree of risk that the complication will occur and the implications for the claimant of such a complication occurring.

---

12   Section 32A Senior Courts Act 1981 (known prior to October 2009 as the Supreme Court Act 1981) and Section 51 County Courts Act 1984

Examples of conditions where these considerations might apply include:

- epilepsy following a head injury;
- mesothelioma or lung cancer following exposure to asbestos fibres;
- sympathetic ophthalmia;
- recurrence of cancer; or
- traumatic arthritis.

2.7 Valuation of the Claim

The valuation of the claim will be based on the evidence (or in the case of a settlement prior to trial, the anticipated evidence) of the claimant, other lay (non-professional) witnesses and the evidence of experts. The lay witnesses in a case may include the claimant, family members or friends, and employers – past, present or prospective. The valuation may be based on medical expert evidence or on any other expert evidence from such disciplines as the court directs (for example, care experts or accountants).

2.7.1 Non-Pecuniary Loss

Valuing damages for non-pecuniary loss (such as for pain, suffering and loss of amenity) is not in any sense a mathematical exercise relying on calculation. The amount of damages awarded is based on the amounts awarded in previous cases even though the facts of each case will normally be unique. Lawyers develop a feel for what a claim is worth and while there is no "right" or "wrong" answer, normally there is an identifiable range of damages within which the court will make an award.[13]

Since 1992, the Judicial Studies Board has attempted to collate the level of damages awarded for different injuries into a small book, *Guidelines for the Assessment of General Damages in Personal Injury Cases*[14] (known as "the JSB Guidelines"). This book has now become the first port of call in assessing general damages, although lawyers will also rely on reported court decisions for further assistance. Medical experts are well advised to take a look at the categories of injuries within their own field, as set out within the JSB Guidelines, in order to appreciate those aspects of the injury or its impact that the court is likely to find most helpful in assessing general damages.[15]

---

13   Lawyers commonly make use of publications such as *Kemp & Kemp: The Quantum of Damages* (Thomson, Sweet & Maxwell) for reports of previously decided cases.

14   *Guidelines for the Assessment of General Damages in Personal Injury Cases* Oxford: Oxford University Press (2010) and now in its 10th edition

15   Some insurers use a computer model for assessing damages (known as 'Colossus'), which is reputed by many lawyers consistently to under-assess damages when compared with court awards. Lord Justice Jackson's 'Review of Civil Litigation Costs: Final Report' (December 2009) has recommended that a working group be set up to establish a uniform calibration for all software systems used in assessment of damages for smaller claims.

2.7.2   Pecuniary Loss

Valuing pecuniary loss is essentially a mathematical exercise. An essential element of the claimant's case is the 'Schedule of Loss', a document in which the detailed valuation of the claim is set out. An example of a schedule of loss is included in Appendix 7. There is no specific format for these schedules, so they vary greatly from case to case and between different lawyers. The schedule of loss should list each of the heads under which damages are claimed and set out for each such head how the claimed damages are calculated.

The lawyers for both claimant and defendant will be looking to see the extent to which the evidence in the case supports the heads of claim and the calculations. This evidence will be both the evidence that the lawyers anticipate that non-expert witnesses will give, which will be contained in witness statements, and also the evidence of experts such as medical and accounting experts instructed in the claim.

For the claimant to be likely to recover damages, most of the heads of claim and the calculations within these will need to be supported directly or indirectly by expert medical evidence. The claimant will not succeed in recovering substantial loss of earnings unless medical evidence confirms that the injury has reasonably resulted in a restriction in the ability to follow paid employment. A claim for the cost of care or for carrying out tasks that the claimant asserts can no longer be carried out will not succeed in the absence of medical evidence that indicates that these restrictions have resulted from the injuries sustained in the accident.

The defendant responds to the claimant's Schedule of Loss with a 'Counter Schedule'. The Counter Schedule sets out the defendant's calculations and those figures that are disputed and those that can be agreed. A trial, in so far as it relates to the value of the claim, will be based around these two documents and an assessment of the evidence each side relies on in support of its own schedule.

2.7.3   Future Pecuniary Loss

Compensation for future losses can be by way of periodical payments or a lump sum payment, or a combination of both. More commonly, damages will be awarded by way of a one-off lump sum payment. This is tax free when received in the hands of the claimant[16] and the claimant is free to spend it as he/she wishes. The amount will have been carefully calculated as representing compensation for future loss of earnings or the amount necessarily and reasonably to be incurred in dealing with the claimant's future additional needs as a result of the injury sustained, or both. However, the claimant is free to spend the award on a luxury cruise, to gamble it away or to invest it all for the benefit of his/her children.

---

16   Hence damages for loss of earnings are calculated net of tax and national insurance contributions

Periodical payments as a way of providing compensation were first introduced in 1996[17] in circumstances where the parties agreed to this. From 1st April 2005, the court has had the power to impose an order for periodical payments on the parties. Periodical payments are sums paid regularly (for example monthly) for a determined period normally to compensate for loss of earnings or to provide for the additional costs of care resulting from the injury. For care costs, the payments will usually be payable for life. Whereas a lump sum to compensate for future losses is calculated by making assumptions as to life expectancy. These assumptions will inevitably in time be proved wrong so that the sum awarded will be too much or too little. A periodical payment, subject to defining an appropriate formula for increasing it to allow for increased future costs, should (theoretically at least) be just what is required and no more or less. Periodical payments are increasingly used in large value claims as part of a compensation "package" involving lump sum payments as well. The annual increases can now be related to a suitable index other than the Retail Prices Index.

To calculate a lump sum value for items of future pecuniary loss the court will start with a valuation based on present day costs. Where there is a loss or cost that will be incurred continuously or at regular intervals, such as loss of earnings or care costs, the court will value the total annual loss at present day values and then multiply it for the number of years for which it will be lost. The actual number of years will be discounted to reflect the number of years in advance that the money is being paid. The discount is applied because money received now is worth more than money received in the future – for example, money received now can be invested to increase its value over time.[18]

Where there is an anticipated one-off cost in the future (for example, an operation in five years' time) the court will discount the current cost to provide adequate money now, which if invested should provide the sum needed at the relevant time in the future.[19] Increases in costs in the future are ignored – the actuarial tables which are used for this exercise allow for future RPI inflation, but not for the higher rates of healthcare and wages inflation.

The limitations of this basis of assessment of loss and of providing full recovery of loss to the claimant is well recognised by the court:

---

17   Section 2 Damages Act 1996 as subsequently amended by section 100 Courts Act 2003

18   Technically, the discount applied to the annual cost is known as the 'multiplier', while the annual cost is known as the 'multiplicand'. The multiplier is applied to the multiplicand to provide a sum now, which if invested in an interest bearing financial instrument, should provide adequate money with which to fund the cost in the future and be used up at the end of that period. The multiplier is found by using actuarial tables, commonly referred to by lawyers as the "Ogden Tables", but more formally entitled, *Actuarial Tables with explanatory notes for use in Personal Injury and Fatal Accident Cases* issued by the Government Actuary's Department (currently in its 6th edition). Lawyers often access these tables and other data relevant to the assessment of damages in *Facts & Figures: Tables for the Calculation of Damages* published by Sweet & Maxwell and the Professional Negligence Bar Association

19   Using the Ogden Tables to identify the appropriate multiplier

*'It is the nature of a lump sum payment that it may, in respect of future pecu-
niary loss, prove to be either too little or too much. So far as the multiplier
is concerned, the [claimant] may die the next day, or he may live beyond his
normal expectation of life. So far as the multiplicand is concerned, the cost of
future care may exceed everyone's best estimate. Or a new cure or less expensive form of treatment may be discovered. But these uncertainties do not
affect the basic principle. The purpose of the award is to put the [claimant] in
the same position, financially, as if he had not been injured.'* [20]

2.8   Costs of Litigation – Why Winning Matters[21]

Generally, the winner in litigation recovers from the other side the cost of bringing
or defending the claim. This means that the loser pays all the costs in the action.
Costs will include the costs of the lawyers, expert witnesses and court fees which
are paid at various stages in the litigation, and which fees have increased greatly
in recent years. Such costs may be out of proportion to, and indeed often exceed,
the damages recovered. This harsh reality means that throughout the claim, the
lawyers on both sides – and particularly for the defendant (more on this below) -
will be concerned about the costs that have been, and are still to be incurred, and
who is to pay them.

For the lawyers, costs (i.e. their fees) are the commercial reason for being in this
line of business, and the costs that can be recovered will depend on the value
of the claim. Fixed costs regimes, which impose a limit on the fees lawyers can
charge in smaller value claims,[22] give the claimant's lawyers an additional interest in maximising the value of the claim and the defendant an additional interest
in minimising its value. The principle of proportionality of costs – that the costs
recovered by the lawyers should be proportionate to the sum in issue[23] – also gives
the lawyers an interest in the value of the claim when seeking to justify to the
court the costs claimed at the end of the litigation process.

---

20   Lord Lloyd in *Wells v Wells* [1999] 1 AC 345 at 363H

21   Lord Justice Jackson's 'Review of Civil Litigation Costs: Final Report' (December 2009) has
proposed fundamental changes to the costs regime in civil litigation, including personal injury
and clinical negligence claims, which might in due course considerably alter the contents
of this Section. The report is available at http://www.judiciary.gov.uk/about_judiciary/cost-
review/jan2010/final-report-140110.pdf

22   From 1st April 2010 a new fixed costs regime has been introduced in road traffic claims with a
value up to £10,000

23   CPR 44.4(2)

2.8.1   Conditional Fee Agreements

The vast majority of personal injury claims and many clinical negligence claims are now funded on the claimant's side by way of 'Conditional Fee Agreements' (also known as 'CFAs'). CFAs are commonly but not always accurately called 'no win, no fee' agreements. These were introduced when Legal Aid was removed from virtually all such claims in April 2000, in order to provide 'access to justice' to litigants. Under a CFA, the claimant's lawyers are only paid for the work they do and the costs they incur, which often includes the fees of medical experts, if the claim is successful. Success for these purposes is generally defined as recovering damages.[24] If the claimant's lawyers are successful, they recover on top of normal 'base' costs an additional sum equivalent to a percentage of the 'base' costs - a percentage up to 100%.[25] This additional sum is to compensate the lawyers for the cases they take on, spend time and money on (as for example in obtaining medical reports), but which do not succeed, whether abandoning the claim as a result of its poor prospects or losing at court.

When a claim funded by a CFA is successful, both the costs and the additional sum to be paid under the CFA will be paid by the defendant. When a claim funded by a CFA is not successful, then normally the claimant will have purchased 'After the Event' (or 'ATE') insurance which will pay the costs of the defendant for which otherwise the claimant would be liable. The losing defendant will have to pay the cost of the premium for such insurance in addition to the base costs and the success fee of the claimant's lawyers.

Some claimants have 'Before the Event' (or 'BTE') insurance, such as may be purchased at very modest cost as an add-on to motor or household insurance. This will provide cover for incurring legal costs on his/her own behalf and the costs of the other side should the claim be lost, up to a defined limit, which is generally adequate for an average claim. Whilst within the limit of the cover provided by the BTE insurance, the claimant is not at risk of paying the costs of the claim. Trades Union members may also have access to funding arrangements that enable them to bring claims without any liability for their own costs or any risk of incurring the other side's costs in the event of losing. These arrangements generally involve the lawyers working under a CFA.

Therefore, except in the exceptional circumstances where the claimant is privately funding the claim without a CFA, or has a CFA but is unable to afford insurance to cover the defendant's costs in the event of losing, the claimant's personal interest in costs is limited.[26]

---

24   Although frequently it is necessary also to 'beat' a defendant's Part 36 offer of settlement in order to recover all costs (see Section 2.8.2 below)

25   In many types of claims these percentage uplifts are now fixed by the *Civil Procedure Rules* 1998 (Part 45)

26   There is a small number of cases which are still eligible for public funding from the Legal Services Commission where the considerations are slightly different, but we leave further consideration of this to other texts

2.8.2   Part 36 – Offers to Settle

To increase the pressure on the parties to compromise each side is entitled, at any stage before as well as after proceedings have been commenced, to make a formal offer to the other side to settle the claim on the basis of a particular amount being paid to the claimant together with costs - the offer being open for acceptance on those terms for 21 days. Where the offer is accepted, this is an end to the claim.[27] Where an offer, whether made by the claimant or by the defendant, is not accepted then the following situations arise:

1.   if the claimant fails to obtain a judgment 'more advantageous' than a defendant's Part 36 offer, almost always the claimant will not only fail to recover his/her own costs from the time the offer was made, but will also be liable for the defendant's costs from that time;

2.   if the claimant obtains a judgment 'at least as advantageous' as an offer the claimant has made to the defendant, then the defendant will almost always be penalised in having to pay additional interest and costs at a higher level to the claimant.

The failure by a party to beat at trial a Part 36 offer of settlement can therefore be disastrous. Indeed, owing to the wording 'more advantageous' or 'at least as advantageous', rather than simply 'beaten' or 'exceeded', the offer needs to be beaten by a safe margin. The claimant may see all of the damages awarded going in discharging his/her own and the other side's costs. The lawyers may recover none of the costs of a large proportion of the claim, including the substantial expenses of a trial (including the attendance fees of experts). The pressure placed on a defendant by a well-positioned claimant's Part 36 offer is significantly less than that on the claimant side, because the nature of the sanction (additional interest and costs at a higher rate) is less damaging and less threatening to a defendant such as a large insurance company.

Conclusion

The process of assessing the value of a claim is not supported effectively by medical evidence that is simply an investigation of the claimant's medical situation. The lawyers and the court are not interested in the medical aspects of a case for their own sake, but focus inevitably on the financial consequences of the injuries sustained. The issue is always what can or cannot be proved to have been suffered, or is likely to be suffered in the future, as a consequence of the injuries sustained. The medical expert's role is to assist the lawyers in the efficient progression of a claim through the litigation process, by dealing both with the issues upon which the lawyers seek expert opinion and those issues relevant to the claim that the expert, using his/her expertise when reporting on the claimant, identifies as material to the claim.

---

27   Such offers by a defendant had, until 6th April 2007, to be backed up by paying into court the sum of money offered ("a payment into court"). That is no longer required of the defendant.

Key-Point Summary

1. The only instrument of civil justice in a claim for personal injury is the award of money (damages).

2. Damages will only be awarded where the claimant can prove four elements of the claim: that the defendant is in breach of a duty owed to the claimant, that the breach of duty caused damage, that the damage suffered is more than minimal, and the claimant can prove the nature of the injury, loss and damage.

3. Civil litigation is an adversarial process, where the claimant has to prove his/her case.

4. All civil cases are decided to the civil standard of proof – on the balance of probabilities.

5. The principle underlying the award of damages is the '100% Recovery Principle'. The court attempts to put the claimant back into the position he/she would have been in in the absence of the accident and the consequent injury, loss and damage.

6. A claimant cannot recover for a loss he/she would have suffered in any event.

7. Damages can be awarded as a lump sum or as periodical payments.

8. Winning does matter, as costs – a substantial sum in most claims – are paid by the losers of the action.

9. Both parties will consider making Part 36 offers of settlement during the claim to increase the pressure on the other side to settle in order to avoid the risk of an increased liability in costs.

Next Steps

In the next chapter, we will explore the progression of a claim - from its inception, the pre-action phase, issuing of proceedings and through to trial.

Developing Your Medico-Legal Mind (2)

Based on your understanding of the legal principles underlying a civil claim for damages in personal injury, answer the following questions:

1.   What does a claimant need to prove in order to succeed in a claim for damages for personal injury or clinical negligence?

2.   What is the 100% Recovery Principle?

3.   What is the difference between 'negligence' and a 'breach of statutory duty'?

4.   In what circumstance might a court reduce the level of damages to be paid to a successful claimant?

5.   What are general damages or generals?

6.   What are special damages or specials?

7.   In what circumstances would a court award provisional damages?

8.   In what circumstances would a court award periodical payments?

9.   What is a Part 36 offer and what function does it have in the litigation process?

10.   Where do lawyers seek guidance on the likely value (or range of values) of an injury?

3

Progression of a Claim

3.1   Civil Procedure Rules 1998
3.2   Structure of the CPR
3.3   Pre-Action Protocols
3.4   Low Value Personal Injury Claims in Road Traffic Accidents
3.5   Commencement of Proceedings
3.6   Court Directions
3.7   Court Control of Expert Evidence
3.8   Legal Professionals Involved in a Case
3.9   Judge's Approach to Conflicting Expert Evidence

Introduction

The entire civil litigation process is controlled and regulated by detailed rules of court. The legal process by which an injured person seeks to claim compensation for an injury sustained is laid down in the *Civil Procedure Rules* 1998 (CPR) with the associated *Practice Directions* and *Pre-Action Protocols*. The CPR came into force in April 1999, introducing new procedural rules that deal with every stage of court proceedings, as well as the conduct of the parties and their lawyers within the proceedings. The CPR also specifically regulate the use of expert witnesses and the duties of experts instructed in a claim. (We will examine the detailed duties of expert witnesses in Chapter 4.)

Chapter Outline

In this chapter, we will examine the fundamental legal principles that underlie the CPR and the specific rules that impose these principles on the parties. We will explain how the parties prepare the claim before proceedings are issued and the role of the court in managing cases. We will also introduce the roles of the legal professionals involved in a case: solicitors, barristers and judges.

3.1   Civil Procedure Rules 1998

In July 1996, Lord Woolf, the then Master of the Rolls (the senior civil judge), presented his final report entitled Access to Justice, on his proposals to reform the civil justice system. In the first section of the report, he detailed the problems in the system that his proposed reforms were seeking to address:

> 'The defects I identified in our present system were that it is too expensive in that the costs often exceed the value of the claim; too slow in bringing cases to a conclusion and too unequal: there is a lack of equality between the powerful, wealthy litigant and the under resourced litigant. It is too uncertain: the difficulty of forecasting what litigation will cost and how long it will last induces the fear of the unknown; and it is incomprehensible to many litigants. Above all it is too fragmented in the way it is organised since there is no one with clear overall responsibility for the administration of civil justice; and too adversarial as cases are run by the parties, not by the courts and the rules of court, all too often, are ignored by the parties and not enforced by the court.'[1]

His assessment of the use of experts in litigation was also the subject of much discussion within the legal profession:

> 'There is widespread agreement with the criticisms I made in the interim report of the way in which expert evidence is used at present, especially the point that experts sometimes take on the role of partisan advocates instead of neutral fact finders or opinion givers.'[2]

In essence, Lord Woolf wanted a system of justice that was fair, cost-effective, easy to use, comprehensible to litigants and efficient. To achieve this, he rewrote the procedural rules of the civil courts. His revision of the rules came into force in April 1999 and created a new framework for the conduct of litigation in the civil courts.

---

1   *Access to Justice - Final Report to the Lord Chancellor on the civil justice system in England and Wales* by The Right Honourable the Lord Woolf, Master of the Rolls (July 1996) (Ch 1 para 2)

2   As Above (Ch 13 para 5)

3.1.1   Court Managed Litigation

Since April 1999, the court has actively managed cases to ensure the efficient and just disposal of the claim. The parties are required to co-operate with the court and with one another to achieve these aims. This contrasts with the previous system in which the court was largely reactive to the parties' requests for intervention, which resulted in much delay and inefficiency.

Each party is required to adopt a "cards on the table" (face up!) approach to litigation. This means that all the evidence in a case on which a party intends to rely at court is disclosed to the other side. The purpose of this approach is to facilitate the early settlement of claims and to limit the number of claims that actually reach court. The extent to which any particular claim is run on a co-operative rather than a tactical basis varies greatly, depending on the issues in the claim, the personalities of the lawyers, the approach of the insurer and the degree of intervention by the court.

Although 10 years on there is concern that the revision of the CPR has failed to deal satisfactorily with the issue of legal costs – indeed may have had the effect of increasing such costs – it is generally recognised amongst those old enough to recall operating under the previous system that the process of civil litigation has been improved by the CPR. As Lord Justice Jackson stated in his recent report[3]:

> 'Those reforms have brought huge benefits to civil litigants. Far more cases are settled before issue. Those cases which are contested proceed far more swiftly from issue to trial. We no longer have the repeated tragedy (for such it was) of meritorious claims being 'struck out' for want of prosecution.
>
> The case management function, which the court has assumed following the Woolf reforms, prevents cases from being parked indefinitely whilst the parties or their lawyers attend to other matters. The creation of tracks for cases ensures that each type of case receives an appropriate allocation of resources and degree of attention from the court.
>
> The fast-track ensures that the lower-value cases are brought to trial with expedition and that the trial costs (although not pre-trial costs) of such cases are fixed.'

---

3   Review of Civil Litigation Costs, Preliminary Report (2009)

3.2 Structure of the CPR

The CPR continue to develop, with the introduction of the 55th series of amendments on 6 April 2011.[4] Currently, there are 79 'Parts' dealing with civil proceedings (each Part draws together rules that relate to a particular stage or aspect of the litigation process), from how to start proceedings through to enforcement of the judgments obtained. The rules in each Part are supported by 'Practice Directions', which generally give directions and guidance supportive of the rule to which they refer. Participants in the litigation process must give equal regard to the rules and the practice directions.

The CPR and practice directions are printed with commentaries by several publishers, as a hefty white, green or brown covered book[5] and more recently in a variety of electronic formats as well as being available on the internet. It is unnecessary for expert witnesses to be familiar with the whole of the CPR, though many of the deadlines given to expert witnesses arise directly from the programme for the litigation imposed by the court or the CPR.[6] Part 35 of the CPR and its practice direction relate specifically to expert witnesses and these are considered in detail in Chapter 4.

3.2.1 Overriding Objective

The overriding objective of the CPR is set out in the first rule. It is the standard by which the entire CPR is to be interpreted and applied:

The overriding objective

CPR 1.1 (1) These Rules are a new procedural code with the overriding objective of enabling the court to deal with cases justly.

(2) Dealing with a case justly includes, so far as is practicable -

(a) ensuring that the parties are on an equal footing;

(b) saving expense;

(c) dealing with the case in ways which are proportionate -

(i) to the amount of money involved;

(ii) to the importance of the case;

(iii) to the complexity of the issues; and

(iv) to the financial position of each party;

---

4   The CPR, Practice Directions and Pre-Action Protocols can be found at http://www.justice. gov.uk/civil/procrules_fin/index.htm

5   These are known in the legal profession, perhaps unsurprisingly, as the "White Book", "Green Book" or "Brown Book".

6   It is essential that experts check that they can meet such deadlines before accepting instructions to act in a particular claim.

(d) ensuring that it is dealt with expeditiously and fairly; and

(e) allotting to it an appropriate share of the court's resources, while taking into account the need to allot resources to other cases.

Application by the court of the overriding objective

CPR 1.2   The court must seek to give effect to the overriding objective when it -

(a) exercises any power given to it by the Rules; or

(b) interprets any rule.

Duty of the parties

CPR 1.3   The parties are required to help the court to further the overriding objective.

In the first section of the CPR the important principle of 'Proportionality' is introduced. The principle of proportionality means that the expense incurred in bringing a claim should be proportionate to its value, complexity and importance. This principle underlies how the court manages the litigation and the way the parties should conduct themselves. The parties are also required to co-operate with the court as it seeks to deal with cases 'justly' and can be penalised in costs if they do not do so.

3.2.2   Court Management

The court, in pro-actively managing its proceedings, must apply the overriding objective in all of the decisions that it makes:

Court's duty to manage cases

CPR 1.4   (1) The court must further the overriding objective by actively managing cases.

The court's powers, in seeking to further the overriding objective, include:

1. requiring a party or his legal representative to attend the court;

2. holding a hearing by telephone;

3. directing a separate trial of an issue or the hearing of a preliminary issue;

4. excluding an issue from consideration;

5. taking any other step or making any other order for the purpose of managing the case and furthering the overriding objective.[7]

---

7   See CPR 3.1

All decisions taken by the court in relation to the progress of a claim will be made to give effect to these objectives. These will include, for example, decisions as to the nature and number of medical experts to be permitted to provide reports or give evidence, whether one or both parties should be entitled to rely on such evidence, and whether it should be provided by a single joint expert.[8] It will also include decisions as to what, if any, clarification of the medical expert report needs to be given by the medical expert.

3.3   Pre-Action Protocols

A third tier of guidance beyond the CPR and practice directions is provided by the 'Pre-Action Protocols' (PAPs). PAPs detail the steps that should be taken by the parties prior to the commencement of proceedings and are intended to facilitate the early settlement of claims by the parties.[9]

PAPs have been drawn up with substantial input from practitioners involved in the applicable area of litigation and represent good practice in the conduct of litigation. A failure to comply with the relevant PAPs can have a significant impact on the manner in which the claim once commenced in court is dealt with and can have a significant costs impact against the interest of a party failing to comply with the relevant PAP.

PAPs relevant to compensation claims in which medical experts will be instructed are:

- Pre-Action Protocol for the Resolution of Clinical Disputes;
- Pre-Action Protocol for Personal Injury Claims; and
- Pre-Action Protocol for Disease and Illness Claims.

In addition, from 30th April 2010, the Pre-Action Protocol for Low Value Personal Injury Claims in Road Traffic Accidents has been introduced. This is different in nature from the others, and is dealt with further in Section 3.4 below.

A fundamental principle in all PAPs is that the claimant's solicitor should set out in detail the nature of the claim and the damages sought in a 'Letter of Claim' sent to the defendant (or the defendant's insurer). In turn, the defendant should respond in detail within a fixed period and provide all documentation relevant to the main issues indicated in the claim.

---

8   A detailed consideration of the rules in respect of the appointment of a single joint expert is given in Section 4.5 below.

9   A review process was instigated during 2009 to review all of the Pre-Action Protocols (not just those relevant to personal injury claims).

The aims of PAPs are set out in the Practice Direction – Pre-Action Conduct:

1. to encourage the exchange of information about the prospective legal claim;

2. to enable parties to settle the issues between them without the need to start proceedings; and

3. to support the efficient management by the court and the parties of proceedings that cannot be avoided.[10]

In relation to the use of experts, the Practice Direction - Pre-Action Conduct states:

> When the evidence of an expert is necessary, the parties should consider how best to minimise expense.[11]

Annex C provides the parties with guidance on instructing experts at this pre-action stage.

PAPs are important because the court will take into account a party's compliance or non-compliance with them in making court management orders such as:

- orders refusing an extension of time in which to carry out a particular procedural step;[12]
- orders for costs – where 'conduct before as well as during the proceedings, and in particular the extent to which the parties followed any relevant pre-action protocol' are expressly relevant;[13]
- orders that money be paid into court where a party has without good reason failed to comply with a rule, practice direction or relevant PAP;[14]
- orders to strike out a statement of case for failure to comply with a rule, practice direction or court order;[15]
- orders to deny a successful party an award of interest or awarding interest at a lower rate than would normally be applied;[16] and
- orders awarding interest at a higher rate against a losing party.[17]

All of these sanctions are designed to encourage the parties in an action to pursue the claim following best practice. PAPs encourage all parties to co-operate in bringing the claim forward in a cost-efficient manner and to avoid overly adversarial behaviour and tactics.

---

10   Practice Direction – Pre-Action Conduct para 1.1 and 1.2

11   Practice Direction – Pre-Action Conduct para 9.4

12   CPR 3.1(4)

13   CPR 44.3(5)(a)

14   CPR 3.1(5)

15   CPR 3.4(2)

16   Practice Direction – Pre-Action Conduct para 2.3(3)

17   Practice Direction – Pre-Action Conduct para 2.3(4)

> The expert has to meet the solicitor's deadline for producing the expert report. Pre-Action Protocols impose time constraints on the parties, as does the timetable imposed by the court once the claim is issued, and there can be implications for costs if a party does not meet these deadlines. If there is any doubt whether such deadlines can be met, the expert must refuse the instruction.

3.3.1 Pre-Action Protocol for the Resolution of Clinical Disputes

The PAPs of most relevance to medical experts are those concerning clinical negligence, personal injury, and disease and illness claims. The most detailed of these protocols is the Pre-Action Protocol for the Resolution of Clinical Disputes. A summary of the stages is set out below:

1. Medical records are obtained by the claimant's lawyers

2. Expert evidence is obtained by the claimant's lawyers

3. A Letter of Claim is sent by the claimant's lawyers containing:

    (a) a clear summary of facts;

    (b) the main allegations of negligence;

    (c) a description of the claimant's injuries;

    (d) an outline of financial loss incurred;

    (e) a chronology;

    (f) copies of relevant documents (core medical records etc); and it can also include

    (g) an offer of settlement (Part 36 offer), in which case there must be a medical report dealing with the injuries, condition and prognosis of the claimant.

4. Within 4 months[18] the health care provider should reply:

   (a) with a reasoned response;

   (b) making clear what issues of breach of duty or causation are admitted, and which denied and why;

   (c) making admissions where possible which are intended to be binding;[19]

   (d) providing copies of key documents; and if relevant

   (e) responding to any claimant's Part 36 Offer and may also make a counter-offer of settlement.

5. Proceedings can now be commenced if negotiations/ mediation etc are at an end.

Expert Reports in Clinical Disputes

The Pre-Action Protocol for the Resolution of Clinical Disputes provides that:

4.1   In clinical negligence disputes **expert opinions** may be needed:—
   - on breach of duty and causation
   - on the patient's condition and prognosis
   - to assist in valuing aspects of the claim.

4.2   The civil justice reforms and the new Civil Procedure Rules will encourage economy in the use of experts and a **less adversarial expert culture**. It is recognised that in clinical negligence disputes, the parties and their advisers will require flexibility in their approach to expert evidence. Decisions on whether experts might be instructed jointly, and on whether reports might be disclosed sequentially or by exchange, should rest with the parties and their advisers. Sharing expert evidence may be appropriate on issues relating to the value of the claim. However, this protocol does not attempt to be prescriptive on issues in relation to expert evidence.

4.3   Obtaining expert evidence will often be an expensive step and may take time, especially in specialised areas of medicine where there are limited numbers of suitable experts. Patients and healthcare providers, and their advisers, will therefore need to consider carefully how best to obtain any necessary expert help quickly and cost-effectively. Assistance with locating a suitable expert is available from a number of sources.

   [Emphasis and punctuation is as provided in the PAP.]

---

18   Extended from 3 months as of October 2010

19   Therefore, if the proposed defendant admits a breach of duty or causation of injury in the letter it will have to justify to the court subsequently reneging on such an admission when proceedings are commenced.

The Pre-Action Protocol for the Resolution of Clinical Disputes therefore seeks to give the parties considerable say in the use of medical experts, in contrast to CPR 32.1, 35.1 and 35.7.[20] This apparent conflict arises because a clinical negligence claim may necessitate the use of a larger number of medical experts than a typical personal injury claim, owing to the difficult issues involved and the additional issue (breach of duty) on which expert evidence is required.

3.3.2   Pre-Action Protocol for Personal Injury Claims

The procedure in the Pre-Action Protocol for Personal Injury Claims is similar to (but simpler than) the Pre-Action Protocol for the Resolution of Clinical Disputes. The first step is the requirement for a detailed 'Letter of Claim' from the claimant, rather than obtaining documents relevant to liability. The defendant is then required to give a reasoned response within 3 months. The letter of claim should provide sufficient information to enable the defendant (or normally the insurer) to assess liability and make an estimate of the likely size of the claim.

No further investigation of liability should then be carried out on behalf of the claimant until the defendant has responded (though the claimant's solicitor will normally suggest documents considered by the solicitor to be relevant to the issue of liability in the letter of claim). If the defendant then denies liability, it should give reasons and disclose in its letter of reply any documents material to the issue of liability.

Before any party instructs an expert, it should give the other party a list of the name(s) of one or more experts in the relevant specialism(s) it considers to be suitable to instruct, so that if possible an expert who is mutually acceptable to the parties is instructed. As a result, it is hoped that the report will be accepted by both parties.

The Pre-Action Protocol for Personal Injury Claims aims to create a process in which achieving an early settlement in the case is more likely, though litigation remains the ultimate step.

---

20   See Section 3.7 Court 'Control of Expert Evidence' and Section 4.5 'Single Joint Experts', below, which emphasise the court's control over the use of experts.

Pre-Action Protocol for Personal Injury Claims – Jointly Selected Experts

When a medical expert report is to be obtained, the pre-action protocol encourages the parties to identify an expert who is acceptable to both sides:

> 2.14   The protocol encourages **joint selection** [emphasis added] of, and access to, experts. The report produced is not a joint report for the purposes of CPR 35… The protocol promotes the practice of the claimant obtaining a medical report, disclosing it to the defendant who then asks questions and/or agrees it and does not obtain his own report. The protocol provides for nomination of the expert by the claimant in personal injury claims because of the early stage of the proceedings and the particular nature of such claims. If proceedings have to be issued, a medical report must be attached to these proceedings. However if necessary after proceedings have commenced and with the permission of the court, the parties may obtain further expert reports. It would be for the court to decide whether the costs of more than one expert's report should be recoverable.

> 2.15   Some solicitors choose to obtain medical reports through medical agencies, rather than directly from a specific doctor or hospital. The defendant's prior consent to the action should be sought and, if the defendant so requests, the agency should be asked to provide in advance the names of the doctor(s) whom they are considering instructing.

The claimant will instruct the expert and disclose the report to the defendant, unless the claimant chooses not to rely on the report. The claimant can choose not to disclose the report if it is not considered to be favourable, or for any other reason is not considered to be satisfactory. The decision not to rely on a report has implications for costs and for the tactical development of the case. If the claimant chooses not to rely on an expert report, the cost of the report is not recoverable from the defendant and the defendant will be aware that an expert was instructed by the claimant, and as the report was not disclosed will presume that it gave an unfavourable opinion.[21]

Therefore a 'Jointly Selected Expert' under the pre-action protocol is an expert instructed by the claimant alone and is contracted only to the claimant. This is in contrast to a 'Single Joint Expert', who is instructed by both parties. We deal with this distinction further in Section 4.5.1 below.

---

21   However the court has a discretion under CRP 35.4 to require the unfavourable report obtained under the PAP to be disclosed as a condition of allowing the party to rely on a subsequent report (*Edwards-Tubb v J D Weatherspoon Plc* [2011] EWCA Civ 136)

The practice under the Pre-Action Protocol for Personal Injury Claims therefore is as follows:

3.15 Before any party instructs an expert he should give the other party a list of the **name**(s) of **one or more experts** in the relevant speciality whom he considers are suitable to instruct.

3.16 Where a medical expert is to be instructed the claimant's solicitor will organise access to relevant medical records.

3.17 **Within 14 days** the other party may indicate **an objection** to one or more of the named experts. The first party should then instruct a mutually acceptable expert (which is not the same as a joint expert)…

3.18 If the second party objects to all the listed experts, the parties may then instruct **experts of their own choice**. It would be for the court to decide subsequently if proceedings are issued, whether either party had acted unreasonably.

3.19 If the **second party does not object to an expert nominated**, he shall not be entitled to rely on his own expert evidence within that particular speciality unless:

(a) the first party agrees

(b) the court so directs, or

(c) the first party's expert report has been amended and the first party is not prepared to disclose the original report.

3.20 **Either party may send to an agreed expert written questions** on the report, relevant to the issues, via the first party's solicitors. The expert should send answers to the questions separately and directly to each party.

3.21 The cost of a report from an agreed expert will usually be paid by the instructing first party: the costs of the expert replying to questions will usually be borne by the party which asks the questions.

[…]

5.1 Where the defendant admits liability in whole or in part, before proceedings are issued, any medical reports obtained by agreement under this protocol should be disclosed to the other party. The claimant should delay issuing proceedings for 21 days from disclosure of the report… to enable the parties to consider whether the claim is capable of settlement.

[Emphasis and punctuation is as provided in the PAP]

3.3.3   Pre-Action Protocol for Disease and Illness Claims

The Pre-Action Protocol for Disease and Illness Claims combines features from the other two pre-action protocols. It is expressed to cover claims involving 'any illness physical or psychological, any disorder, ailment, affliction, complaint, malady or derangement other than a physical or psychological injury solely caused by an accident or other similar single event'[22] and is not limited to diseases occurring in the workplace.

The practice under the Pre-Action Protocol for Disease and Illness Claims is as follows:

1.   The occupational health records and personnel records of the claimant are obtained by the claimant's lawyer from the defendant, and the general practitioner records will also normally be obtained.

2.   The claimant's lawyer sends the defendant a letter of claim 'as soon as there is sufficient information available to substantiate a realistic claim':

   (a)   containing a clear summary of the facts and the main allegations of fault;

   (b)   outlining the financial loss incurred;

   (c)   identifying any relevant documents.

3.   The letter of claim may, but need not, be accompanied by a medical report.[23]

4.   The defendant should acknowledge the letter of claim within 21 days and provide a reasoned answer within 3 months of the acknowledgement admitting the claim or explaining why it is not admitted.

The PAP notes that expert opinions in such claims will usually be needed 'on knowledge, fault and causation; on condition and prognosis; and to assist in valuing aspects of the claim'.

It also emphasises that a flexible approach should be adopted in obtaining medical expert reports, and that the parties should decide whether to instruct experts jointly, and whether to disclose their reports sequentially or by exchange.[24] Where the claimant sends a medical report with the letter of claim, the defendant will be entitled to obtain its own medical report. Where instructing a single joint expert is considered appropriate, then a procedure is suggested for the expert's nomination and instruction.[25]

---

22   Para 2.2

23   Para 6.8

24   Para 9.2

25   Para 9.5 – 9.10

3.4   Low Value Personal Injury Claims in Road Traffic Accidents

New rules, pre-action protocols and practice directions have been introduced to simplify the procedure for road traffic accident personal injury claims. A new claims process now operates for claims where the level of general damages for pain, suffering and loss of amenity is at least £1,000 and total damages do not exceed £10,000 (excluding interest and vehicle related damages). The process only applies to accidents after 30 April 2010.

The process is broken down into three stages and the costs recoverable for each stage are fixed. There will be consequent pressure on the claimant's solicitor to keep the time spent on the process to a minimum.

It is intended to be a largely electronic (paper-less) process.[26] A claim is notified to defendants and insurers in a standard form and the insurer must make a decision on liability within 15 business days ('Stage 1'). Only claims where an admission of liability is made by the defendant's insurer and where there is no allegation of contributory negligence - other than failure to wear a seatbelt - will remain in the process (moving into 'Stage 2'). All other claims will be dealt with under the normal court-based procedure.

Once the defendant's insurer has made an admission of liability, the claimant's solicitor prepares and submits a settlement pack, which will include any medical reports. The report may already have been obtained prior to reaching Stage 2, and indeed, it may be that only on receipt of the medical report does it become apparent that the claim has a value that would put it within this process. Once the report has been provided to the claimant's solicitor, there is only one opportunity to request that the expert correct any factual errors before the report is sent to the defendant.[27]

The expectation is that in most cases one report will suffice, but where one expert cannot deal with all the elements of the injury, a further report from a medical expert in a different discipline may be obtained.[28] On the recommendation of those two experts up to a maximum of 4 reports may be obtained, each from a different discipline.[29] Follow-up reports may be obtained on the recommendation of the medical expert, for example, where more time is required before a prognosis can be determined or where the claimant's treatment is continuing.[30]

---

26   See PD 8B and the Pre-Action Protocol for Low Value Personal Injury Claims in Road Traffic Accidents ('The RTA Protocol')

27   RTA Protocol para 7.2

28   RTA Protocol para 7.4

29   RTA Protocol para 7.5

30   RTA Protocol para 7.6

In contrast to the Pre-Action Protocol for Personal Injury Claims, the claimant's solicitor is not required to nominate a medical expert to the defendant. There is no requirement for a jointly selected expert. Apparently, those representing the interests of the insurers felt that current procedures for the selection of experts were effective without the need for the insurer to be involved. In contrast with the normal court based process, there is no provision for the defendant/insurer to put any questions to the medical expert, or even to challenge the quality or expertise of the medical expert selected by the claimant. Not only is there no ability for the defendant/insurer to question the report, but further, the process does not provide for the defendant/insurer to obtain or to rely on its own medical reports.

Where the value of the claim is not agreed between the parties on the basis of the submitted settlement pack, there will be a court determination that will be without an oral hearing, unless the parties request one or the court orders it ('Stage 3'). If the defendant/insurer considers that the medical evidence on which to make an offer is inadequate, then by refusing to make an offer the defendant/insurer will cause the claim to leave the process and so enter the normal (and more expensive) court-based procedure in which it can then obtain its own medical evidence or question the claimant's expert.

Although the committee developing the new process produced a medical report form for use by medical experts, it has not been adopted and does not appear in the current version of the CPR. The process anticipates that the medical expert will provide, where appropriate, an opinion as to the impact of any failure to wear a seat belt on the claimant's injuries. The medical report form, which was not adopted, also contained a section relating to the wearing of a seatbelt.

In cases where the claimant was not wearing a seatbelt, the medical expert was to have been expected to express an opinion as to the extent to which each of the injuries suffered would have been prevented, less severe or no different. While the expert will no doubt wish to assist those instructing him/her and the court, the opinion is, as always, covered by the expert's duty to express an opinion within his/her area of expertise. The expert should make it clear, if asked to address this issue, if he/she considers that it falls outside his/her expertise or where he/she is not able to reach a definite opinion.[31]

3.5   Commencement of Proceedings

Where proceedings have not been compromised as a result of following the relevant pre-action protocol or by negotiation between the parties and do not fall to be dealt with under the new claims process (see Section 3.4 above), the claimant commences proceedings by issuing a 'Claim Form' at the court and by paying the appropriate fee (which varies depending on the value of damages expected to be recovered – this value is provided by the claimant at this stage).

---

31   PD35 para 2.2 and 2.4 and Chapter 4 below

All personal injury claims can be issued in the County Court but only claims with a financial value of £50,000 or more can be commenced in the High Court (except in relation to clinical negligence where there is no minimum value for issue in the High Court).[32] There is, therefore, a substantial overlap of jurisdiction between the local County Court and the High Court, though the High Court is only found in regional centres. The court in which claims are issued is chosen by the solicitor involved and is essentially a matter of professional preference or based on the local reputation of the court, both its management and judiciary. In practice, claims for damages of several hundred thousand pounds are commonly issued and heard in the County Court. In addition, the courts can transfer cases between themselves when it is considered appropriate (on application of the parties or by a court's own decision). The County Court will generally transfer the case to the court that is local to the defendant.

The claim form and the claimant's statement of case - called the 'Particulars of Claim' - must then be served on the defendant. The particulars of claim must have attached to it a report from a medical practitioner 'about the injuries which he alleges in his claim.'[33] It must also have attached 'a schedule of details of any past and future expenses and losses which he claims'[34], generally referred to as the 'Schedule of Loss'.[35] The defendant is required either to admit the claim, or to serve a 'Defence', which sets out the basis on which the defendant takes issue with the claimant's claim.

The defendant is required to respond to the schedule of loss in a document referred to as the 'Counter Schedule'. The defendant is not required at this stage to produce any medical evidence. The parties then complete 'Allocation Question-naires', which are sent into the court and the court will consider to which 'Track' the claim should be assigned.

3.5.1   Tracks

All cases will be assigned by the court to one of three tracks. Cases in each track are managed differently by the court to support the principle of proportionality. The three tracks are:

1.   Small Claims Track

2.   Fast Track

3.   Multi-Track.

---

32   High Court and County Courts Jurisdiction Order 1991

33   PD16 para 4.2

34   PD16 para 4.3

35   See 2.7.2 above

Small Claims Track

This track is for straightforward cases with a value of no more than £5,000 and where the damages for pain and suffering and loss of amenity do not exceed £1,000. Expert evidence will be in the form of written reports only. Court directions will be given without a hearing.

Fast Track

This track is for:

- claims outside the small claims limit and with a value up to £25,000 (for claims issued after 6th April 2009, £15,000 prior to that date – CPR26.6(4));
- where one day (5 hours) of court time only is considered adequate for the trial; and
- where expert evidence will be limited to a maximum of 2 experts (in different fields) per side.[36]

On allocation to the fast track, the court will give directions for the trial setting a period with a three week window for the trial date, not more than 30 weeks in the future. Court directions will be given without a hearing.

From 1 April 2010, the new fast track claims process for personal injury claims arising out of road traffic accidents after 1 April 2010 with a value between £1,000 and £10,000 has been introduced (see Section 3.4 above). This is not part of the current fast track and has a different and simplified procedure. Medical expert evidence will only be in the form of written reports – there will be no oral evidence.

Multi-Track

This track is for all other claims. After allocation to the multi-track the court will normally hold a Case Management Conference (often abbreviated by lawyers to 'CMC') with the parties' representatives. This takes about 30 minutes and the court will decide what directions for the progression of the case should be given. These directions will normally include a timetable leading to a trial window, perhaps 6 months in the future.

---

36 In practice given the time limit, there is little opportunity for disputed medical evidence to be heard in a Fast Track case and any case where there is disputed medical expert evidence will be moved to the Multi-Track.

3.6 Court Directions

The court issues directions to the parties generally reflecting the principles set down in the relevant pre-action protocol. Court directions will require the parties to disclose any relevant documents and to exchange witness statements. The court will also deal with permission to rely on expert evidence in proceedings (including the evidence of medical experts) and will identify whether only the claimant or both parties may rely on expert evidence. The court will direct the specialities of the experts whose reports the parties may rely upon and the date any such reports are to be disclosed or exchanged. If permission is given to both parties to instruct experts, then there will be directions for the experts of similar specialities to meet and discuss the claim, and to provide a joint statement setting out areas of agreement and disagreement (with reasons for disagreement).

Court directions will also be given for the claimant to provide an updated schedule of loss (in the light of the final medical evidence) and for the defendant to respond to this schedule in a counter-schedule.

At the CMC, it will not normally be apparent whether or not there will be conflicting medical opinions or the extent of any medical dispute that will need to be resolved at trial. The defendant may well not have obtained any medical evidence at this stage. The court therefore defers the question of whether or not the parties should have permission to rely on the oral evidence of medical experts at trial (to enable them to be cross-examined) to a future date, nearer to the likely trial date. The issue will then be resolved at a further CMC or 'Pre-Trial Review'. Parties may have to apply to the court subsequently for alterations to court directions if they consider, for example, that experts in further areas are needed or if the defendant seeks to challenge the expert evidence that the claimant has obtained. The parties may also apply if for any reason it has not proved possible to comply with the directed time limits.

At the CMC, a trial date or a trial window - a period ranging from a few days to several weeks or even months - will be provided for. Where medical experts are likely to give oral evidence, a trial date within the trial window will be found that suits all the parties and the availability of their experts, or at least as many of them as possible, consistent with the effective use of court time.

3.7 Court Control of Expert Evidence

Expert evidence is only admissible on matters for which such specialist knowledge is required and therefore if such knowledge is not required the expert will normally be prevented from giving any such evidence. The court is also concerned to control the use of experts in order to ensure that the claim is managed proportionally to the issues in the claim and its value.

3.7.1   Purpose of Expert Evidence

Where a court requires specialised knowledge to decide matters, it will admit expert evidence. The evidence of a medical expert may be necessary in any number of circumstances:

1. to explain or interpret facts that a judge or lawyer would be unable to understand without medical expertise;

2. to understand the implications of a particular injury;

3. to understand the relevance of test results or the significance of an entry in the medical records;

4. to obtain a medical opinion that would be beyond the ability of the judge or lawyer to provide;

5. to understand the expected degree of disability resulting from an injury;

6. to assess the likelihood of further recovery or future complications of an injury; and

7. to understand the appropriate treatment (or acceptable range of treatments) in the specific circumstances faced by a doctor involved with treating the claimant.

3.7.2   The Court's Powers

The court has a general power to control evidence and can exclude evidence even if it is relevant and in the correct form. It will exercise this controlling power whenever giving directions or hearing a party's application in the course of proceedings:

CPR 32.1   (1)   The court may control the evidence by giving directions as to -

    (a)   the issues on which it requires evidence;

    (b)   the nature of the evidence which it requires to decide those issues; and

    (c)   the way in which the evidence is to be placed before the court.

    (2)   The parties are required to help the court to further the overriding objective.

The court has an express power to restrict the expert evidence allowed in relation to a claim:

CPR 35.1   Expert evidence shall be restricted to that which is reasonably required to resolve the proceedings.

In deciding how to exercise this power, the court will take into account such matters as:

- the overriding objectives under Part 1 of the CPR;
- the potential for the narrowing of issues;
- proportionality and costs;
- whether written reports alone will suffice or whether oral evidence and cross examination is necessary; and
- the use of single joint experts.

3.7.3 Limiting Experts' Fees

The court has the power to limit 'the amount of a party's expert's fees and expenses that may be recovered from any other party'.[37] This is a limit on the amount of the expert's charges that can be recovered from the other side, but not on the charges the expert can seek from the instructing party. Proportionality may dictate that the recoverable fees are limited in a smaller value case, even though the expert evidence may be reasonably required and obtained at the reasonable market rate. For obvious economic reasons, the lawyers for the party concerned will normally be anxious to limit the expert's fees to the amount they are able to recover from the other side.

In the case of a single joint expert, that is an expert who is instructed by both parties, the court can limit the amount of fees payable to that expert.[38]

CPR 35.8 (4) The court may, before [a single joint] expert is instructed –

(a) limit the amount that can be paid by way of fees and expenses to the expert; and

(b) direct that some or all of the relevant parties pay that amount into court.

(5) Unless the court otherwise directs, the relevant parties are jointly and severally liable for the payment of the expert's fees and expenses.

3.8 Legal Professionals Involved in a Case

There are three types of legal professional involved in the majority of cases that come to trial:

- solicitors
- barristers
- judges.

---

37 CPR 35.4 (4)

38 Single joint experts are considered in more detail in Section 4.5 below.

3.8.1 Role of the Solicitor

In a typical personal injury claim, the claimant who wants professional assistance to manage his claim will instruct a solicitor. This may in fact involve using a free-phone number to speak to a solicitor many miles away in response to an advertisement, rather than walking into a solicitor's office on the high street to speak to a solicitor across a desk. The defendant may well be dealt with initially by an insurance company or claims handler rather than a solicitor, with a firm of solicitors only becoming involved when proceedings are issued by the claimant. Thereafter, the extent to which the insurer continues to run the case varies from insurer to insurer and from case to case.

In practice, the person handling the claim in the solicitor's office may not be a qualified solicitor. Members of the Institute of Legal Executives or unqualified 'para-legal' staff do much of the day-to-day case work. A solicitor, however, remains responsible for their work on the case and has the day-to-day control of the litigation on behalf of the party on whose behalf he/she is instructed.

The solicitor will maintain a file and manage the litigation (usually with the assistance of case management software), deal with correspondence and communicate with the solicitor for the other party to the litigation. The solicitor for the claimant will be responsible for ensuring that appropriate funding is in place to cover the cost of making the claim and potentially also of losing it (whether such funding be insurance based, Trades Union based or private funds), as well as obtaining the claimant's detailed instructions, collating the necessary documentation, finding witnesses and preparing witness statements.

The extent to which a barrister is used in a claim depends on the solicitor, who in consultation with the claimant will decide whether a barrister needs to be instructed. Practice amongst solicitors varies. Many solicitors are content to draft statements of case and schedules and to assess the value of the claim. Many solicitors will also attend procedural court hearings, such as a CMC, while others will instruct a barrister to do all of this on their behalf. Even when it comes to a trial, some solicitors will appear on behalf of their clients and argue the case, while others will instruct a barrister.

3.8.2 Role of the Barrister

A barrister is a self-employed lawyer.[39] Although barristers are commonly involved in relatively small claims, the larger a claim becomes the more likely it is that the solicitor will instruct a barrister. Barristers work within 'Chambers' with a number of other self-employed barristers. Being in a chambers is essentially a way for a barrister to share administrative and marketing costs with other barristers. In recent years, chambers increasingly market themselves collectively and many chambers now specialise in particular areas of law.

---

39   A barrister is also known as 'counsel'.

The training and experience of a barrister is more focused upon litigation and presenting a claim before a court than that of a solicitor. Although courts require or expect a greater quantity of written submissions than used to be the case, the barrister is still primarily an advocate, skilled in presenting a case to a judge and cross-examining witnesses. As such, a barrister is often better placed to assess the likely outcome of a court hearing. The barrister does not maintain a file for each case, but is briefed (sent instructions and relevant papers) only when his/her assistance is required.

In the field of personal injury, clinical negligence and industrial disease claims, once instructed the barrister will usually perform the following functions:

- draft the statement of case;
- prepare the schedule or counter schedule;
- advise on the merits of the claim and its value;
- advise on the evidence required for the case;
- advise in conference (a meeting) with the solicitor, the party and with experts;
- appear for the party at procedural hearings;
- represent the party at negotiation meetings; and
- appear at trial.

The barrister may also advise the solicitor on the identity of an appropriate expert for the case and draft questions for clarification of the expert reports.

3.8.3   Role of the Judge

The Procedural Judge will normally be a District Judge in the County Court or regional High Court, or a Master in the High Court in London. The Procedural Judge will determine the procedural issues in the case, including the use to be made of experts. This determination is performed with reference to the CPR and the facts of the particular case. There may be other procedural issues relating to the disclosure of documents or payment of interim damages that will also be determined at this level. These hearings are often now heard on the telephone, but if in court will normally be heard in a private room (although legally in fact open to the public).

The expert medical evidence is prepared for the trial judge who will assess the evidence in the very small minority of cases that reach trial. Depending on the value of the claim, or how complicated it is, the trial judge may be a High Court Judge, a Circuit Judge (in the County Court) or a District Judge (also in the County Court). Masters (in the High Court) also hear some disputed matters.

In addition, cases are heard by barristers and solicitors sitting as part-time judges in the High Court (Deputy High Court Judge) or County Court (Recorder or Deputy District Judge). There is no presumption that the judge hearing the case has any experience of personal injury, clinical negligence or industrial disease litigation, or even of cases involving medical expert evidence. The expertise of a judge is as a judge, not as an expert in any particular area of law or type of dispute. It is the judge's role to decide the facts, on the balance of probabilities. It is also for the judge to decide what weight to attach to an expert's evidence.

The court is not bound to accept such evidence simply because it comes from someone designated as being an expert. Where there is a conflict between the evidence of experts, a judge exercises his/her judgement in deciding which opinion to prefer, although the judge is required to give a coherent and reasoned opinion for rejecting expert evidence. The judge can even make his own assessment and come to a conclusion unsupported by either side's expert's evidence, although the judge must give good reason for doing so and must not take on the role of expert.[40]

So, for example, when faced with different opinions from 2 experts on the period of acceleration of symptoms from a pre-existing condition as a result of an accident, the judge may decide on a period between those given by the experts if there is no reason to disregard the opinion of either. It is also for the judge to decide whether the proffered expert has sufficient expertise to be treated as an expert and whether the expert is assisting the court from matters within his/her expertise

3.9   Judge's Approach to Conflicting Expert Evidence

It comes as a surprise to many medical experts the manner in which a judge makes a decision as to which expert's evidence is to be preferred and which rejected. In the absence of any medical expertise of his/her own and faced with differing opinions from two honest and respectable medical experts, the judge has to assess which expert's opinion is more likely to be correct. The judge does this in much the same way as when deciding any conflict in the evidence in a case.

The classic explanation of this assessment process is in the much quoted passage of Lord Justice Stuart-Smith:[41]

> 'The court has to evaluate the witness and the soundness of his opinion.
> …this involves an examination of the reasons given for his opinions and the extent to which they are supported by the evidence. The judge also has to decide what weight to attach to a witness's opinion by examining the internal consistency and logic of his evidence; the care with which he has considered the subject and presented his evidence; his precision and accuracy of thought as demonstrated by his answers; how he responds to searching and informed cross-examination and in particular the extent to which a witness faces up to and accepts the logic of a proposition put in cross-examination or is prepared to concede points that are seen to be correct; the extent to which a witness

---

40   *Huntley v Simmons* [2010] EWCA Civ 54

41   *Loveday v Renton* [1990] 1 Med LR 117 at 125

has conceived an opinion and is reluctant to re-examine it in the light of later evidence, or demonstrates a flexibility of mind which may involve changing or modifying opinions previously held; whether or not a witness is biased or lacks independence

[…] There is one further aspect of a witness's evidence that is often important; that is his demeanour in the witness box. As in most cases where the court is evaluating expert evidence, I have placed less weight on this factor in reaching my assessment. But it is not wholly unimportant; and particularly in those instances where criticisms have been made of a witness on the grounds of bias or lack of independence… the witness's demeanour has been a factor that I have taken into account.'

It is important for all professionals involved in a claim to understand the approach of a judge to conflicting expert evidence, even though most cases are settled before they reach court. In making decisions about settling the claim, the parties' lawyers are mentally projecting the evidence into a courtroom situation and making assessments of how the judge would be likely to respond to the evidence. The quality and content of the expert reports will form an essential part of this assessment prior to a settlement being negotiated by the parties.

Conclusion

The entire progression of a claim, from its intimation through to trial, is controlled by court rules (including here practice directions and pre-action protocols). Compliance with court rules ensures that the parties will minimise the cost of running the claim, while enhancing the chances of an early settlement. Once proceedings are commenced, it is the court rather than the parties that manages the litigation. In particular, the court will set down the programme (ending in a trial) and issue directions to the parties that have to be followed, failing which the court may well impose sanctions or financial penalties in costs. The court also controls the use of experts in the claim.

Key-Point Summary

1. The *Civil Procedure Rules 1998* and associated practice directions and pre-action protocols are the framework within which all claims are brought before the court.

2. The overriding objective of the CPR is to deal with cases justly, while introducing the principle of proportionality into the administration of justice.

3. The court actively manages cases, giving directions to the parties on how the case should progress.

4. Pre-action protocols are important guidance, representing best practice for the lawyers in preparing claims, with penalties in costs for any party that does not follow them.

5. The Pre-Action Protocol for Personal Injury Claims encourages the joint selection of a mutually acceptable medical expert (who is then instructed by the claimant's solicitors), enabling the parties to settle the claim without having to obtain a second expert report.

6. The court has the power to impose on the parties a single joint expert (who is instructed by both parties), although there is no presumption in favour of instructing a single joint expert and in clinical negligence cases the parties have considerable say in the use of medical experts.

7. Experts must ensure that they do not confuse their position as a jointly selected or mutually acceptable medical expert instructed by one party, with that of a single joint expert instructed by both parties.

8. In managing cases, the court places cases into one of three tracks depending on the value and importance of the case – the small claims track, the fast track, and the multi-track. Larger cases (with a value above £50,000) can be heard in the County Court or the High Court and cases can be moved from one court to another as appropriate to achieve the overriding objective.

9. The likely decision of the judge at trial is a critical concern for all parties in a claim, and the assessment by the parties of how the judge will approach the evidence will be an important factor in their approach to settlement negotiations and in making decisions on offers to settle from the opposing party.

10. The judge's role is to decide facts and to assess expert opinion evidence in order to reach a decision. Judges look for accuracy and consistency in expert evidence and a clear rationale to support the opinions reached by the expert.

Next Steps

In the next chapter, we will explore the roles and duties of an expert witness instructed to give evidence in a civil claim.

Developing Your Medico-Legal Mind (3)

Based on your understanding of the *Civil Procedure Rules 1998*, answer the following questions:

1. What is the overriding objective of the CPR and how does this principle affect decisions of the court?

2. What is the purpose of pre-action protocols and what penalties can the court impose on parties that do not follow them?

3. Which pre-action protocols are most relevant to the conduct of claims in personal injury litigation?

4. What is the intention of the CPR in respect of the joint selection of expert witnesses?

5. Which party instructs a jointly selected expert?

6. What factors affect whether proceedings are commenced in the County Court or High Court?

7. How does the court manage cases and upon what information about the claim does it base its management decisions?

8. What are 'tracks' and what are the distinguishing features of each track?

9. What is the purpose of expert evidence in proceedings?

10. How do judges assess expert witnesses and their evidence?

4

Role and Duties of the Expert Witness

4.1   Duties of Experts
4.2   Content of Expert Reports
4.3   Amendments to Reports
4.4   Written Questions to Experts
4.5   Single Joint Experts
4.6   Court Orders
4.7   The Joint Discussion (or Meeting of Experts)

Introduction

All expert witnesses preparing evidence for civil litigation must comply with the rules in Part 35 (CPR 35) and the practice direction to Part 35 (PD35).[1] There is also extremely useful guidance for experts in interpreting and complying with these rules in the Protocol for the Instruction of Experts to give Evidence in Civil Claims (Protocol)[2], published by the Civil Justice Council and annexed to PD35.

Chapter Outline

1   Experts should remain alert to the possibility that in specialist courts, additional guidance may supplement the CPR. If unsure, ask your instructing solicitor, who should know if there are any additional requirements.

2   PD35 states that experts and those instructing them are expected to have regard to the guidance contained in the Protocol.

In this chapter, we will outline the key themes relating to expert evidence in the CPR. We will comment on those rules that relate directly to the form and content of expert reports, and illustrate the importance of these rules both in the writing of the report and in understanding the decision-making process that the court has to undertake should an action come to trial.

4.1 Duties of Experts

Many of the rules that are contained within Part 35 existed before 1998 and Lord Woolf's drafting of the CPR. However, Part 35 does contain for the first time a clear and authoritative statement of the law, so far as it relates to the duties of expert witnesses.

Adherence to the framework of rules within Part 35 is mandatory. Reports that do not comply with these rules may be excluded from litigation, leaving the party seeking to rely upon the evidence in severe difficulties. Reports that do not comply with the CPR also reflect extremely badly on the competence of the expert. It is fundamental to the duties of an expert witness to produce evidence that complies with all of the requirements of CPR 35, PD35 and the Protocol.

4.1.1 The Expert as Fact Finder

In a personal injury claim, the role of the medical expert is to establish, as accurately as possible, what the injuries, symptoms, effects and consequences[3] of the accident have actually been. Since much of the detail in the factual basis of a personal injury report will come directly from the claimant who is seeking compensation, the quality of the presentation of this evidence and the expert's evaluation of it is of the utmost importance.[4]

Two points arise:

1. good note-taking of discussions with the claimant is essential; and where relevant

2. information from the claimant should be reported in the claimant's own words, rather than being glossed into technical medical language by the expert.

---

3   See Section 6.1 below for an explanation of the medico-legal use of these terms

4   In this regard, effective questioning and careful observation of the claimant during the examination are essential skills for experts to develop, though these are beyond the scope of this book.

These two disciplines enable the lawyers and the court to address any dispute between the claimant and the expert about what took place at the interview and examination.

Any notes relating to the interview or examination, whether held on paper or electronically, must be retained until the conclusion of the litigation - i.e. until settlement of the claim or court judgment and the conclusion of any appeal process. The expert will be unlikely to know when any of these stages has been reached in the absence of communication from the instructing lawyer. The notes should also be retained following the conclusion of the injury litigation in case of any claim by a party against any of the professionals in the action. Such a claim may not come to the attention of the expert until as much as seven years after the conclusion of the injury claim (there is a 6 year limitation period in claims alleging such professional negligence) or even longer in the case of a child claimant and therefore, as a rule of thumb, the expert is well advised to keep the notes in relation to an adult claimant appropriately filed for at least 10 years.

4.1.2   GMC Guidance

Acting as an expert witness also carries responsibilities in respect of an expert's professional standards. The GMC Guidance Acting as an Expert Witness[5] provides:

> 15. You must keep up to date in your specialist area of practice. You must also ensure that you understand, and adhere to, the laws and codes of practice that affect your work as an expert witness. In particular, you should make sure that you understand:
>
> • how to construct a court-compliant report;
> • how to give oral evidence; and
> • the specific framework of law and procedure within which you are working.

More specifically the GMC Guidance provides:

> 10. You must make sure that any report that you write, or evidence that you give, is accurate and is not misleading. This means that you must take reasonable steps to verify any information you provide, and you must not deliberately leave out relevant information.
>
> [...]
>
> 12. Your advice and evidence will be relied upon for decision-making purposes by people who do not come from a medical background. Wherever it is possible to do so without being misleading, you should use language and terminology that will be readily understood by those for whom you are providing expert advice or opinion. You should explain any abbreviations and medical or other technical terminology that you use.

---

5   July 2008, available at http://www.gmc-uk.org

It is important that the expert's Terms and Conditions of service are clear. The Protocol for the Instruction of Experts to give Evidence in Civil Claims provides useful guidance as to what should be agreed between the expert and the solicitor before accepting instructions. (See Appendix 5 – Para 7)

4.1.3   CPR Part 35

Many of the principles underlying Part 35 are drawn directly from the judgment of Mr Justice Cresswell in an Admiralty case called *The Ikarian Reefer.*[6] The judge, having been forced to sit through a relatively straightforward case for the best part of six months, is reported to have been extremely annoyed by the conduct of the expert witnesses in court.

In his judgment, he took the unusual step of setting out the duties and responsibilities of expert witnesses in civil cases:

'...because I consider that a misunderstanding on the part of certain expert witnesses... as to their duties and responsibilities contributed to the length of the trial...

The duties and responsibilities of expert witnesses in civil cases include the following:

1.   *Expert evidence presented to the Court should be and should be seen to be the independent product of the expert uninfluenced as to form or content by the exigencies of litigation...*

2.   *An expert witness should provide independent assistance to the Court by way of objective unbiased opinion in relation to matters within his expertise... An expert witness in the High Court should never assume the role of the advocate.*

3.   *An expert witness should state the facts or assumptions on which his opinion is based. He should not omit to consider material facts which detract from his concluded opinion...*

4.   *An expert witness should make it clear when a particular question or issue falls outside his expertise.*

5.   *If an expert's opinion is not properly researched because he considers that insufficient data is available then this must be stated with an indication that the opinion is no more than a provisional one...*

---

6   Cases involving ships are called 'Admiralty cases' and are known by the name of the ship at issue in the litigation. This particular case involves a fire in the engine room of the *Ikarian Reefer* that led to the ship running aground.

6. *If after exchange of reports, an expert witness changes his view on a material matter... such a change of view should be communicated... to the other side without delay and when appropriate to the court.*

7. *Where expert evidence refers to photographs, plans, calculations... survey reports or other similar documents these must be provided to the opposite party at the same time as the exchange of reports...*[7]

Cresswell J's *Ikarian Reefer* principles first appear in rule 35.3:

CPR 35.3 (1) It is the duty of experts to help the court on the matters within their expertise.

(2) This duty overrides any obligation to the person from whom experts have received instructions or by whom they are paid.

4.1.4   Narrowing the Area of Dispute

To help the court (or the judge trying the case) experts must seek to limit the areas of contention between the parties, and so simplify the dispute and the judge's eventual task:

> *'There are generally many "irreducible and stubborn facts" upon which agreement between experts should be possible and in my judgment the expert advisers of the parties, whether legal or scientific, are under a special duty to the court in the preparation of such a case to limit in every possible way the contentious matters of fact to be dealt with at the hearing. That is a duty which exists notwithstanding that it may not always be easy to discharge.'*[8]

4.1.5   Independence

Expert witnesses owe a duty to the court as well as a duty to exercise reasonable skill and care in providing their services to the party instructing them.[9] This simple and straightforward concept seems to cause many experts far more problems than it ought. That one party is paying the expert's fee does not mean that the expert needs to give a favourable opinion to that party or even to temper an unfavourable one. The requirement is simply that the expert demonstrates the independence of mind and the strength of character to give an unbiased opinion.

---

7   [1993] 2 Lloyd's Rep 68

8   *Graigola Merthyr Co Ltd v Swansea Corporation* [1928] 1 Ch 31 at p38

9   This duty to the court does not apply where experts are instructed in an advisory capacity, such as to help a solicitor to identify the key medical issues in a case or to advise or comment on the work of a single joint expert, rather than to prepare evidence for the purpose of proceedings. See Protocol paras 5.1-5.3

> 'There is no conflict between the duty owed by an expert to his client and his overriding duty to the court. His duty to the client is to perform his function as an expert with the reasonable skill and care of an expert drawn from the relevant discipline. This includes a duty to perform the overriding duty of assisting the court. Thus the discharge of the duty to the court cannot be a breach of duty to the client. If the expert gives an independent and unbiased opinion which is within the range of reasonable expert opinions, he will have discharged his duty both to the court and his client. If, however, he gives an independent and unbiased opinion which is outside the range of reasonable expert opinions, he will not be in breach of his duty to the court, because he will have provided independent and unbiased assistance to the court. But he will be in breach of the duty owed to his client.'[10]

As the Protocol states:

Protocol   4.3   Experts should provide opinions which are independent, regardless of the pressures of litigation.[11] In this context, a useful test of 'independence' is that the expert would express the same opinion if given the same instructions by an opposing party…

The potential difficulties for an expert in maintaining this independence have been recognised by the courts:

> 'The area of expertise in any case may be likened to a broad street with the [claimant] walking on one pavement and the defendant walking on the opposite one. Somehow the expert must be ever mindful of the need to walk straight down the middle of the road and to resist the temptation to join the party from whom the instructions come on the pavement. It seems to me that the expert's difficulty … is much increased if he attends the trial for days on end as a member of the litigation team. Some sort of seduction into shared attitudes, assumptions and goals seems to me almost inevitable.'[12]

Even without being present in the courtroom for days, the feeling of being part of a team can develop during conferences with the instructing side, especially where discussions of the case and the evidence of the 'opposing' experts take place.

An independent and unbiased opinion is far more helpful to the lawyers in negotiating a settlement than an exaggerated opinion that is only exposed as such once substantial costs have been incurred on the back of it. Worse still is the situation where an exaggerated opinion collapses under the pressure of cross-examination in court. Any competent solicitor will say that an opinion that is not supported by the evidence is extremely costly, misleading and ultimately damaging to a cli-

---

10   Lord Dyson in *Jones v Kaney* [2011] UKSC 13 at para 99

11   Note the repetition of the first *Ikarian Reefer* principle, although with 'pressures' replacing 'exigencies', perhaps for ease of understanding

12   Thorpe LJ in *Vernon v Bosley* (No1) [1997] 1 All ER 577 at 612

ent's case. It is therefore important that when assisting a party as part of a team of experts involved in a case, the sense of being a 'team player' is not allowed to come into conflict with the duty to assist the court and express an independent and unbiased opinion.

The expert owes his/her duty to the court, and failure to comply with that duty can have serious implications for the party instructing the expert as well as for the expert him/herself. The Protocol sets out the position as follows:

Protocol 4.7 Experts should be aware that any failure by them to comply with the Civil Procedure Rules or court orders or any excessive delay for which they are responsible may result in the parties who instructed them being penalised in costs and even, in extreme cases, being debarred from placing the experts' evidence before the court. In *Phillips v Symes* Peter Smith J held that courts may also make orders for costs (under section 51 of the Supreme Court Act 1981)[13] directly against expert witnesses who by their evidence cause significant expense to be incurred, and do so in flagrant and reckless disregard of their duties to the Court.

There is also a duty of care owed by experts to the party instructing them, as there is in any contract to provide services. However, the duty of care owed to that party is subject to the obligations imposed on the expert by the CPR. Until 30 March 2011, the expert had the benefit of immunity from being sued for anything said in the course of giving evidence and in preparation for giving evidence, which included his/her conduct in a joint discussion and in the preparation of a joint statement. That immunity has now ceased to exist as a result of the decision of the Supreme Court in *Jones v Kaney*.[14] The position now is that the expert witness can be sued for damages by his/her client for negligence in relation to the expert's participation in any legal proceedings. It has been suggested that:

> 'The most likely broad consequence of denying expert witnesses the immunity accorded to them [hitherto] will be a sharpened awareness of the risks of pitching their initial views of the merits of their client's case too high or too inflexibly lest these views come to expose and embarrass them at a later date. I for one would welcome this as a healthy development in the approach of expert witnesses to their ultimate task (their sole rationale) of assisting the court to a fair outcome of the dispute (or, indeed, assisting the parties to a reasonable pre-trial settlement).
>
> The other signal advantage of denying immunity to expert witnesses is, of course, that in the no doubt rare case where the witness behaves in an egregious manner such as is alleged in the instant case or, indeed, otherwise causes his client loss by adopting or adhering to an opinion outside the

---

13 From 1st October 2009 the Supreme Court Act 1981 has been renamed the Senior Courts Act 1981
14 *Jones v Kaney* [2011] UKSC 31

permissible range of reasonable expert opinions, the wronged client will enjoy, rather than have denied to him by rule of law, his proper remedy.' [15]

This potential liability of the expert witness to be sued by his/her client for negligence in performing the services of an expert witness will extend to reports prepared for the purposes of litigation, any out of court statements, such as in a conference with the client and instructing lawyers and in a joint statement pre-pared following a discussion between experts, and the giving of evidence itself.

> There is no excuse for an expert witness not to be familiar with the require-ments of the CPR (Part 35, PD 35 and the Protocol). These rules are funda-mental to producing expert reports and giving oral evidence and familiari-ty with these rules will help the expert to perform the role of expert witness appropriately.

In addition to this liability for any negligence, at all times experts remain subject to their professional codes of ethics and may in appropriate instances of bad con-duct or apparent incompetence be referred by the judge to their professional body for consideration of disciplinary proceedings. The Protocol states:

Protocol   4.1   Experts always owe a duty to exercise reasonable skill and care to those instructing them, and to comply with any relevant professional code of ethics. However when they are instructed to give or prepare evidence for the purpose of civil proceedings in England and Wales they have an overriding duty to help the court on matters within their expertise (CPR 35.3). This duty overrides any obligation to the person instructing or paying them. Experts must not serve the exclusive interest of those who retain them.

An expert must always ensure that there is no possible conflict of interest when producing a report and that there is no possible appearance of bias. For example, when advising in a clinical negligence claim, it is important to draw attention to any possible connection that the medical expert may have with any party being made the subject of possible criticism.

The standard court direction in clinical negligence claims in the High Court includes the direction that:

Experts shall, at the time of producing their reports, produce a CV giving details of any employment or activity which raises a possible conflict of interest.

---

15   Lord Brown in *Jones v Kaney* at para 67 and 68

4.1.6   Duty to Co-Operate with the Court Process

The expert's duty to the court also includes a requirement to co-operate with the court process.

Protocol   9.1   Experts should confirm without delay whether or not they accept instructions. They should also inform those instructing them (whether on initial instructions or at any later stage) without delay if:

    (a)   instructions are not acceptable because, for example, they require work that falls outside their expertise, impose unrealistic deadlines, or are insufficiently clear;

    (b)   they consider that instructions are or have become insufficient to complete the work;

    (c)   they become aware that they may not be able to fulfil any of the terms of appointment;

    (d)   the instructions and/or work have, for any reason, placed them in conflict with their duties as an expert; or

    (e)   they are not satisfied that they can comply with any orders that have been made.

Therefore by taking on medico-legal work, it must be recognised by the busy medical practitioner that the medico-legal practice must be given proper priority. This can become even more difficult when it comes to the possibility of being required to attend at court:

Protocol   19.1   Experts instructed in cases have an obligation to attend court if called upon to do so and accordingly should ensure that those instructing them are always aware of their dates to be avoided and take all reasonable steps to be available.

The solicitor has a corresponding obligation to ascertain the expert's availability before the trial date is fixed, keep experts updated with court timetables, give consideration to whether experts could give evidence by a video-link, and inform experts immediately if trial dates are vacated.[16]

The attendance of a witness at court can be enforced by the issue and service of a witness summons. Normally, an expert should attend without the need for service of a witness summons, but on occasions an expert may be served in order to require attendance. Whether or not a witness summons is served, the expert has an obligation to attend and the instructing party has an obligation to pay the expert's fee.[17]

---

16   Protocol para 19.2

17   Protocol para 19.3

4.1.7   Investigating Claims

The medical expert's role is to identify the relevant facts, to carry out such examination as is appropriate and to express an opinion. It is not for the medical expert to become involved in the exercise of gathering evidence in the case.

An example of an unfortunate over-involvement of a medical expert in obtaining evidence in a claim is the case of *Williams v Jervis*.[18] The defendant's expert, having produced his report, came into possession of an earlier report that had been obtained in the same case by the claimant's lawyers. The claimant's lawyers, as they were entitled so to do, had not disclosed the report to the defendant. This undisclosed report was not favourable to the claimant's case and the defendant's expert in his own opinion evidence agreed with it.

The defendant's expert then sent the report anonymously to his instructing solicitors, who in turn disclosed it to the claimant's lawyers. On investigation at trial, it transpired that the defendant's expert had heard of the existence of the other unfavourable report when he happened to discuss the case with a colleague who was the author of the report. The expert had asked for a copy of it and so created the difficulty for the parties.

In his judgment, the judge stated:

> *'In putting himself in the position of being in possession of [the undisclosed report], [the defendant's expert] displayed very poor judgement. Moreover, the way he dealt with the report and part of the evidence he gave about it in court were not straightforward. He misled his instructing solicitors and I reject the evidence he gave that he had any doubt about the source of the report even if it did arrive in a brown envelope with no covering letter. Accepting, as of course I do, that [the defendant's expert] has no legal training, his claim that he thought his conduct consistent with the discharge of his duties to the court as an expert witness is, in the light of the vast number of medico-legal cases he undertakes, untenable...'*

An expert is instructed to report and should limit investigations to strictly medical investigations, and not become involved in the more general investigation of the claim in which he/she is instructed.

4.1.8   Restrictions on Expert Evidence

Before April 1999 when the CPR came into force, it was the parties who managed the litigation and they would frequently instruct a multitude of expert witnesses. In his final report, Lord Woolf concluded that many of these instructions were unnecessary, time-consuming and disproportionate to the value of the claim.

---

18   [2008] EWHC 2346

Part 35 begins with a rule that restricts the availability of expert evidence and the number of expert witnesses that can be relied upon in a case. The parties are required to justify to the court why any expert is necessary and the particular disciplines that are necessary. It is for the court to rule if expert evidence in any particular discipline, or any at all, is necessary to resolve the proceedings:

CPR 35.1   Expert evidence shall be restricted to that which is reasonably required to resolve the proceedings.

4.1.9   Form of Expert Evidence

Rule 35.5 requires that expert evidence is put before the court in the form of a written report:

CPR 35.5   (1)   Expert evidence is to be given in a written report unless the court directs otherwise.

(2)   If a claim is on the small claims track or the fast track, the court will not direct an expert to attend a hearing unless it is necessary to do so in the interests of justice.

This rule places great weight on the written report. In smaller cases, there will be no oral evidence should the matter come to court. In larger cases, the report will be taken as read and will stand as the expert's evidence-in-chief[19], so that the expert will not expand upon or explain his/her report in oral evidence and cross-examination of the witness on the contents of the expert's written evidence will proceed without delay.

A high-quality report is now essential. All of the evidence that the expert witness wants to bring to the attention of the court needs to be set out in writing and will be read before the expert witness arrives at court. In practice, the written report is important at a far earlier stage of proceedings because approximately 98% of cases will be abandoned or will settle by negotiation based substantially upon the written reports of the experts in the case.

4.2   Content of Expert Reports

The required content of expert reports is first addressed in CPR 35.10, with greater detail set out in PD35 paras 3.1-3.9. Further guidance is provided in paras 13.1-13.15 of the Protocol. The purpose of these requirements is to make sure that all of the information relevant to the decision-making process of the court is contained in the report:

CPR 35.10   (1)   An expert's report must comply with the requirements set out in practice direction 35.

---

19   The evidence adduced in court by a party from its own witnesses.

(2) At the end of an expert's report there must be a statement that the expert understands and has complied with their duty to the court.

(3) The expert's report must state the substance of all material instructions, whether written or oral, on the basis of which the report was written.

PD35 3.2 An expert's report must:

(1) give details of the expert's qualifications;

(2) give details of any literature or other material which the expert has relied on in making the report;

(3) contain a statement setting out the substance of all facts and instructions which are material to the opinions expressed in the report or upon which those opinions are based;

(4) make clear which of the facts stated in the report are within the expert's own knowledge;

(5) say who carried out any examination, measurement, test or experiment which the expert has used for the report, give the qualifications of that person, and say whether or not the test or experiment has been carried out under the expert's supervision;

(6) where there is a range of opinion on the matters dealt with in the report –

(a) summarise the range of opinion, and

(b) give reasons for the expert's own opinion;

(7) contain a summary of the conclusions reached;[20]

(8) if the expert is not able to give an opinion without qualification, state the qualification; and

(9) contain a statement that the expert –

(a) understands their duty to the court, and has complied with that duty; and

(b) is aware of the requirements of Part 35, this practice direction and the Protocol for Instruction of Experts to give Evidence in Civil Claims.

---

20 Note that there is no requirement for a 'summary report', only a straightforward 'summary of conclusions'

PD35 3.3   An expert's report must be verified by a statement of truth in the following form:

'I confirm that I have made clear which facts and matters referred to in this report are within my own knowledge and which are not. Those that are within my own knowledge I confirm to be true. The opinions I have expressed represent my true and complete professional opinion on the matters to which they refer.'[21]

The expert's written evidence in a case will be comprised of the expert's report, the expert's answers to questions of clarification, and the joint statement produced by the experts prior to trial. All of these may be subject to cross-examination should a case reach court. The requirements in the CPR and the Protocol will, if properly followed, help to ensure that the expert's evidence is adequate. If the rules are followed, the expert report will demonstrate that the expert has the appropriate qualifications and relevant experience to give opinions in the case. It should also show the basis of the expert's opinions. The report will also confirm - and it will generally be taken at face value - that the expert has understood and complied with his/her duty to the court in the proceedings.

PD35 3.1   An expert's report should be addressed to the court and not to the party from whom the expert has received instructions.

By requiring the expert to expressly refer to the duty to the court and to address the report to the court and not to the instructing party, the role of the expert as an independent and objective professional is emphasised. In practice, this outlaws the practice of producing a report addressed directly to one party, but does not mandate that the report is headed 'To the Court'. A statement that the expert has been 'instructed to produce a Part 35 report for the court' is an elegant way of informing everyone involved that the expert has read and is conscious of the requirements of the CPR.

The Protocol makes reference at para 13.5(ii) to the need for an expert to refer to an awareness of the requirements of the 'practice direction on pre-action conduct'. PD35 does not require a statement to this effect although it notes the existence of further guidance on experts (not 'to experts' or 'for experts') in Annex C to the Practice Direction - Pre-Action Conduct. This guidance is for the parties and their legal advisers and refers to the procedure by which, where a single joint expert is not used, the claimant should if possible chose an expert acceptable to the defendant.

---

21   The Expert's Declaration and Statement of Truth are mandatory statements in an expert report. There are many, often lengthy, statements and declarations generated by various professional bodies that do not comply with the far easier and simpler requirement laid down by the court. See Section 4.2.14-15

4.2.1   Instructions

It is by no means the universal practice for solicitors, when instructing experts, to provide any or any adequate guidance as to what is required either generally of a medical expert report or specifically in relation to a particular case. As Lord Woolf noted:

> 'From the comments I have received on this point it appears that solicitors' instructions vary from detailed to perfunctory. 'Please provide your usual report' is an example that has been mentioned to me, and it may well be that this is adequate for an experienced expert who is frequently instructed by the same solicitor. Many experts have, however, indicated that they would welcome more detailed and explicit instructions, and I have no doubt that solicitors would benefit from guidance in this area.' [22]

The situation persists with perfunctory or inadequate solicitors' instructions still being provided to medical experts. The medical expert is therefore frequently on his/her own as to what is required when writing the report. The Protocol provides guidance for lawyers as to what is required as a minimum and encourages medical experts to respond positively should they feel the need for clarification of what is required of them.

Protocol   8.1   Those instructing experts should ensure that they give clear instructions, including the following:

    (a)   basic information, such as names, addresses, telephone numbers, dates of birth and dates of incidents;

    (b)   the nature and extent of the expertise which is called for;

    (c)   the purpose of requesting the advice or report, a description of the matter(s) to be investigated, the principal known issues and the identity of all parties;

    (d)   the statement(s) of case (if any), those documents which form part of standard disclosure and witness statements which are relevant to the advice or report;

    (e)   where proceedings have not been started, whether proceedings are being contemplated and, if so, whether the expert is asked only for advice;

    (f)   an outline programme, consistent with good case management and the expert's availability, for the completion and delivery of each stage of the expert's work; and

    (g)   where proceedings have been started, the dates of any hearings (including any Case Management Conferences and/or Pre-Trial Reviews), the name of the court, the claim number and the track to which the claim has been allocated.

---

22   *Access to Justice – Final Report* (see above) Chapter 13 para 56

8.2   Experts who do not receive clear instructions should request clarification and may indicate that they are not prepared to act unless and until such clear instructions are received.

There is an element of proportionality in what is provided by way of detailed instructions and the time spent by the lawyers in providing such instructions. A whiplash type injury with 4 weeks of symptoms does not require or merit the same length of instructions as would be expected of a claim in clinical negligence for an adverse event following brain surgery. However, the principle remains the same – the medical expert should understand the purpose of the report and what he/she is being asked to report on, and if in doubt must ask the instructing solicitor for clarification of the instructions.

The substance of all material instructions that the expert has received, whether in writing or orally, is to be included in the report. The expert should summarise the instructions to enable the judge to understand what issues the expert is reporting upon. It is intended that by disclosing the substance of the instructions, the objectivity and impartiality of the expert will be emphasised and encouraged. Any instruction, for example, not to mention an unfavourable aspect of the case, even if given on the telephone as a supplemental instruction to a letter of instruction, would have to be included in the report. The Protocol states:

Protocol   13.15   The mandatory statement of the substance of all material instructions should not be incomplete or otherwise tend to mislead. The imperative is transparency. The term "instructions" includes all material which solicitors place in front of experts in order to gain advice. The omission from the statement of 'off-the-record' oral instructions is not permitted. Courts may allow cross-examination about the instructions if there are reasonable grounds to consider that the statement may be inaccurate or incomplete.

The expert's report must state the 'substance of all facts and instructions which are material to the opinions expressed in the report or upon which those opinions are based': [23]

I have been asked specifically to express an opinion as to:

1.   the likelihood the claimant would have developed symptoms of anxiety or depression in the absence of the accident; and

2.   the date at which it would have been reasonable for the claimant to have returned to full time employment following the accident.

---

23   PD35 3.2(3)

Many experts with established relationships with solicitors understand what the solicitor requires and therefore the expert need simply state his/her own understanding of the instructions:

I am instructed by Sue Quickly & Co to write a medical report on Mr Smith. I have interpreted this instruction as follows:

1. I am to interview Mr Smith and perform a medical examination;

2. I am to identify any injuries Mr Smith has on presentation and give opinion, on the balance of probabilities, as to their causation;

3. I am to give a prognosis, on the balance of probabilities, for any injuries that I consider are caused by the accident and where appropriate suggest further treatment to improve prognosis;

4. I am to give an opinion on the likely consequences arising from any such injuries and whether the consequences claimed by Mr Smith are reasonable and attributable to the accident; and

5. I am to set out my findings and conclusions in a report that complies with the requirements of CPR Part 35.

Before agreeing to provide an expert report, the expert must make sure that the instructions received from the solicitor are clear. Clarifying instructions before commencing the work will usually save time and money, and sometimes even the professional relationship between the expert and the solicitor.

4.2.2 Details of Qualifications

An expert has to show that he/she has the appropriate expertise to express an opinion on the issues addressed in the report. Normally, this can be stated briefly within the report – two or three paragraphs at the start of the expert report summarising the expert's qualifications is usually sufficient, with the option of a CV appended to the report if further detail is likely to be required.

The expert's CV should show the expert's expertise and experience of dealing with the medical aspects relevant to the claim. It is also a good discipline to check that the CV, whether included within or appended to the report, is sufficient to establish the expert's credibility in dealing with the issues in dispute in that particular claim.

If the issues to be addressed are particularly specialised or esoteric or if a clear difference of opinion develops between experts, then it may be advisable to provide or make available a more detailed CV with reference to all posts held, research undertaken and papers published.

The Protocol states:

> Protocol   13.16   The details of experts' qualifications to be given in reports should be commensurate with the nature and complexity of the case. It may be sufficient merely to state academic and professional qualifications. However, where highly specialised expertise is called for, experts should include the detail of particular training and/or experience that qualifies them to provide that highly specialised evidence.

The expert's relevant experience of the issues in a case is a significant factor in the court's analysis of the need for a party to instruct a particular expert in the first instance. It is also important in the analysis of the opinion by the lawyers during negotiations between the parties and by the judge should the matter come to court. An expert whose CV clearly indicates particular expertise in the matters before the court is more likely to be given instructions to produce a report and the report itself is likely subsequently to carry much greater evidential weight.

> It is important that the expert's CV makes clear the expert's expertise and experience of dealing with the medical issues in the case. This information may influence the court in allowing a party to call the expert. Experts must make sure that the CV set out in the report is relevant to the issues in dispute – a generalised CV that does not address the medical issues in the dispute is not helpful.

The expert must be accurate in providing details of expertise and relevant experience. Inaccuracies, even if not dishonestly provided, can be fatal to the expert's credibility:

> 'When asked about his curriculum vitae he gave oral evidence about his experience as a consultant and said he had performed about 2,000 terminations. However, the defendant had done its homework and had obtained figures for the terminations performed over the years at… Hospital. They disclosed that in fact a very low number of terminations had been performed – probably one of the lowest rates in the whole country, and Mr X is not the only surgeon at the hospital performing these operations. Eventually Mr X did admit that he must have been wrong about his figures. Asked how he felt about that he said he did not think it was important.
>
> Another matter is that Mr X told me he had given evidence before in court and, asked whether that was mainly on behalf of [claimants] or defendants, he replied that the split was 80% [claimant] to 20% defendant. However

again after further questioning, some of it by me, Mr X admitted he had never given evidence on behalf of any defendant in court.' [24]

Not surprisingly, the judge considered these important matters in assessing the reliability of the expert's evidence.

4.2.3 Literature

It is extremely important that experts ensure that they give details of literature and papers they have relied upon in reaching an opinion.[25] This becomes only too clear to the expert who under cross-examination seeks to justify his opinion by reference to literature not previously and expressly disclosed to the other party in good time prior to trial.

The other side is entitled to have the opportunity to consider such literature in order to challenge the expert's reliance upon it, interpretation of it, or its application to the facts of the present case. Not only the other side's expert, but also its lawyers are entitled to this opportunity. If the case has to be adjourned, then there will be issues as to who should pay the substantial costs – the costs of the lawyers and of the experts - resulting from such an adjournment. If the court declines an adjournment, then the expert may not be permitted to rely on the undisclosed literature, with potentially very damaging consequences on the court's approach to the reliability or reasonableness of the expert's opinion.

> The purpose of providing references to medical literature is to support the opinions expressed by the expert. All references provided in the report should be directly relevant to the evidence and generalised lists of references, which the expert habitually adds to each report, should not be used.

An unnecessary proliferation of references must be avoided. The expert should be selective in identifying only the most relevant and appropriate literature and should normally list only the key papers published in reputable journals. When relying on a text book, it is important to ensure that the text book is appropriate to the matter in issue and that it is the appropriate edition (generally the most recent edition, although in the case of clinical negligence, the edition current at the time of the alleged negligence is likely to be relevant on issues of standard of care):

'Mr X relied on page 7 of the 1972 edition... The matter which caused me considerable concern was that since 1972 there have been further editions of this, albeit basic, textbook, and in particular a third edition was published six years before the [claimant's] operation and a fourth edition was published

---

24   *Rhodes v West Surrey and North East Hampshire* HA [1998] Lloyds Law Reports: Medical 246

25   PD35 3.2(2)

two years after. The importance of these later editions is that the word "clumsiness" has been removed.' [26]

In many cases, it will suffice to provide relevant footnotes within the report or a short list of references to relevant texts at the end of the report. However, if it becomes apparent that there is a significant difference of opinion between the experts, then the expert should be given the opportunity by the instructing solicitor to consider whether it is necessary to expand the list of relevant and material texts. Once it becomes clear that there is a dispute between the experts, copies of the texts material to the dispute should be provided to their respective instructing lawyers by each expert, as it is unlikely that the lawyers on either side will have these texts or easy access to them. The court's directions, which the expert should (but may well not) have seen, may order that any literature relied upon by an expert is to be disclosed to all parties within some specific period prior to the trial.

The court directions used in clinical negligence claims in the High Court normally provide:

> *Any unpublished literature upon which any expert witness proposes to rely shall be served at the same time as service of his report together with a list of published literature. Any supplementary literature upon which any expert witness proposes to rely shall be notified to all other parties at least one month before trial. No expert witness shall rely upon any publications that have not been disclosed in accordance with this direction without leave of the trial judge on such terms as to costs as he deems fit.*

4.2.4 Factual Basis of the Evidence

Experts need to establish a reliable factual basis for the opinions that they wish to express later in the report. This requires of the expert both the ability to identify all facts that are relevant to the claim and the ability to differentiate between discrete categories of factual evidence in the report. The court's assessment of the expert report will initially be focussed upon the expert's apprehension of the factual basis.

As far as the lawyers are concerned, an essential element of presenting the case is establishing facts to the required standard of proof. Facts that are accepted as true by all parties are known as 'agreed facts', while facts that are disputed between the parties are known as 'asserted facts' or 'alleged facts'. All witnesses will give evidence as to what they perceive the facts to be. Witnesses of fact can only give evidence of what they perceived of the events at the time, while expert witnesses will usually give both evidence of fact and evidence of opinion.

---

26   See *Rhodes v West Surrey and North East Hampshire* HA (as above)

> In expert witness workshops, when we ask groups of doctors for a definition of a 'fact', the suggestion usually arises that a fact is something that can be demonstrated to be true, such as the result of a measurement or a test. A dictionary definition of 'fact' introduces the concept of a fact being something that is indisputably shown to be the case. In court, a fact is something that is perceived through one or more of the five senses of a witness. That a perceived fact may be hotly disputed does not exclude it from the evidence, as it is the judge's role to assess competing facts (perceptions) to decide what the 'true' facts are for the purposes of the case.

Expert witnesses are able to increase their range of perception beyond the limits of the five senses through the use of scientific tests and experiments, which allows greater factual accuracy to be established. The use of such experiments and tests will often clarify factual disputes between the parties. However, lawyers are entitled to challenge tests and experiments carried out by experts, by challenging the methodology adopted, the calibration of the equipment used to carry out the test or the relevance of the test results to the issues to be decided in the case.

Facts may be provided to the expert in different ways:

- the history or other information provided by the claimant;
- the witness statements provided to the expert by the instructing solicitor;
- information gleaned from medical records;
- the results of examinations or tests carried out by others; or
- the results of observations, examinations or tests carried out by the expert him/herself.

We have seen above that PD35 3.1-3 introduce specific requirements for the presentation of factual evidence. In summary, the expert is required to differentiate three categories of fact:

1. given facts (relevant to the opinions expressed); [PD35 3.2(3)]

2. facts within the expert's own knowledge; [PD35 3.2(4)] and

3. facts (and possibly opinions) taken from the work of other experts. [PD35 3.2(5)]

The purpose of this requirement is to allow the court to consider the quality and integrity of the factual basis of the report. For each issue in dispute, the court will seek to understand those facts that the expert has taken into account in reaching his/her opinion and, crucially, the basis of those facts and the weight given to each by the expert.

The Statement of Truth addresses this distinction between different types of fact when it requires the expert to confirm his/her belief that 'the facts … within my own knowledge' are true. The expert cannot confirm the truth of facts where such facts have been provided by another (for example, facts from the claimant or the medical practitioner whose medical records have been provided to the expert), although the fact that those facts were provided by the claimant or recorded by other medical practitioners can be confirmed by the expert.

In addition to reporting on the facts provided by the claimant and providing factual evidence from the expert's own medical examination, the expert may also give relevant factual evidence based on observations not specific to an observer with medical expertise. For example, the expert may observe the claimant arriving or leaving for the appointment – on the stairs or in the car park – and find those observations relevant to an opinion as to the degree of actual disability.[27]

All of these types of facts can be provided by the expert and may be material to the expert's opinion.

Therefore, an expert report will fall short of the required standard if the factual basis for an opinion is not set out clearly in the report.

4.2.5   Incident/Accident Details and Subsequent Events

When describing the history of an accident, the expert should give those factual details that are relevant to the medico-legal issues to be addressed in the report. For example, in a report on injuries sustained in a car accident, an orthopaedic surgeon may be concerned to address issues such as:

1.   where the claimant was sitting in the car;

2.   the angle of collision;

3.   the severity of the collision;

4.   whether the claimant was wearing a seat belt;

5.   whether the car was fitted with headrests;

6.   whether the claimant was able to brace before impact;

7.   whether the claimant was able to get out of the car unaided; and

8.   whether the claimant was taken to hospital.

---

27   See further at Sections 7.4.4 and 7.4.5 below

For a psychiatrist, other issues may also be relevant, such as:

1. whether the claimant saw the oncoming vehicle before the collision;

2. what the claimant saw, heard and felt during and immediately after the accident; and

3. who else was in the car and how the claimant reacted to his/her own injuries and the injuries of these others in the car.

Details, such as the colour of the car, are factual issues that are irrelevant to the medical expert's opinion and should be omitted.

Sometimes, the precise circumstances of an accident are an issue in dispute between the parties. The expert must appreciate that if the report includes a detailed description of the circumstances of the accident, this must be an accurate record of what the claimant has said. If the version in the report differs materially from that given in the proceedings by the claimant (for example in the statement of case or in a witness statement), then the claimant's credibility in relation to those and other facts may be attacked on the basis of such inconsistencies. To resolve the issue the expert could become a witness of fact at the trial as to what the claimant said during the interview about the circumstances of the accident – a situation that experts should seek to avoid.

The description of the accident as given by the claimant may be lengthy, so if the expert seeks only to summarise this description there is a greater risk of the version recorded in the report being an inaccurate record of what was said. While describing a road traffic accident may generally be straightforward, descriptions of other accidents and particularly accidents at work can often be difficult to understand clearly without photographs of equipment, plans of the workplace or knowledge of the process involved.

If providing a detailed description of the accident in the report is relevant, then the expert must make sure that he/she understands all relevant matters and that the claimant is in agreement with the details that the expert has recorded. It is generally best practice, therefore, for an expert to give only a brief summary of the accident in the report save where the detail is material to the opinions expressed, and when providing details, to ensure that the claimant has had the opportunity to confirm the correctness of the description.

4.2.6 Examination Findings

The examination the expert carries out will generally be fundamental to the opinions that will follow later in the report. The expert will report his/her direct evidence as to the claimant's condition on the day of the interview and examination.

The expert should briefly describe the type of examination that he/she has carried out, so that the lawyers understand what methodology the expert has adopted. It is unnecessary to give a full explanation of the technical terms in the Examination or Mental State Examination section, as any relevant findings will be explained in the Opinion and Prognosis section that follows. However, short explanatory notes can be very helpful in increasing the lawyers' comprehension of the report.

It is important that the expert should take the time to set out clearly all of the examination findings in the report, even where no abnormality or adverse finding is detected. There are two reasons for this:

1. the results of a detailed examination set out in the report reassures the lawyers and the court that the expert has carried out the examination to the required professional standard;[28] and

2. should the case come to court, a challenge may arise as to whether a particular aspect of the examination was carried out at all, as there may be no reference to it in the report.

Therefore, recording the examination to an appropriate level of detail provides the basis for opinions that will be expressed in the Opinion and Prognosis section.

4.2.7   Factual Disputes

It may happen that the parties have different versions of events that are material to the expert's opinion. It may also be that the opinion of the expert would change depending on which version of events the expert uses as the basis for his/her opinion. The expert is therefore faced with a difficulty that cannot be resolved without the court's decision on the facts at issue.

The solution, however, is straightforward and is dealt with clearly in the Protocol:

Protocol   13.11   Where there are material facts in dispute experts should express separate opinions on each hypothesis put forward...

Therefore, where there are factual disputes in the evidence, the expert should express separate opinions on each of the factual bases. How this is set out in the report will depend on the extent of the factual disagreements. Where there are limited conflicts in the evidence, the expert may choose to deal with both sets of facts in the same section within the factual basis of the evidence. As the conflicts in the evidence multiply, it may be necessary to have two separate sections dealing with the factual evidence brought forward by each party.

---

28   Protocol Para 4.1: '...to exercise reasonable skill and care...and to comply with any relevant professional code of ethics.'

Experts have the authority only in limited circumstances to express an opinion in favour of one or other of the disputed versions:

Protocol   13.11   They should not express a view in favour of one or other disputed version of the facts unless, as a result of particular expertise and experience, they consider one set of facts as being improbable or less probable, in which case they may express that view, and should give reasons for holding it.

It may be, for example, that an expert's specialist knowledge of a particular medical condition enables him/her to conclude that the claimant's version of events cannot be correct – for example, such symptoms cannot be caused by or are not consistent with this condition or such complaints cannot persist for such a period or in such a manner given the nature of the condition. However, there are probably limited situations in which the expert can confidently dismiss one set of facts entirely. In most cases, the expert will need to express a separate qualified opinion on each of the factual bases.

The importance of expressing separate opinions is perhaps best illustrated by conflicts between medical records and lay witnesses present at the material time. If an expert forms an opinion, for example, that the GP records should be relied upon, because these appear to be contemporaneous and there is no apparent reason for them to be mistaken, and so chooses to discount the evidence of the claimant or the claimant's family, then the expert has created a vulnerability in his/her opinion evidence. Should the court take the view that, on the balance of probabilities, the evidence of the claimant is to be preferred, then the expert would be left without a valid opinion and would provide no assistance to the court or to the parties on that matter.

The expert should therefore be careful before proceeding only on the factual basis as provided by the instructing solicitor. In expressing opinion on the basis of facts set out in a letter of instruction or in witness statements from only one side of the claim, the expert will often be providing a one-sided report and may be ignoring 'facts in dispute' material to the provision of expert opinion.

4.2.8   Disputes between Medical Records and the Claimant's Account

Some medical experts adopt the practice of only reading the claimant's medical records after having carried out the interview and examination, the claimant by then having left the consulting room. The motivation for this practice is laudable, namely that the expert can avoid preconceptions about the claimant and have a clear perception of the injuries. However, a practical difficulty with this method arises when the information from the claimant about his/her previous medical history conflicts with the medical records.

Conflicts commonly arise in the claimant's account of his/her previous medical history when this is compared to the clinical records. Possible reasons for these conflicts are:

1. some claimants are trying to manipulate the situation to their advantage;

2. some claimants can be very nervous about seeing a medical expert and do not give a clear account;

3. people are often poor at giving a clear history, whether out of embarrassment or because of a poor or selective memory;

4. medical records may be incomplete, inaccurate or the records may even belong to another person;

5. miscommunication commonly occurs between doctors and lay-people;

6. some claimants overstate their injuries to try to convince the medical expert there is actually something wrong with them; and

7. some claimants understate their injuries so as not to be seen to 'make a fuss'.

Claimant solicitors complain that at interview medical experts expect too much accuracy from claimants regarding their previous medical history and then leap to the conclusion that the claimant is in some way dishonest. We have some sympathy with this view, as for many claimants the environment of a medical interview and examination is nerve-wracking and can even generate anxiety and fear.

Sometimes, a claimant will arrive at the examination with written or printed notes. The expert may appreciate this preparation and the aide memoire may contribute to an effective interview. The claimant may have produced the notes on the advice of lawyers aware of the difficulty the claimant has in giving an accurate or complete history without such help. Alternatively, the claimant may be trying to make a prepared statement for reasons good or bad. The expert must not jump to conclusions as to the validity of these prepared notes.

Some claimants may see the expert as 'working for the other side', even if this should not be the case when the expert is acting in accordance with the CPR, and adopt a defensive or aggressive stance. Whatever the reason, experts should be aware that giving an accurate previous medical history under the conditions of a medical interview and examination can be difficult for some claimants.

4.2.9   Opinion Evidence

All witnesses are entitled to give relevant evidence of facts of which they have direct experience. Witnesses are not normally entitled or permitted to give evidence of opinion. A witness attempting to do so in court would be stopped by the judge.

In contrast to witnesses of fact, an expert witness has an elevated status in court proceedings and is entitled to express an opinion, so long as it is within his/her area of expertise. Therefore, unless and until the witness proves appropriate expertise, he/she will not be treated as an expert and will be prevented from expressing any opinion. Once the expert has established his/her credentials before the court, careful attention will be given to the factual basis for any opinion expressed and the reasoning process that the expert has followed in reaching a conclusion.

4.2.10 Fact and Opinion

Fact and opinion must be clearly distinguished. For the lawyers and the court when approaching the expert report, this division within the report structure is essential to achieving an accurate interpretation of the text. As the Protocol states:

Protocol 13.9   When addressing questions of fact and opinion, experts should keep the two separate and discrete.

13.10 Experts must state those facts (whether assumed or otherwise) upon which their opinions are based. They must distinguish clearly between those facts which experts know to be true and those facts which they assume.

Once the expert begins to mix fact and opinion, it becomes difficult for the readers of the report to clearly identify what the expert's opinion is and the basis for it.

4.2.11 Qualified Opinion

We have already addressed the issue of qualified opinion:

PD35 3.2   (8)   If the expert is not able to give his opinion without qualification, state the qualification;

It is also important to explain the reason why an opinion may need to be qualified, or even not be addressed in the report.

PD35 2.4   Experts should make it clear -

(a) when a question or issue falls outside their expertise; and

(b) when they are not able to reach a definite opinion, for example because they have insufficient information

It should be clear to an expert when a matter lies outside his/her area of expertise, and the temptation to try to assist the instructing solicitor or the court by trespassing onto an area outside the expert's expertise should be avoided. At the point where an expert steps beyond the boundary of his/her expertise, not only does the expert cease to be an expert, but the expert's credibility within his/her area of expertise and credibility as an independent witness may suffer significant damage.

For example, where a claimant is demonstrating non-organic signs on examination, the orthopaedic expert should be wary about expressing an opinion as to the psychological causation of these signs, unless comfortable that this is an area in which he/she has appropriate expertise and experience. A statement in the report advising an assessment by an appropriate expert is the best way to deal with such a situation.

It may happen that an expert is unable to provide a concluded opinion, for example in relation to prognosis, because the recovery is incomplete or further imaging or test results are required. It may be that the opinion is dependent on the reliability of a particular fact, such as when the claimant first developed symptoms, and there is a difference between what appears in the GP notes and what the claimant states to the expert. In both these categories of case, the opinion must expressly be qualified so that the reader of the report can understand the nature and strength of the opinion expressed. The further steps needed to clarify the opinion should also be set out.

4.2.12   Range of Opinion

Specific provision is made to make clear how an expert should deal with a situation where there is a range of professional opinion on a particular matter:

PD35 3.2   (6)   where there is a range of opinion on the matters dealt with in the report -

  (a)   summarise the range of opinion, and

  (b)   give reasons for the expert's own opinion

Medical experts often comment that the possible range of opinion in many cases is so vast that a discussion of it would be more difficult than expressing the opinion itself. These experts point out that not only is the likelihood of recovery for a claimant within a given time frame difficult to predict, but also the complex nature of many injuries means that there are no scientific studies in the literature that can provide guidance. The expert has to look at the medical facts and form an opinion without the luxury of reference to a body of medical opinion.

The Protocol attempts to clarify how establishing a range of opinion needs to be carried out:

Protocol	13.12	If the mandatory summary of the range of opinion is based on published sources, experts should explain those sources and, where appropriate, state the qualifications of the originator(s) of the opinions from which they differ, particularly if such opinions represent a well-established school of thought.
	13.13	Where there is no available source for the range of opinion, experts may need to express opinions on what they believe to be the range which other experts would arrive at if asked. In those circumstances, experts should make it clear that the range that they summarise is based on their own judgement and explain the basis of that judgement.

It is paragraph 13.13 that probably represents the most common situation that experts have to address. The expert is required not only to express an opinion him/herself, but having done so, to address the opinions of colleagues with whom the expert would probably disagree. The experienced medical expert will tend to be more familiar with the range of opinions that opposing experts might come up with in such cases.

However, in reaching an opinion on a subject where there is no published basis for the opinion (for example, the period of recovery, the period during which symptoms might in any event have developed to a similar level, the timing of future degeneration or the need for future medical intervention), the expert would probably have considered a wider range of periods before settling on a particular period in the light of the facts of the case. The expert can describe the basis of his/her assessment, making it clear that the opinion is based on the expert's own experience of dealing with such injuries in his/her medical practice. An expert who does not set out this process in the report is unlikely at trial to be able to justify convincingly the opinion he/she has expressed. In any event, an opinion expressed without explanation of the basis for it will only carry limited weight.

For example, take the question of how long it is likely to be before the claimant, who suffered injury affecting her hip, would probably require a hip replacement operation. The expert would probably take into account factors such as:

- the nature of the injury;
- the degree of progression that has been observed on x-ray since the accident;
- the age of the claimant and the likely level of activity in the coming years; and
- his/her own experience of similar cases in clinical practice.

The expert will then, based on his/her own assessment of these factors, be able to express a maximum range and to identify within it, with reasons, the range that the expert considers to be appropriate in this particular case. A paragraph in the report will suffice to make clear the basis of the assessment to the lawyers and the court.

4.2.13 Summary of Conclusions

A summary of conclusions is mandatory. The Protocol states:

Protocol   13.14   A summary of conclusions is mandatory. The summary should be at the end of the report after all the reasoning...

All of the users of the expert report - client, solicitor, another expert, barrister and judge – will be expected to have read the entire report and to have considered it carefully. An extensive 'summary report' (an executive summary) designed for readers who do not have the time or need to read the detailed report is unnecessary.

A summary of conclusions is a useful discipline to impose on the report writer, as it brings together in one place all the conclusions in the report and allows these to be compared with the instructions upon which the report is predicated. It can also act as a useful starting point for a reader to establish the context of the report he/she is about to read.   It can also be a point of reference from which to compare the conclusions of opposing experts.

The summary of conclusions should normally consist of a summary of the expert's concluded opinion in response to each of the issues that the report has addressed. This summary should be short, to the point and be placed at the end of the report.

The Protocol provides further guidance:

Protocol   13.14   ...There may be cases, however, where the benefit to the court is heightened by placing a short summary at the beginning of the report whilst giving the full conclusions at the end. For example, it can assist with the comprehension of the analysis and with the absorption of the detailed facts if the court is told at the outset of the direction in which the report's logic will flow in cases involving highly complex matters which fall outside the general knowledge of the court.

Particularly in complex or complicated cases – more often found in clinical negligence or industrial disease claims - the summary placed at the beginning of the report, combined with a brief summary of the factual background and an introduction to the medical issues, can provide a very useful aid to a proper understanding of the body of the report on a first reading.

4.2.14 Expert's Declaration

There are many, often lengthy, statements and declarations generated by medical experts and suggested by various professional bodies that do not comply with the far easier and simpler requirement laid down in PD35.

The authors recommend a declaration at the end of every report that complies with the requirements of the rules, practice direction and the Protocol by setting out the declaration and the statement of truth as detailed in PD35. However, we also suggest that experts include a further statement (set out below in italics), which will provide additional comfort to the parties and the court that the expert has understood fully his/her duties:

> **Declaration**
>
> I confirm that I understand my duty to the court and have complied with that duty.
>
> *Where I am not able to give my opinion without qualification, I have stated the qualification.*
>
> I am aware of the requirements of CPR Part 35, the Practice Direction to Part 35 and the Protocol for the Instruction of Experts to give Evidence in Civil Claims.

4.2.15 Statement of Truth

The form of words for the Statement of Truth is mandatory:[29]

> I confirm that I have made clear which facts and matters referred to in this report are within my own knowledge and which are not. Those that are within my own knowledge I confirm to be true. The opinions I have expressed represent my true and complete professional opinions on the matters to which they refer.

In an expert report, all the opinions expressed are verified as being the 'true and complete professional opinion' of the expert. This requirement has put an end to the pre-CPR practice of experts who would write a "side-letter" to the solicitor that qualified the opinion expressed in the report.

---

29   PD35 3.3

Prior to the introduction of the CPR, many experts used to act as if they owed their primary duty to the side that instructed them. A favourable medical expert report on a claimant, produced by a so called "claimant-friendly" expert, might be accompanied by a side-letter that pointed out that the claimant's account was in fact inconsistent and implausible. It was not only claimant-friendly experts who behaved in this manner, "defendant-friendly" experts would also produce exculpatory medical reports while, in a side-letter, advising early settlement of the claim. Nor was this practice limited to personal injury claims. Such experts behaved in a similar manner in clinical negligence and industrial disease claims as well.

Since the introduction of the CPR, it would be impossible for any independent expert to honestly sign a Statement of Truth if he/she were to have any reservation about the written conclusions or where the written conclusions were not to represent the complete opinion of the expert.

The report should be signed and the signature dated. In an expert report in a civil claim, it is unnecessary to sign and date every page. In addition, the report itself should have a date on the front page for ease of reference (and to distinguish the report from any earlier or later reports). Often both the examination date and the date of signing off the report will be provided. If the signing date and the examination date (where there is an examination) are within a day or two of each other, the examination date will suffice. Where there is an extended period between the examination date and the signing date, the expert would be wise to expect to face questioning on this point should the matter come to court, as the delay may be thought indicative of the report having gone through a number of amendments or re-drafts during that period.

4.3   Amendments to Reports

An expert may be asked by a party's lawyers to amend his/her report. Such a request can cause anxiety on the part of the expert who fears that his/her independence may thereby be compromised. In fact, there are circumstances in which it is appropriate for the expert to consider and make amendments to a report. The Protocol deals with this issue as follows:

Protocol   15.2   Experts should not be asked to, and should not, amend, expand or alter any parts of reports in a manner which distorts their true opinion, but may be invited to amend or expand reports to ensure accuracy, internal consistency, completeness and relevance to the issues and clarity. Although experts should generally follow the recommendations of solicitors with regard to the form of reports, they should form their own independent views as to the opinions and contents expressed in their reports and exclude any suggestions which do not accord with their views.

Amendments necessary to achieve accuracy, internal consistency, completeness, relevance to the issues and clarity are all appropriate for the expert to make. In many instances, the amendments requested are not material to the opinions expressed and the expert can make changes without undue concern.

However, requests to alter or vary facts set out in the report do require very careful scrutiny. Issues do sometimes arise regarding what was or was not said by a claimant during a medical interview and examination. It is essential that medical experts keep good notes of these interviews. A claimant who says he is a smoker at interview may seek to deny that information later, on hearing from the solicitor that he has just diminished the damages he may receive. If the expert has a note that the claimant said he was a smoker, then clearly the report should not be amended.

A request to alter or vary an opinion will require even more careful consideration and the expert must be satisfied that any resulting changes do not put the expert in conflict with his/her duty to the court and with the contents of the Statement of Truth. Beyond this, an expert may wish to revise or change an opinion so that it is no longer consistent with the opinion expressed in the report. This may be as a result of further information coming to light, a subsequent examination of the claimant or even because of the expert's consideration of matters raised in the report of another expert in the case. The expert may simply, on reflection, have changed his/her mind. In such circumstances, two actions are required:

1. the change of opinion must be communicated to the lawyers and the parties without delay; and

2. the change of opinion must be explained to the instructing lawyers and party, as they are entitled to understand the process that has resulted in the change of opinion, particularly if the change is to the detriment of that side's case.

If a change of opinion were to result in an opinion that is more favourable to the instructing party and so is to the detriment of the other side's case, then it is important to set out the reasoning in order to explain fully why the change of opinion is justified. Otherwise, the apparent inconsistency could cause the expert to lose credibility before the court and the revised opinion may not be given due weight.

The procedure to follow in such circumstances is set out in the Protocol:

Protocol 15.4 Where experts significantly alter their opinion, as a result of new evidence or because evidence on which they relied has become unreliable, or for any other reason, they should amend their reports to reflect that fact. Amended reports should include reasons for amendments. In such circumstances those instructing experts should inform other parties as soon as possible of any change of opinion.

15.5 When experts intend to amend their reports, they should inform those instructing them without delay and give reasons. They should provide the amended version (or an addendum or memorandum) clearly marked as such as quickly as possible.

We must emphasise that a change of opinion, and this includes a change of opinion within a report where the expert continues to support the case of the party by which he or she is instructed, must be communicated to the instructing lawyer without delay[30] (the lawyer being under a duty to pass on that change of opinion to the other party in the case). The client is entitled to know, as soon as is practicable, the basis for a change that may have disastrous and expensive consequences. In failing to communicate the reasons clearly and immediately, the expert is likely to complicate what is almost certainly in any event a difficult situation.

Where a change of opinion occurs at a discussion between experts, the Protocol suggests a slightly different approach:

Protocol 15.3 Where experts change their opinion following a meeting of experts, a simple signed and dated addendum or memorandum to that effect is generally sufficient. In some cases, however, the benefit to the court of having an amended report may justify the cost of making the amendment.

In our opinion, experts should not simply sign a document recording their change of opinion, but as more generally with any change of opinion (and for the same reasons) should give reasons for the change. If it is necessary to give a detailed explanation for the change of opinion, then it is probably best to follow the suggested alternative of an amended report offering full reasons for the change of opinion. Particularly at this late stage in the litigation, the instructing party is entitled to know why the expert has had a change of mind and is no longer willing to be supportive of the client's case.

---

30   see Protocol 4.6

4.4   Written Questions to Experts

To facilitate the comprehension by the parties of expert reports, and to assist the parties in having the experts address those aspects of the case that the lawyers regard as most important, any party may now send written questions to an expert witness on his/her report:

CPR 35.6   (1)   A party may put written questions about an expert's report (which must be proportionate) to –

        (a) an expert instructed by another party; or

        (b) a single joint expert appointed under rule 35.7.

    (2)   Written questions under paragraph (1) –

        (a) may be put only once;

        (b) must be put within 28 days of service of the expert's report; and

        (c) must be for the purpose only of clarification of the report, unless in any case –

            (i)   the court gives permission; or

            (ii) the other party agrees.

    (3)   An expert's answers to questions put in accordance with paragraph (1) shall be treated as part of the expert's report.

    (4)   Where –

        (a) a party has put a written question to an expert instructed by another party; and

        (b) the expert does not answer that question,

        the court may make one or both of the following orders in relation to the party who instructed the expert –

            (i)   that the party may not rely on the evidence of that expert; or

            (ii) that the party may not recover the fees and expenses of that expert from any other party.

The expert is entitled to be paid for answering the questions by the party asking them.[31] Although the starting point in the CPR is for one set of questions only from each party, the parties may agree to more than one set of questions being asked of the experts – often without telling the experts instructed in the case. The CPR also refer to questions being asked within 28 days of service of the report by one party on the other, but in practice the expert will have no knowledge of this date and the serving of the report could well be many months after the report has been sent off by the medical expert to the instructing solicitor.[32]

When questions duly arrive, the case is unlikely to be fresh in the expert's mind. Answering even a few questions may require the expert to spend a significant amount of time in familiarising him/herself with the details of the case. This is in itself a powerful reason for ensuring that all the likely relevant medico-legal issues are addressed in the original report.

Questions may be asked 'for the purpose only of clarification of the report'.[33] Sometimes, however, a party will use the right to send questions to the expert as a tactic to elicit more information than might appear at first sight to be mere 'clarification' of the report. The term clarification is not defined or explained in the CPR. Whilst it has been said by the court that the questions should not normally amount to cross-examination by post or require the expert significantly to expand on the existing report, it has also been said that questions that 'assist the just disposal of the dispute' are appropriate.[34] In practice, the lawyers are often left with inadequate medical expert reports and have little alternative but to raise questions in order to get the experts to deal with the medico-legal issues that have not been addressed.

Common examples of the need to address questions to medical experts relate to issues in respect of causation of injury, loss and damage and to seeking the expert's opinion on the various heads of claim being made. Hence questions may seek to clarify the difference between the condition of the claimant as a result of the accident and the condition as it probably would have been in any event, and to clarify the nature of the restrictions resulting from the accident in terms of ability to pursue employment or to carry out particular tasks. As the answers that the expert will give will form part of the expert's evidence and as the expert report will include both the Expert's Declaration and a signed Statement of Truth, there is no need to include these elements a second time when responding to questions.

Where the expert does not consider that the questions are appropriate as clarification, the Protocol indicates that the parties and their experts should attempt to sort out disputes as to the appropriateness of questions for themselves:

---

31   PD35 6.2

32   Protocol para 14.1 advises instructing solicitors to tell experts when their reports are disclosed to the other party

33   CPR 35.6(2)(c)

34   See for example *Mutch v Allen* [2001] All ER D 121

Protocol 16.3 Where experts believe that questions put are not properly directed to the clarification of the report, or are disproportionate, or have been asked out of time, they should discuss the questions with those instructing them and, if appropriate, those asking the questions. Attempts should be made to resolve such problems without the need for an application to the court for directions.

If they are unable to resolve the issue by agreement, then the matter will be resolved by a hearing at court (to which the expert will not be a party and will not be present).

A failure to provide answers to questions is likely to be disastrous for the party on whose behalf the defaulting expert is instructed. The whole of the expert's evidence in the case may be excluded or the instructing party may be unable to recover any of the costs of that expert from the other party. In the latter case, the costs of the expert will fall on the party or the lawyer, or more probably, the instructing lawyer will refuse to pay the expert or will seek to recover any costs already paid. In either case, the expert's reputation, at least with the instructing solicitor, will be irrecoverably damaged. However irritating or apparently irrelevant the questions an expert receives appear to be, and however inconvenient the timing, the expert must provide written answers, unless the court on application orders otherwise.

4.4.1 Format for the Response

There is no prescribed format for the provision of answers to questions. These may be provided in a letter addressed to the lawyer asking them or in a document headed 'Response to Questions from...' The document containing the answers, whether in the form of a letter or an addendum report or some other document, should set out each question in full, followed by the answer. Not only does this make the document stand alone as a comprehensible whole, but it is a good discipline for ensuring that each question is fully considered and answered. The expert must proceed on the basis that there is a reason for each question asked and that the lawyers have expressed them in the form that they have for a particular purpose.

4.5 Single Joint Experts

Rule 35.7 gives the court power to direct that both parties share one expert witness – a single joint expert.

CPR 35.7 (1) Where two or more parties wish to submit expert evidence on a particular issue, the court may direct that the evidence on that issue is to be given by a single joint expert.

However, both the Pre-Action Protocol for the Resolution of Clinical Disputes and the Pre-Action Protocol for Disease and Illness Claims[35] suggest that this should be a matter for the parties themselves. This is recognised to some extent in PD35 7(e).

PD35	7	When considering whether to give permission for the parties to rely on expert evidence and whether that evidence should be from a single joint expert the court will take into account all the circumstances in particular whether:
	(a)	it is proportionate to have separate experts for each party on a particular issue with reference to –

        (i)   the amount in dispute;

        (ii) the importance to the parties; and

        (iii) the complexity of the issue;

	(b)	the instruction of a single joint expert is likely to assist the parties and the court to resolve the issue more speedily and in a more cost-effective way than separately instructed experts;
	(c)	expert evidence is to be given on the issue of liability, causation or quantum;
	(d)	the expert evidence falls within a substantially established area of knowledge which is unlikely to be in dispute or there is likely to be a range of expert opinion;
	(e)	a party has already instructed an expert on the issue in question and whether or not that was done in compliance with any practice direction or relevant pre-action protocol;
	(f)	questions put in accordance with rule 35.6 are likely to remove the need for the other party to instruct an expert if one party has already instructed an expert;
	(g)	questions put to a single joint expert may not conclusively deal with all issues that may require testing prior to trial;
	(h)	a conference may be required with the legal representatives, experts and other witnesses which may make instruction of a single joint expert impractical; and
	(i)	a claim to privilege makes the instruction of any expert as a single joint expert inappropriate.

On any issue seen by the parties as potentially significant in the dispute or of significant impact upon the value of the claim, the parties will tend to resist the appointment of a single joint expert. Each side would generally want its own expert witness in each area of expertise, as there are clear disadvantages to the parties in having to share a single joint expert with whom they cannot communicate privately. There is also a more general concern that the imposition of a single joint

---

35   See Sections 3.3.1 and 3.3.3 above

expert in technical cases may amount to the abdication of decision-making by the judge to that of the appointed single joint expert.

As well as the court directing that there will be a single joint expert, the parties may also agree between themselves that they will instruct a single joint expert when the issue to be reported on is considered unlikely to be particularly contentious.

> The single joint expert is at risk of being nobody's friend. One or more of the parties may be unhappy with the expert's report and parties may wish to cross-examine the expert should the case come to trial.

Each party may separately instruct the single joint expert, although in most cases the parties will agree one set of instructions between themselves before these are sent to the single joint expert. Disputes between the parties can arise over the issues that the expert should address. This results in the expert receiving instructions from each party and having to set out the substance of both sets of instructions in the report, before addressing all of the matters raised by the parties.

4.5.1 Comparison of a Single Joint Expert and a Jointly Selected Expert

A single joint expert is instructed by both parties to report to them jointly and is an expert with whom neither party has a right of private access separate from the other side. This means no private communication takes place between a party and the single joint expert to discuss the contents of the report or to seek clarification of it and any written communication, for example for clarification of the report, must be copied to the other party, together with any response. In practice, this means that if the single joint expert does not deal clearly with all relevant aspects of the claim, any clarification or explanation must be obtained by questions in writing with copies sent to all other parties and the responses similarly shared. It is rare that a meeting is arranged between the expert and all the parties.

In contrast, a jointly selected expert is instructed by the claimant alone. The solicitor can discuss the report with the expert confidentially in correspondence, on the telephone and in conference. The expert report need never be disclosed to the other side.[36] The position is the same in relation to any other expert instructed by just one party.

---

36   See Section 3.3.2 above

It is essential that the medical expert is clear as to the basis upon which he/she is instructed, and by whom, before preparing an expert report. Unfortunately, the distinction between a jointly selected expert and a single joint expert is not always fully appreciated by instructing solicitors, so the expert may need to check the basis of instruction before preparing the report.

4.5.2 Status of a Single Joint Expert's Report

Where the parties are committed to a single joint expert, whether by an order of the court or by agreement between themselves, the report as it is written will stand as the only expert evidence in that discipline in the case.

Each party is stuck with that expert even in a situation where, once the report is received, the expert is regarded by either or both sides as having taken an unreasonable position – for example, the expert has "fallen for" everything the claimant has said or has "serious reservations" about the credibility of the claimant or has taken an extreme view on some other aspect of the case. In such circumstances, a party may choose to incur the cost of obtaining further expert evidence and, if materially different to the single joint expert's evidence, seek to persuade the court to permit the previous court order or agreement to be overridden "in the interests of justice". The outcome of such an application to the court is generally uncertain.

Even where the court does order a single joint expert to be appointed, it is possible that each party may then appoint "shadow experts" to advise on the evidence of the single joint expert. Even though shadow reports are not used to support applications to the court for further experts to be permitted, they may well be used to provide the basis for cross-examination of the single joint expert by each party should the matter reach court. Such shadow experts may even sit in court in order to brief the lawyers during the evidence and cross-examination of the single joint expert.

Owing to the limitations inherent in opposing parties sharing an expert, single joint experts are appointed less frequently than was thought likely when the CPR were first introduced.

4.6 Court Orders

The court manages proceedings by way of directions given to the parties. These are in the form of court orders.[37] A failure to comply with a court order may result in the court imposing sanctions on the party guilty of such failure, whether it is the party, the lawyer or the expert witness who is personally at fault.

---

37 See Sections 3.2.2, 3.6 and 3.7 above.

4.6.1   Notice of Court Orders

Often the expert is not made aware by the solicitors of the contents of court orders affecting the expert and with which the expert is expected to comply. This difficulty has, at least in theory, been overcome by an amendment to PD35:

PD35	8	Where an order requires an act to be done by an expert, or otherwise affects an expert, the party instructing that expert must serve a copy of the order on the expert. The claimant must serve the order on a single joint expert.

Therefore, when required to provide an expert report once proceedings are under way or to arrange a joint discussion and joint statement, the expert should be provided with a copy of the court order setting out that requirement and the court's timetable with which the expert has to comply.

Where an instructing solicitor imposes a tight deadline on an expert because of an order of the court, the expert may wish to request a copy of the order to ascertain on what date it was made. The tight deadline may in fact be caused by the solicitor forgetting until the last moment to notify the expert of the order. Once the date of the order is known then frank discussions between the solicitor and the expert about meeting the order can ensue. In an extreme case, the expert may wish to make his/her own application to the court for directions to resolve difficulties.

4.6.2   Seeking Directions from the Court

In CPR 35.14, an expert is given the power, without any involvement from the instructing lawyer, to ask the court for directions.

CPR 35.14 (1)   Experts may file written requests for directions for the purpose of assisting them in carrying out their functions.

(2)   Experts must, unless the court orders otherwise, provide copies of the proposed request for directions under paragraph (1) –

(a)   to the party instructing them, at least 7 days before they file the requests; and

(b)   to all other parties, at least 4 days before they file them.

(3)   The court, when it gives directions, may also direct that a party be served with a copy of the directions.

It is unlikely that an expert will ever need to make such an application and this power is rarely exercised. However, this provision is an effective stick that an expert can wave under the nose of a solicitor who is in some way preventing or delaying the expert from carrying out his/her duty. For the most part, solicitors who do not co-operate with expert witnesses do so out of oversight or incompetence rather than malice, and the required notification of the expert's intention to seek directions from the court is sufficient to markedly change attitudes. Single joint experts may also resort to threatening solicitors with this power, in order to receive appropriate instructions or necessary information.

The Protocol gives the following guidance regarding applications to the court by expert witnesses:

Protocol   11.1   Experts may request directions from the court to assist them in carrying out their functions as experts. Experts should normally discuss such matters with those who instruct them before making any such request. Unless the court otherwise orders, any proposed request for directions should be copied to the party instructing the expert at least seven days before filing any request to the court, and to all other parties at least four days before filing it. (CPR 35.14).

       11.2   Requests to the court for directions should be made by letter, containing:

          (a)   the title of the claim;

          (b)   the claim number of the case;

          (c)   the name of the expert;

          (d)   full details of why directions are sought; and

          (e)   copies of any relevant documentation.

4.7   The Joint Discussion (or Meeting of Experts)

During the progression of a case, it is likely that there will be at least one meeting of experts.

PD35 9.1   Parties must consider, with their experts, at an early stage, whether there is likely to be any useful purpose in holding an experts' discussion and if so when.

Under CPR 35.12 the court may direct such a discussion and in practice it will be required now in all cases where permission is given to more than one party to instruct experts of a similar discipline, unless there is no material disagreement between the experts.

The purpose of the discussion is to facilitate the efficient conduct of the litigation. The Protocol suggests that the discussion might also identify any actions that may help to resolve the outstanding points of disagreement in the expert evidence.[38]

---

38   Protocol 18.10(d)

The discussion need not be held face to face and will often be held on the telephone. However, a face to face meeting will normally be necessary in more complicated cases.

4.7.1   Object of the Discussion and the Expert's Role

One of the important objectives of the CPR is to assist the parties by providing a process where the parties have the best opportunity to compromise a claim without the need for a court hearing. A discussion between the experts is part of this process. The object of the discussion is, where possible, to extend areas of agreement and to narrow the issues that remain in dispute.

CPR 35.12 (1)   The court may, at any stage, direct a discussion between experts for the purpose of requiring the experts to –

    (a) identify and discuss the expert issues in the proceedings; and

    (b) where possible, reach an agreed opinion on those issues.

(2)   The court may specify the issues which the experts must discuss.

(3)   The court may direct that following a discussion between the experts they must prepare a statement for the court setting out those issues on which –

    (a) they agree; and

    (b) they disagree, with a summary of their reasons for disagreeing.

(4)   The content of the discussion between the experts shall not be referred to at the trial unless the parties agree.

(5)   Where experts reach agreement on an issue during their discussions, the agreement shall not bind the parties unless the parties expressly agree to be bound by the agreement.

It should be noted that where issues do remain in dispute, the purpose of the discussion is to produce a summary of the reasons for the disagreement, and in appropriate cases, what can be done to resolve these disputes:

PD35 9.2   The purpose of discussions between experts is not for experts to settle cases but to agree and narrow issues and in particular to identify:

    (i) the extent of the agreement between them;

    (ii) the points of and short reasons for any disagreement;

    (iii) action, if any, which may be taken to resolve any outstanding points of disagreement; and

    (iv) any further material issues not raised and the extent to which these issues are agreed.

We must emphasise that the objective is not for the experts to reach a compromise on behalf of the parties. There is an important difference between varying or adjusting an opinion following discussion, which may result in creating an area of agreement where previously there was disagreement, and in being prepared to agree a point outside the range of an opinion held by the expert in order to reach what may be seen as a sensible compromise of opinions. Narrowing issues is for experts; compromising an opinion is for the lawyers or the judge.

In stating the points of agreement and disagreement, it is essential that the experts apply the civil standard of proof and the appropriate legal tests, referring expressly to the balance of probabilities and addressing causation of injury and damage as appropriate.[39]

The lawyers must not give, and the experts must not accept, instructions not to reach agreement during such discussions on areas within their competence. In complying with his/her duty to the court, the expert must remain independent:

PD35 9.7   Experts must give their own opinions to assist the court and do not require the authority of the parties to sign a joint statement.

The expert's duty remains at all times to help the court on matters within his/her expertise, the duty which overrides any obligation to the person from whom he/she has received instructions.[40]

4.7.2   Agenda for the Discussion

In a straightforward case no purpose is likely to be served by a formal agenda and the experts are unlikely to be provided with one. PD35 provides for discussing and agreeing whether an agenda is necessary and what it should contain:

PD35 9.3   Where the experts are to meet, the parties must discuss and if possible agree whether an agenda is necessary, and if so attempt to agree one that helps the experts to focus on the issues which need to be discussed. The agenda must not be in the form of leading questions or hostile in tone.

There are cases where an agenda can be very useful for the experts to guide them in their discussions. An agenda should ensure that the experts do address the issues which the lawyers need to have addressed in order to resolve the dispute.

---

39   We address these issues in detail in the chapters that follow
40   CPR 35.3

The Protocol gives further assistance in preparing an agenda:

Protocol 18.5 The parties, their lawyers and experts should co-operate to produce the agenda for any discussion between experts, although primary responsibility for preparation of the agenda should normally lie with the parties' solicitors.

18.6 The agenda should indicate what matters have been agreed and summarise concisely which are in issue. It is often helpful for it to include questions to be answered by the experts. If agreement [of the agenda] cannot be reached promptly or a party is unrepresented, the court may give directions for the drawing up of the agenda. The agenda should be circulated to experts and those instructing them to allow sufficient time for the experts to prepare for the discussion.

In clinical negligence claims in the High Court, the standard court directions, which are obligatory only in such cases where they are part of the court order in fact made, reflect this in providing as follows:[41]

Unless otherwise agreed by all parties' solicitors, after consulting with the experts a draft agenda which directs the experts to the remaining issues relevant to the experts' discipline, as identified in the statements of case shall be prepared jointly by the claimant's solicitors and experts and sent to the defendant's solicitors for comment at least 35 days before the agreed date for the experts' discussions.

[Claimants' solicitors and counsel should note the obligation to prepare the draft agenda jointly with the relevant expert. Experts should note that it is part of their overriding duty to the court to ensure that the agenda complies with the following direction:]

The use of agendas is not mandatory. Solicitors should consult with the experts to ensure that agendas are necessary and, if used, are reasonable in scope. The agenda should assist the experts and should not be in the form of leading questions or hostile in tone. An agenda must include a list of the outstanding issues in the preamble.

Where it has been impossible to agree a single agenda, it is of assistance to the experts if the second agenda is consecutively numbered to the first.

---

41   These directions can be found at http://www.hmcourts-service.gov.uk/cms/9793.htm

4.7.3 People Present at the Meeting of Experts

PD35 gives clear guidance on who should be present at an experts' meeting and the roles that they should adopt:

PD35 9.4 Unless ordered by the court, or agreed by all parties, and the experts, neither the parties nor their legal representatives may attend experts discussions.

PD35 9.5 If the legal representatives do attend –

    (i)   they should not normally intervene in the discussion, except to answer questions put to them by the experts or to advise on the law; and

    (ii) the experts may if they so wish hold part of their discussions in the absence of the legal representatives

Therefore the claimant, defendant, insurer or representative of the healthcare provider clients will not normally be present, and if in a particular case the lawyers are present they will have a very limited role. Even in a case where there is a fear of improper influence from one side, by use of a good draft agenda and if necessary by making a recording of the meeting, the presence of lawyers can usually be avoided. [42]

4.7.4 The Joint Statement

It is essential that the conclusions from the discussion are not only put into writing, but that a document containing these conclusions is signed by the experts:

PD35 9.6 A statement must be prepared by the experts dealing with paragraphs 9.2(i) - (iv) above. Individual copies of the statements must be signed by the experts at the conclusion of the discussion, or as soon thereafter as practicable, and in any event within 7 days. Copies of the statements must be provided to the parties no later than 14 days after signing.

Signing off on a summary of the discussions is essential, whether the discussion is face to face or on the telephone. In a hotly disputed and complex case, the task of the scribe of this document will be a very important one. Lawyers will look to the precise wording of the statement in order to resolve issues in the claim or to assess their prospects of success on those issues should the matter proceed to trial. Whilst there may be an attraction in leaving one's opposite number to carry out the drafting, the draftsperson is likely to have a considerable advantage in ensuring that his/her views are best represented in the joint statement.

---

42   *Hubbard v Lambeth, Southwark & Lewisham* HA [2001] EWCA 1455

Should an expert alter his/her previously expressed opinion in the joint discussion, then it is important to explain why. The party instructing that expert and the legal advisers are entitled to a proper explanation for the change of opinion upon which the claim or defence has up to that point been based:

> PD35 9.8   If an expert significantly alters an opinion, the joint statement must include a note or addendum by that expert explaining the change of opinion

4.7.5   Status of the Discussion and Agreement at Trial

The deliberations and discussions at the meeting of experts will not be referred to at the trial unless the parties agree.[43] Where agreement on an issue is reached by the experts, this agreement will not bind the parties unless the parties agree to be bound by the agreement.[44] In the absence of a binding agreement, the statement prepared by the experts at the conclusion of the meeting may still be produced to the court by either party. In practice, an expert giving evidence on oath in court will be in the greatest difficulty if he/she seeks without good reason to renege on concessions made in the discussion and recorded in the statement.

Conclusion

The role and duties of an expert witness are codified in CPR Part 35 and its associated practice direction and annex. By being familiar with the rules and following them, the expert is able to meet the specific requirements of expert evidence and to perform the role to an appropriate professional standard. The expert has at all times to act in accordance with his/her overriding duty to help the court on matters within his/her expertise.

Key-Point Summary

1.   Adherence to Part 35 and its associated practice direction is mandatory.

2.   The rules relating to expert evidence are written to help the expert perform the role effectively and experts should follow the rules carefully.

3.   An expert has an overriding duty to help the court on matters within his/her expertise.

4.   An objective and unbiased opinion is far more helpful to the lawyers involved in the claim than an opinion weighted towards the instructing party.

---

43   CPR 35.12(4)

44   CPR 35.12(5)

5. Once proceedings have been commenced, an expert must ensure that he/she is able to meet the timetable laid down by the court before accepting an instruction to provide evidence.

6. The required form and content of expert evidence is clearly set out in PD35 3.2.

7. An expert must make clear the basis for each opinion expressed, when an opinion is qualified, and where relevant deal with the range of professional opinion on the matter.

8. An expert must not make amendments to a report that distorts his/her true opinion.

9. An expert's written answers to questions of clarification form part of the expert report.

10. The court has the power to order that evidence on a particular topic or in a particular field be given by a single joint expert.

11. An expert should be notified by his/her instructing solicitor of the content of any court order that affects the expert in performing his/her role as an expert.

12. The statement produced at the end of a joint discussion must not only set out the areas of agreement and disagreement, but must also set out the reasons for any disagreement.

Next Steps

In the next chapter, we will explore the civil standard of proof and the particular difficulties that applying this standard creates for the medical mind.

Developing Your Medico-Legal Mind (4)

Based on your understanding of the CPR Part 35, answer the following questions:

1. What is the duty of an expert?

2. What is the standard of practice expected of an expert witness by the courts?

3. When an expert expresses an opinion beyond his/her own area of expertise, what status does such evidence have in the proceedings?

4. What is an important principle underlying the expression of factual information in an expert report?

5. In what circumstances may the court order an expert to pay the costs of one of the parties?

6. How should experts deal with factual disputes in the evidence?

7. What alterations to expert reports are permitted?

8. If an expert changes his/her opinion, what actions must he/she take?

9. How does the court treat an expert's answers to questions of clarification posed by a party?

10. What discussions are permitted between a single joint expert and the parties?

11. When should an expert be notified about court orders that affect the expert?

12. What is the mandatory wording that must be included in the Statement of Truth?

5

Proof

5.1   Civil Standard of Proof
5.2   Decision-Making in Civil Litigation
5.3   Applying 'On the Balance of Probabilities'
5.4   Establishing Proof

Introduction

For medical experts, one of the most challenging aspects of producing opinion evidence is to correctly apply the civil standard of proof. The 'medical mind' has inherent difficulties in grasping the absolute importance of applying this standard in every case, no matter how inconsequential or devastating the facts of the case may have been for the parties involved. As medical evidence is essential for parties who are seeking to prove or defend a claim, medical experts have to be able to apply the civil standard of proof to every opinion they express in their reports.

Chapter Outline

In this chapter, we will explore the standard of proof applied by the courts in civil litigation. We will highlight some of the inherent difficulties in applying the standard of proof to evidence and show its fundamental importance when expressing coherent expert opinion.

5.1   Civil Standard of Proof

In a civil case, the claimant has the burden of proof, which means that the claimant must prove his/her case to the civil standard of proof, namely, 'on the balance of probabilities'.[1] The claimant must therefore satisfy the judge that it is 'more likely than not' that his/her injuries and the consequential claimed losses were caused by the defendant's negligence or other breach of duty.

The outcome of the whole case is decided on this standard of proof. Once a point has been proved to the judge's satisfaction on the balance of probabilities (i.e. that it is more likely than not), the lawyers will treat the decision on the point as an established fact – for the purposes of the litigation certainty on the point has been established.

> 'In our legal system, if a judge finds it more likely than not that something did take place, then it is treated as having taken place. If he finds it more likely than not that it did not take place, then it is treated as not having taken place. He is not allowed to sit on the fence. He has to find for one side or the other. Sometimes the burden of proof will come to his rescue: the party with the burden of showing that something took place will not have satisfied him that it did. But generally speaking a judge is able to make up his mind where the truth lies without needing to rely upon the burden of proof.'[2]

Consider the following illustration of applying the standard of proof to evidence. Let us assume that there is a factual dispute as to whether a road traffic accident occurred in daylight or in darkness. If having heard all the evidence on this point the judge finds as more reliable the evidence of the witnesses who say it was daylight, and so finds that it was more likely than not daylight at the time of the accident, then for all purposes of the case it was daylight and the case will be resolved on that basis. Visibility at the time of the accident will no longer be an issue in the case and the fact that the lights on the vehicle were known to be defective will be no longer relevant in the proceedings.

When medical experts allow themselves to consider the ramifications of the civil standard of proof, their reaction is usually one of disbelief, tinged with deep

---

1   In criminal cases, the prosecution must prove the case to a standard of proof where the jury is 'sure' of the defendant's guilt before it may convict – the standard of being 'sure' used to be worded as 'beyond a reasonable doubt'.

2   In *re B (Children)(FC)* [2008] UKHL 35 at para 32

anxiety. The contrast between the civil standard of proof and the scientific proof that is the basis of medical practice is glaringly obvious: in civil litigation there is little, if any, regard paid to the 95% probability often demanded in scientific proof. Medical experts have to understand that the law is not searching for absolute truth – which would require a very high degree of probability or a superhuman judge – but is rather applying a set of man-made rules in order to resolve disputes.

> ## Science seeks truth, while the law does justice.[3]

Understandably, most medical experts are uncomfortable with being required to apply their hard-earned scientifically-based medical expertise in what is, to their minds, an imperfect and artificial system of rules. Some experts find writing reports in which they apply the civil standard of proof so unnatural and unreal that they will, when they express their opinions, use almost any phrase other than 'on the balance of probabilities'. This lack of comfort in applying the civil standard of proof is often even greater in clinical negligence claims, where the expert is asked to assess, on the balance of probabilities, the quality of medical treatment provided by another practitioner. The expert often recoils from giving an opinion that another practitioner's practice fell below an appropriate standard of care, when to the medical mind the assessment is made to such an inadequate standard of proof.

Judicial recognition of the difficulty that there can be for the medical expert, familiar with applying scientific or medical standards of proof, in providing opinion in a legal context can be found in the following excerpt from a Scottish case, *Dingley v The Chief Constable, Strathclyde Police*[4], The issue in *Dingley* was whether the development of multiple sclerosis had been caused by physical injury sustained in a motor accident. Medical science was not able to demonstrate the connection between the two, and reliance was placed on epidemiological evidence.

> *'In ordinary (non-lawyers') language, to say that one regards something as 'probable' is by no means to say that one regards it as 'established' or 'proved'. Yet in the civil courts, where we say that a pursuer[5] must prove his case on a balance of probabilities, what is held to be probable is treated as 'proved'. I do not suggest that any lawyer will be confused by this rather special meaning of the word 'proved'. But speaking very generally, I think that the civil requirement of a pursuer – that he satisfy the court that upon the evidence his case is probably sound – would in ordinary language be regarded as very different from, and less stringent than, a requirement that his case be established or proved. More importantly in the context of such a case as the*

---

3   See the discussion of this concept in Jasanoff, S. (1997) *Science at the Bar: Law, Science and Technology in America.* Cambridge, Ma: Harvard University Press

4   (1998) SC 548 at 603 (Lord Prosser)

5   In Scottish law, a 'claimant' is called a 'pursuer'

present, the fact that the two concepts are distinct in ordinary language, but the same in this legal context, seems to me to give rise to a risk of ambiguity or misunderstanding in the expressed opinions of expert witnesses. And this risk will be increased if the expert in question would normally, in the exercise of his profession, adopt an approach to such issues starkly different from that incumbent upon a court.

Whether one uses the word 'scientific' or not, no hypothesis or proposition would be seen as 'proved' or 'established' by anyone with any form of medical expertise merely upon the basis that he had come to regard it as probably sound. (Indeed, I think even the word 'probable' would be reserved for situations where the likelihood is thought to be much more than marginal). And even if, in relation to any possible proposition or hypothesis, such an expert even troubled to notice that he had come to the point of regarding it as not merely possible but on balance 'probable' then I think he would regard that point as one from which he must set off on further inquiry, and by no means as being (as it is in the courts) a point of arrival. Mere marginal probability will not much interest him. But it must satisfy a court.'

5.1.1   Applying the Standard of Proof

In civil litigation, the same standard of proof is applied in every case. It is applied to a claimant's mild symptom of pain as a consequence of a 'slip and trip' accident, in the same way that it is applied to catastrophic injuries as a consequence of a motorway pile-up. Whether the case is banal or exceptional, the civil courts apply exactly the same standard of proof.

It is unlikely that any professional in daily practice, other than a lawyer, would be familiar with making important decisions, with profound consequences, on the balance of probabilities. It might, therefore, be assumed that in every day professional practice only unimportant decisions of little consequence would be made on such a basis. In reality, we in fact make relatively few mundane decisions by applying the standard on the balance of probabilities.

Let us consider a very simple decision to see whether it is one where we would commonly apply the balance of probabilities as the standard of proof:

I will/will not take an umbrella when I go out today.

Faced with making such a decision, how would we decide whether or not to take an umbrella? The first element of an analysis of the umbrella carrying decision-making process is the intriguing question as to whether we would begin from an unbiased standpoint or whether in fact we would actually have a preference for one option or the other before we begin. For example, you may choose to 'dress down' rather than carry an umbrella.

In which case, the balance of probabilities does not figure in the reasoning process because the standard applied is one of personal preference.

However, let us assume for the purposes of our discussion that we have no preference for being either with or without an umbrella. We would probably begin by considering the factors relevant to the decision:

1. the current weather conditions;

2. the likelihood of rain, based on weather forecasts;

3. the intensity and longevity of any forecast of rain;

4. the amount of time in our schedule when we may be exposed to the rain;

5. the cost and quality of the clothes we are wearing;

6. the importance of being dry during our likely activities; and

7. the level of perceived inconvenience of carrying an umbrella.

After identifying each of these factors, we would probably assign to them a relative importance. For example, if the current weather was threatening and the forecast was for heavy rain, perhaps we would give most weight to factors 1-3. If factors 1-3 were unremarkable, but we were planning to wear our best clothing to attend a job interview, then we would give far more weight to factors 5 and 6. At the end of the reasoning process we would make a decision – one that is made, not on the balance of probabilities, but rather on the likely consequences that would result from making that decision.

The more significant the likely consequence is, the lower the standard of proof we would be likely to apply to the decision, such that only a 10% chance of rain would be enough to persuade us to take the umbrella if the consequences of not doing so – turning up at the job interview soaked and bedraggled – would have important consequences.

Conversely, if we were intending to go out in a T-shirt and jeans for a coffee and a chance to read the paper, perhaps then a 70% chance of rain would be necessary before we would take the umbrella.

In everyday life, even a mundane choice about taking an umbrella is not one that is generally, if ever, made on the balance of probabilities. So the civil standard of proof is in its essence conceptual rather than pragmatic and it is its conceptual unfamiliarity that causes medical experts (and others) difficulty and discomfort when applying it to factual issues in a dispute.

5.1.2   Differential Decisions

We suggest that on the balance of probabilities is a standard that would normally only apply to decision-making in everyday life in two specific circumstances:

1. where the differential in outcome (in terms of the likely consequences) would be inconsequential; or

2. where the differential in outcome (in terms of the likely consequences) resulting from delaying the decision would be so unacceptably large that an immediate decision effectively forces itself upon us.

5.2   Decision-Making in Civil Litigation

In civil litigation, there are very few inconsequential decisions to be made. If no importance rests on the decision, then for all practical purposes the decision is irrelevant and the parties will not waste time and money seeking an opinion upon it. There are also no forced decisions to be made, for everything in compensation claims will have happened months or even years before the claim began. Deadlines set by the court are counted in weeks and months, not minutes and seconds.

The decisions that have to be made in a medical expert's practice are neither inconsequential nor forced and so fall outside the two types of decision that are typically made on the balance of probabilities. Yet, decisions in medico-legal practice are likely to profoundly affect the outcome of the litigation and are made without any pressure of time.

In the context of a personal injury claim, hundreds of thousands or even millions of pounds may rest upon the opinion the medical expert expresses. Such sums may represent the only opportunity for a claimant to re-establish some degree of quality of life after an accident. On the other side of a claim, a defendant may have to live with the knowledge that he/she bears the responsibility for the injuries suffered by the claimant and may suffer heavy financial consequences from the court's decision. Even where the compensation is for a few thousand pounds, this sum may be very significant for the parties involved in the action.

Similarly, the financial consequences to a medical insurer or health care provider of many thousands of small claims being supported (or not) by medical experts also mean that apparently minor decisions are in fact extremely important. In a clinical negligence claim, not only are large sums of money involved but also the professional reputation of one or more medical practitioners may be in the balance. In industrial disease claims, there may be many other potential claimants who have been similarly exposed to the same agent, such that the court's decision could affect thousands of other claims.

So, while medical experts are told that they 'only' have to express an opinion on the balance of probabilities and that they do not need to be anywhere near 'sure', they are also expected by the lawyers to get the answer right and to present a rationale to justify their opinion. Their opinions need to be firmly based in medical practice and, whenever possible, in the scientific context of their speciality. Indeed, in conference with counsel prior to a court hearing, or during cross-examination in court, the medical expert can expect to have to justify a difficult opinion, reached on the balance of probabilities by reference to both professional experience and scientific reasoning.

This is a paradoxical situation - lawyers seek opinions resting on the balance of probabilities on the one hand, while demanding a scientific rationale on the other. The demand for scientifically supportable opinions from medical experts continues even though the science to support such opinions often does not exist. For example, the law requires that it be told what would have happened to a claimant in the absence of an accident or an adverse event, while demanding a logical, scientifically supported and expert basis for assessing, on the balance of probabilities, that which can never be known to a scientifically validated degree of certainty.

Medical experts are therefore required to assess hypothetical situations, such as 'had the accident or adverse event not occurred, on the balance of probabilities, would the claimant have developed any disease or symptoms and if so when and with what consequences?' and to respond with a logical rationale to satisfy the lawyers and the court. Everyone involved in the process (judges, lawyers and medical experts) agrees that this is a profoundly difficult task, yet it is one that the medical expert must engage with in a manner that is useful to the lawyers in progressing the claim, and that will withstand potentially vigorous cross-examination should such an opinion be challenged in court.

5.3   Applying 'On the Balance of Probabilities'

We have seen that the claimant in civil litigation must prove that the elements of his/her claim are more likely than not to be (or have been) as asserted in the claim. What the claimant cannot prove to this standard of proof, he/she cannot recover. In response, a defendant therefore seeks to establish uncertainty, at least to the point where it cannot be said that something is more likely than not, so as to prevent the claimant from proving the claim.

The civil standard of proof applies to resolving issues of fact, deciding issues of breach of duty (such as negligence), and proving causation of loss and damage in relation to those matters that have occurred by the date of trial. A case that illustrates how the courts apply the civil standard of proof and some of the complexities that arise in its application is *Hotson v East Berkshire Area Health Authority*[6]:

---

6   [1987] AC 750

The infant plaintiff[7] Stephen Hotson fell from a tree, sustaining a fracture of the left femoral epiphysis. He was taken to a hospital where staff negligently failed to diagnose the injury and sent him home. After 5 days he was taken to hospital again and the correct diagnosis was made. He was operated upon, but suffered avascular necrosis of the epiphysis, involving immediate disability. The Health Authority admitted negligence.

The trial judge found that even if the defendants had correctly diagnosed and treated Stephen on his first admission, there was a 75% risk that his injury would have followed the same course as in fact it did. The trial judge awarded Stephen damages for the loss of the 25% chance that, if the injury had been promptly diagnosed and treated, there would have been no avascular necrosis.

The House of Lords reversed this judgment holding that the trial judge's finding of fact showed that it was more likely than not (75:25) that the avascular necrosis itself was an inherent complication of the original injury, and so Stephen had failed to prove causation – i.e. that the Health Authority's admitted negligence had caused the avascular necrosis.

If however Stephen had proved that there was a 51:49 prospect that the avascular necrosis resulted from the negligent delay, as opposed to the fall from the tree, he would have recovered full compensation for the consequences of his disability – i.e. he would have proved that it was more likely than not that the avascular necrosis was caused by the negligent delay in diagnosis.

In order to be awarded damages, the claimant has to show that there is a more than 50% chance (i.e. on the balance of probabilities) that the accident or adverse event, or as in Stephen Hotson's case the failure to correctly diagnose, caused the injuries complained of. If this is achieved then there is no 'legal' doubt – as far as the court is concerned, the accident or adverse event (or failure to diagnose or treat appropriately) did cause the injuries, and damages will be awarded on that basis.

Life-Expectancy

If the life expectancy of the claimant were to become an issue in assessing the damages to be awarded to the claimant, then the judge will hear evidence on what the claimant's life expectancy now is, on the balance of probabilities. This will be expressed as the point in the future at which not more than 50% of the relevant cohort will still be alive and therefore the point at which the claimant will, on the balance of probabilities, be dead. On the basis of the expert evidence, the judge will decide the date of death of the claimant and then this becomes the period for which any lump sum award of damages for future care will be assessed.[8]

---

7   Prior to 1999 'claimants' were known as 'plaintiffs'

8   Although it is possible now by awarding periodical payments to avoid the inherent risk of over or under-compensating the claimant on this basis. See Section 2.7.3 above.

Factual issues

In a clinical negligence claim, the medical expert evidence will generally have a fundamental role in establishing liability to pay damages. When the factual picture is incomplete, the court often turns to the medical experts involved in the case to give opinions on what the likely factual position would have been at a particular time.

Let us consider a case where resolving the issue as to what would have been an appropriate treatment depends upon what the patient's temperature would have been on a particular occasion when it was not in fact taken. The judge will hear all the factual evidence from the patient, the patient's family, the treating doctor and nursing staff. Then the judge will hear opinion evidence from the medical experts, as to the likely temperature based on various known or presumed factors.

Having heard all of the evidence, and having formed his/her view of the quality and reliability of this evidence, the judge will decide the issue as to what is more likely than not to have been the patient's temperature on that particular occasion – the temperature for which there is at least a more than 50% probability on the available evidence.

5.4   Establishing Proof

Proof is always established on the available evidence. Such evidence may be the claimant's word, assertion or recollection. It may involve a careful analysis of the claimant's medical records over many years, or close scrutiny of x-rays, scans or test results. It may involve many files of documents. It may be informed by the results of learned studies. It may involve contributions from a variety of experts in various fields.

When an expert is asked to express an opinion as to when, in the absence of the injury sustained, a claimant would have suffered symptoms or a particular level of symptoms from a degenerative condition, the expert will never be able to provide an opinion based on scientific proof. However, based on an analysis of the images of the relevant joints and bones taken on various occasions, information as to the extent of prior symptoms, the age of the claimant, his/her level of activity, and possibly assisted by relevant published papers, the medical expert will usually be able to identify a range of possible periods by which significant symptoms would reasonably be expected to occur. Then, on the balance of probabilities, the expert can usually identify a narrower range based on the particular facts of the case.

Many of the issues that the medical expert is required by the parties to resolve are issues that are simply not addressed in the course of medical practice, and which have no sound basis in medical science:

By how many years have the symptoms that would have arisen due to the claimant's pre-existing asymptomatic degenerative condition been brought forward by the accident? [9]

When, in the absence of this accident, is it likely that the claimant would have suffered this condition?

How do the consequences of the sensory deficit resulting from the injury compare with those to be expected in any event without the accident?

Had the claimant's condition been correctly diagnosed within 6 hours of his admission to hospital, what would the outcome have been?

By applying medical expertise and scientific knowledge, with reference to the expert's professional experience and to the literature, the medical expert can usually provide an answer to the lawyers that is an expression of the expert's medical expertise. It is an answer that can never be tested in any scientific way, yet the expert has to, and should be able to, give a justified rationale for an opinion on the basis of what is more likely than not.

When hearing expert evidence, a judge is not permitted simply to select one professional opinion over another, without having a basis for his/her preference. The role of the judge is to assess every aspect of the evidence and to decide which opinion is more likely to be correct, on the balance of probabilities. For expert evidence, this begins with establishing the relevance of the expert's qualifications and expertise, the methodology adopted by the expert, any assumptions made by the expert, the expert's apprehension of the factual basis, and the rationale for the opinions/conclusions that he/she has reached.

It is essential, therefore, that the reasoning process that supports an expert opinion should be no less detailed or nuanced than an opinion an expert would seek to give based on a scientific standard of proof: it simply adopts the civil standard of proof for testing each element of the reasoning process that takes the expert from the factual basis to an opinion. The opinion an expert gives may not be capable of proof in a scientific sense, but in giving an opinion the medical expert should apply a depth of practical expertise and scientific knowledge to justify the opinion. Tempting though it may be for medical experts to believe that the lawyers seek only an intelligent guess, it is never a guess that is required.

---

9   In Section 6.4, we will examine how an expert needs to approach giving opinions on symptoms that have been 'brought forward'.

Conclusion

Applying the civil standard of proof to both factual and opinion evidence is fundamental to the role of a medical expert. Every fact has to be considered in the light of this standard as does every expert opinion. The difficulty is that the standard 'on the balance of probabilities' is only ever used in very limited circumstances in everyday life and the conceptual difficulty of the test provides medical experts with a good deal of discomfort. This does not however excuse the expert being unwilling to engage with the civil standard of proof and to use it when producing his/her evidence for the court.

Key-Point Summary

1. In civil litigation, the claimant has the burden of proof.

2. In civil litigation, every case is determined to the standard of proof of 'on the balance of probabilities'.

3. On the balance of probabilities is rarely used as a basis for determining professional decisions, except in civil litigation.

4. Large sums of money can rest on the opinion of a medical expert, so the expert must be comfortable with applying the civil standard of proof to each opinion in his/her evidence.

5. Even though the standard of proof to be applied represents a very low level of certainty from a scientific viewpoint, opinions must be supported by a clear rationale based on the expertise and experience of the expert and, so far as is possible, have a scientific basis.

Next Steps

In the next chapter, we will explore the fundamental legal principles that underpin the court's assessment of medical evidence.

Developing Your Medico-Legal Mind (5)

Based on your understanding of proof in the civil courts, answer the following questions:

1. What is the effect of the following opinion:

    If the index accident had not occurred then it is as likely as not that he would still have required the hip operation.

2. How does a medical expert reach a firm opinion on an issue where there is no decisive factual evidence and there are no studies in the literature on the point at issue?

3. What is the essential difference between an educated guess and an opinion given on the balance of probabilities?

4. In a case involving a missed diagnosis of cancer, expert evidence indicates that a claimant's prospects of long term survival have diminished from 60% to not more than 50%: what proportion of the compensation for the consequences of that loss of life will the claimant receive?

5. In a case involving a missed diagnosis for cancer, expert evidence indicates that a claimant's prospects of long term survival have diminished from not more than 50% to 5%: what proportion of the compensation for the consequences of that loss of life will the claimant receive?

6

Opinion Evidence

6.1   Causation of Damage
6.2   Giving Opinions on Causation
6.3   Industrial Disease Claims and 'Material Contribution'
6.4   'Acceleration' and 'Exacerbation'
6.5   Prognosis and Future Risk
6.6   Consequences of Injuries

Introduction

The opinion section of an expert report is of fundamental importance. The opinions expressed by the medical expert will ultimately determine whether or not the claimant will be able to pursue a claim for damages for personal injury, industrial disease or clinical negligence. All opinion evidence must be expressed in terms that are clear, concise and reliable. This demands of the expert the ability to express medical opinions in a manner that is meaningful to the lawyers and the court.

Chapter Outline

In this chapter, we will explore three fundamental issues in a claim where expert opinion is essential:

1. causation of damage;

2. prognosis and future risk; and

3. consequences of injuries.

The parties in a claim have to rely on medical experts to assess these issues, which are often far from straightforward. Both the legal principles and their practical application to the facts of the case can cause problems for medical experts, for lawyers and for the court.

6.1   Causation of Damage

Judges and lawyers alike want to know what injuries, if any, the claimant has actually suffered as a result of the accident. Usually, there is little difficulty in identifying the injury (or injuries) that the claimant has presented with. However, one of the most important purposes of a medical expert report is to distinguish between those injuries, symptoms and effects that have been caused by the accident (or adverse event) from those that have not. Lawyers use the term 'causation' to describe this issue.

A claimant can only recover damages for the consequences arising from the accident and not for anything that would probably have occurred or been suffered in any event. A claimant must therefore prove that his/her loss was caused by the relevant accident. To proceed with a claim, the claimant's medical evidence must establish which of the claimant's complaints since the accident and which of the concerns in relation to the claimant's medical health for the future are a consequence of the accident. It must also establish that these complaints and concerns would not have arisen in the absence of the accident or adverse event.

> Lawyers use the term 'but for' when addressing the issue of causation: 'but for the accident, the claimant would not have suffered...'

The issue of causation is generally not part of a medical practitioner's assessment of a patient and is not written about in medical reports to colleagues. For the most part, causation is irrelevant to medical practice - a patient is as a patient is and what would have been the situation were circumstances to have been different is of no, or very little, significance. Most medical experts do not recognise or understand the fundamental importance of the issue of causation to lawyers and to the litigation process. Having a clear understanding of causation is one of the fundamental components of the medico-legal mind.

The primary importance of causation in medico-legal practice alerts us to the issue that some of the technical language in a medical expert report is inter-disciplinary, with some terms having specific meaning and significance only in a medico-legal context. Terms that are used interchangeably in everyday professional practice may have specific meanings in the medico-legal arena.

When addressing causation, one such area of confusion for medical experts (and alas many instructing solicitors) is the distinction in the medico-legal use of the terms: *Injury, Symptoms, Effects and Consequences.* As most experts are unclear precisely how these terms should be used, many substitute one for another, without realising the detrimental effect this has on the quality and clarity of the evidence. However, once the distinction between these terms is understood, experts can use these terms as an agenda to seek out relevant factual information on these aspects of the claim during the interview and examination of the claimant and during the analysis of medical records. Such information is fundamental to addressing the issue of causation.

Let us define these terms and illustrate how to use them in a report:

Injury	the physical/psychological trauma suffered
Symptoms	the physical/psychological manifestations of the injury
Effects	the physical/psychological limitations experienced by the claimant as a result of the injury/symptoms
Consequences	the restrictions on the activities of daily living, now and for the future, that result from the injury/symptoms/effects

Therefore, to apply these terms in a personal injury report dealing with a claimant injured in a car accident: a soft-tissue *injury* to the claimant's neck caused *symptoms* of severe headaches for two weeks, with the *effect* that the claimant had to rest most afternoons during that period, with the *consequence* that he was unable to work for two weeks after the accident.

In a claim arising out of an injury, not only the causation of the injury itself but of all of the subsequent symptoms, effects and consequences have to be proved by the claimant and must be addressed by the medical expert in the expert report.

The effect of not dealing properly with causation is that the expert evidence prevents the claim being properly assessed or valued, which delays the progress of the claim and initiates the tedious round of correspondence and questions by the lawyers seeking clarification of the expert's opinions.

'Signs' and 'Symptoms'

Doctors make a clear distinction between the terms 'signs' (manifestations of an injury that are objectively ascertainable) and 'symptoms' (manifestations of an injury as reported by the client). Most lawyers do not appreciate this difference, tending to conflate the distinct meanings of these terms. From a legal perspective, signs will either be supportive of (or not supportive of) the injury, symptoms and effects that the claimant claims and so it is important that the expert makes clear what the sign is and what it shows, and how it supports or does not support particular aspects of the claimant's claim.

> The greatest failing in medical expert reports is the inability or unwillingness of medical experts to address causation adequately. It is a daily complaint of lawyers that medical experts do not understand the importance of causation: this complaint applies equally to reports in personal injury, clinical negligence and industrial disease claims.

A lawyer would find the following opinions **unhelpful** because in both examples the evidence does not address what consequences actually resulted from the accident:

> I am asked to consider whether had the accident not happened Mr J would have been able to continue in his employment until retirement age. It is impossible to say whether in the absence of the accident he would have been able to continue in his employment. That is a hypothetical question and is not capable of a scientific answer.

> Based on his account of the circumstances of the accident, his past medical history, scan results and my clinical experience it is my opinion that his pre-existent back problems contribute 10-20% of the present problem while the index event contributes 80-90%.

A lawyer would find the following opinions **helpful** because the evidence provides a clear opinion on causation and gives the rationale that supports the conclusion reached by the expert:

> If the accident had not occurred, Mr J would probably have been able to continue in his current employment until age 60, although it is likely that from about that age, in the light of developing and increasing symptoms, he would have had to find lighter work or reduce the number of hours he worked. As a result of the accident and his subsequent medical retirement, those options are no longer available to him.

I consider it is very unlikely that Mr W will return to work before the age of 65. I am of the opinion that given his pre-morbid functioning, the psychosocial/family disruption, his musculo-skeletal problems and his alcohol intake, he would not have worked to the age of 65 in any event. I consider that the culmination of these factors would almost certainly have resulted in his leaving work before his retirement age of 65. Although it is impossible to be precise, I consider it probable that there would have been a reduction of working life of at least 5 years, resulting in his retirement at the age of 60.

6.1.1   Competing Causes of Injury

If there are a number of possible independent explanations for a condition following an accident, then the 'but for' test must be applied to establish whether the condition was, for legal purposes, caused by the accident. In order to recover damages the claimant must prove that in the absence of the accident that is the subject of the claim (i.e. the negligence or other breach of duty) the injury would probably not have occurred.

Consider the case of *Wilsher*[1], where a premature baby developed retrolental fibroplasia after being given excess oxygen by doctors. The hospital trust whose staff had acted negligently and were responsible for the baby receiving excess oxygen would not be found liable in damages for the consequences to the baby unless it were proved that the negligence probably caused the blindness and therefore that in the absence of that negligence the baby would not have sustained damage. If there were a number of other 'innocent' or non-negligent explanations for the development of the condition, then the claim could not succeed unless it were proved that the damage to the baby's vision would not have occurred 'but for' the excess oxygen.

A second example is the case of *Hotson*[2] in which a boy fell from a tree, sustaining a fracture of the femoral epiphysis. The fracture was negligently missed at hospital, and the boy went on to develop avascular necrosis. Damages for the subsequent damage to the leg would not be recoverable if there was at least a 50% risk of avascular necrosis even had the fracture been appropriately diagnosed. The claimant would not be able to prove that it was more likely than not that the avascular necrosis was caused by the negligence – in other words, he is not able to prove that 'but for' the negligence the avascular necrosis would probably not have occurred in any event. The lawyers will look to the medical expert to give opinion on such issues.

---

1   *Wilsher v Essex Area Health Authority* [1988] AC 1074

2   *Hotson v East Berkshire Area Health Authority* [1987] AC 750, which is discussed in Section 5.3 above

6.1.2 Material Contribution

In very limited circumstances, the 'but for' test is relaxed and it is sufficient if it can be proved by the claimant that the defendant's breach of duty 'materially contributed' to the injury. This will arise in the limited situation where medical science cannot establish the probability that 'but for' an act of negligence the injury would not have happened, but can establish that the contribution of the negligent cause was more than negligible.

Outside the field of industrial disease claims, it is safe to assume that in the absence of instructions to the contrary, the normal 'but for' test applies. However, the medical expert should remain aware of the possibility of needing to address 'material contribution' in circumstances where there are competing causes of injury and there are no scientific means of establishing their relative contribution to that injury. (We address 'material contribution' in Industrial Disease claims in Section 6.3 and in Clinical Negligence claims in Section 8.7.)

6.2 Giving Opinions on Causation

In considering and giving opinion upon each of the claimant's complaints, the medical expert must distinguish clearly between:

1. the present injuries or medical situation and as these would have been but for the accident;

2. the present symptoms and the symptoms as these would have been but for the accident;

3. the present effects (or degree of disability) and what these would have been but for the accident; and

4. the present consequences of the injuries, symptoms and effects on the claimant's daily life, and the consequences as these would have been but for the accident.

Opinions on causation need to be expressed on the period from the accident to the date of the examination or report, and for the future.

The difficulty of forming opinions on causation is that a claimant may have had some symptoms prior to the accident, onto which the symptoms resulting from the injury have been superimposed. There may be pre-existing degenerative changes, asymptomatic prior to the accident but contributing to the situation since the accident or which might do so in the future. There may also be some other unrelated disease or condition that will affect the future. All of these issues can make causation a challenging principle to apply.

When addressing causation, the medical mind is far more comfortable with giving opinions on the situation as it is now than on giving opinions on what the situation would have been in the absence of (i.e. but for) the accident. The medico-legal mind understands that without the second half of the opinion dealing with the 'but for' position, the opinion is incomplete and the claim cannot be valued.

6.2.1 Causation Graphs

A straightforward way to think about causation is to use a 'causation graph', where the X-axis represents the progression of time and the Y-axis deals with the severity of injuries/symptoms/effects. A typical graph for a claimant injured in a road traffic accident is presented below.

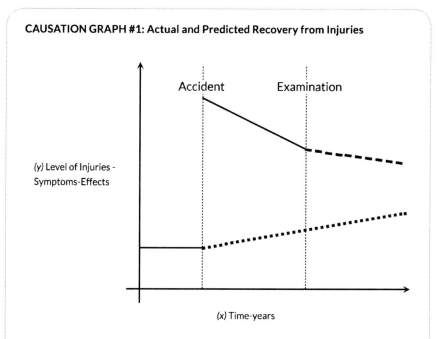

CAUSATION GRAPH #1: Actual and Predicted Recovery from Injuries

Accident   Examination

(y) Level of Injuries -
Symptoms-Effects

(x) Time-years

The solid line illustrates a very low-level of injury/symptoms/effects experienced by the claimant before the accident, with a sudden uplift as the claimant is injured in the accident. Following the accident, there is a gradual improvement in the claimant's situation as the injuries heal and the symptoms diminish. Initially, he returns to work part time before returning to full time work. At the examination date, the medical expert's opinion is that the claimant's medical situation in the future will continue to gradually improve – this is represented by the dashed line – with fewer effects on his activities of daily living.

To deal properly with causation, the medical expert also has to give opinion on the claimant's situation in the absence of the accident, to the date of the report and into the future – this opinion is represented by the lower dotted line. The opinion of the expert as represented on this graph is that there would have been a gradual worsening of the claimant's pre-existing condition over time. The expert will need to consider whether the two lines dealing with the projected future (dashed and dotted post examination date) would eventually meet, which would be the moment when the symptoms that the claimant is likely to suffer as a result of the accident will be equivalent to those that he would have suffered without ('but for') the accident.

The upper and lower lines on the causation graph will be different in every case. If the upper and lower lines meet, either because the claimant's condition improves sufficiently or because of a likely deterioration of a pre-existing condition, then this will be the time-limit for the compensation claim – i.e. the claimant will be back in the position he/she would have been in but for the accident and the 100% Recovery principle will have been met.

In a personal injury claim, the essential questions to be addressed, on the balance of probabilities, are:

> To what extent, and in what way, has the accident affected the claimant's (actual) situation with regard to the injuries, symptoms and effects he/she has suffered and the consequential restrictions on employment and his/her activities of daily living, since the accident and for the future? [Top line]

> But for the accident, what would have been the claimant's (hypothetical) situation with regard to his/her pre-accident condition from the accident date and into the future (i.e. injuries/symptoms) and in regard to any effects and consequences resulting from his/her pre-accident condition over the same period? [Bottom line]

> How much worse off, in terms of consequences, has the claimant been since the accident, is presently, and will be for the future, than would have been the situation in the absence of the accident? [To answer this, the expert describes the differences in injuries/symptom/effects that the space between the top and bottom lines represents and then gives opinion on the consequences that arise from these differences.]

The expert's approach in forming opinions on these questions therefore, as illustrated by the causation graph, is to:

1. identify the situation until now and for the future; (Top line)

2. identify what the situation would have been until now and for the future, but for the accident; (Bottom line)

3. consider if the difference is caused by or attributable to the accident;

4.   describe the difference in terms of injuries/symptoms/effects; (the area between the 2 lines)

5.   interpret the difference the accident has made in terms of consequences: pain, suffering and loss of amenity, restrictions or limitations in activity and consequential restrictions in terms of daily living, employment and special needs.[3]

Experts can apply this approach to causation to any factual situation in a claim. Consider the following examples:

A claimant with a painful arthritic hip injures the same hip in an accident and 12 months afterwards undergoes a total hip replacement. What additional pain and restriction in activity and what treatment did the claimant experience over that which would have occurred "but for" the accident? By what period, if any, was the need for the hip replacement brought forward?

A claimant in his 60's suffers from noise induced hearing loss caused by exposure to excessive noise in the workplace. As a result, his hearing thresholds at particular frequencies are raised. What is the likely impact of this hearing loss in terms of everyday activities (conversation, watching TV, speaking on the telephone) and what is the need for hearing aids? How does that compare with likely age-related hearing loss in the absence of the noise induced hearing loss? When would hearing aids probably have been required in any event?

A claimant suffers a 4th degree perineal tear in childbirth, which is neither recognised nor appropriately treated following the birth. This results in the need for subsequent surgery including a colostomy and persisting residual symptoms. What treatment would have been appropriate had the situation been recognised at the time? How would that treatment compare with the treatment in fact required as a result of the failure to diagnose and treat? How does the current situation and future consequences compare with what would probably have been the situation with appropriate treatment?

Whatever the factual situation, the same logical approach applies. The expert needs to identify and report on the difference that the accident or adverse event has made.

---

3   We recommend that this final element of the opinion, regarding the consequences of the injury be dealt with in its own section. See discussion of report templates in Chapter 10 and Notes to the templates in Appendix 1.

> In assessing which, if any, injuries have been caused by the accident, it is often helpful in less clear-cut cases for the expert to consider whether the likely mechanism of the accident would have caused the injuries complained of and whether the level of symptoms reported by the claimant is consistent with the injuries identified by the expert as having been caused by the accident.

6.2.2 'Egg-Shell Skull' Principle and Causation

The 'Egg-Shell Skull' principle means that someone who causes injury to another person must take that other person as they are. If therefore the injured person has a particular vulnerability, which means that the impact of the accident or injury on them is more severe than would normally be expected, the person who causes the injury is responsible for all of the consequences. Common examples of this might include the impact of a traumatic experience on someone with a vulnerable personality as a result of a history of depression, a soft tissue knee injury in the case of someone still recovering from a previous similar injury, or a prolapsed lumbar disc following an accident in someone with degenerative disease of the spine. In each case, the person causing the injury cannot avoid liability for the consequences being greater than would normally have been expected in a person of reasonable fortitude or constitution.

However these same egg-shell skull issues will be relevant to the question of causation – i.e. what injury or loss resulted from the accident and how that compares with what would probably have occurred in any event. The person with the vulnerable personality might have suffered some further relapses of depression in any event. The claimant with the injured knee might not have been able to return to skiing or working as a carpet layer even in the absence of the second accident. The disc prolapse might well have occurred in any event even in the absence of the second accident so that the subsequent surgery would still have been necessary.

It follows that the medical expert need not be directly concerned with the egg-shell skull principle, but may be concerned with how in the particular case the consequences of the injury, in terms of the claimant's medical condition, can be attributed to the accident and will be concerned with any such vulnerabilities when considering what would have been the situation but for the accident.

6.2.3 Use of Percentages

The expert should always describe in words the difference an accident has made. It is unlikely to be useful for a medical expert to express this difference in terms of a percentage that reflects the difference between aspects of the situation now and the situation as it would have been but for the accident. A common and incorrect approach is for a medical expert to write, for example, that 50% of the symptoms (or pain or discomfort or disability) is attributable to the accident and the balance to the pre-existing condition. While this could be said to address the issue of causation of injury, it wholly fails to address the difference that the accident has made and therefore does not help the lawyers to establish a value for the claim.

The difficulty for the lawyers seeking to value the claim on the basis of a percentage contribution becomes obvious when we consider the following example. Take a claimant with low back pain. The expert's opinion is that 50% of the claimant's symptoms are attributable to the accident and 50% are attributable to his pre-existing condition and would have been present in any event.

1. Does the expert mean that the claimant now has twice as much pain?

2. Does the expert mean that the claimant can only walk half as far?

3. Does the expert mean the claimant can only lift half as much?

This opinion expressed as a percentage could mean that the claimant receives virtually no damages, or that the claimant receives nearly 100% of the damages claimed. If the first 50% (from the pre-existing condition) would not have affected the claimant's ability to work or any activities of daily living at all, or only occasionally, while the second 50% (from the accident) affected the claimant so that he can now no longer work or do anything useful around the home, then the first 50% will have little relevance in terms of damages recovered, whilst the second 50% will attract almost a full award of damages. In contrast, if the first 50% had resulted in the claimant losing employment and being largely unemployable because of the resulting restrictions in activity, the second 50% may actually add very little to the restrictions and the recoverable damages may be extremely small.

An opinion that 50% of the symptoms are attributable to the accident simply does not mean that he will recover 50% of the damages he would have recovered had 100% been attributable to the accident. The expert must explain the differences between the situation as it now is (and will be for the future) and the situation as it would have been but for the accident and how these differences affect the claimant's life. The lawyers can then assess the loss that results from the symptoms that are attributable to the accident.

A lawyer would find the following opinions **unhelpful** because the evidence does not address in grounded and pragmatic language the difference that the accident has made:

> Of his present problems 60% can be attributed to the low back while 40% can be attributed to symptoms and signs in his right lower limb. Of the overall disability arising from the low back and right lower limb, 20% might have been expected to occur even if this accident had not taken place but 80% of his residual symptoms can be attributed to the accident.

She has a past history of suffering from anxiety symptoms. On each occasion this was treated successfully with short term treatment involving anxiolytic medication. She recovered completely from these symptoms. Having had anxiety symptoms in the past this should be viewed as a vulnerability factor to her developing depressive disorder due to the pain and restrictions arising from the accident. I would attribute up to 20% of the causality of the depressive disorder to this pre-existing vulnerability and 80% to the pain and restriction in activities arising from the accident.

I would estimate that of the severity of his low back symptoms at the 5 year point after his accident, two-thirds will be attributable to his long-standing low back problems whereas one-third of the severity will be as a result of the accident and would not have been present if this accident had not occurred. Therefore there will be, at the 5 year point, an increase of 50% in the severity of his symptoms, solely as a result of the accident.

In my opinion, 60-70% of the trouble that he is having in his thoracolumbar spine is attributable to the accident. The treatment he now requires is attributable to the accident and to the pre-existing degenerative changes in the spine. In my opinion, 60-70% of the treatment he now requires to his thoracolumbar spine is attributable to the accident.

A lawyer would find the following opinions **helpful** because the evidence makes clear the difference the accident has made:

… in the absence of the accident, he would probably have developed minor symptoms involving occasional and intermittent low back pain. This would likely have been managed with occasional use of over-the-counter painkillers and perhaps very occasional physiotherapy, but would not have significantly interfered with his work or activities of daily living. There is no indication that he would have developed any lower limb symptoms in the absence of the accident.

She has a past history of suffering from anxiety symptoms. On each occasion these were treated successfully, with full recovery after short term treatments involving anxiolytic medication. By 2007, she seems to have recovered completely from these symptoms. Her having had anxiety symptoms in the past should be viewed as a vulnerability factor to her developing depressive disorder in the future.

In the absence of the accident, there was a significant risk that she would suffer a further depressive disorder at some time in the light of further stressors and adverse life events. Any such depressive disorder caused by adverse life events would have been readily amenable to further similar treatment and recovery. However, it is the pain and restriction in activities arising from the accident that both initiated and perpetuated the current depressive disorder, which is of a far greater magnitude in terms of its physical and emotional impact and from which she has still not yet fully recovered.

As a result of the accident, he continues to suffer symptoms in his low back and right lower limb, resulting in the restrictions in activity described above. I consider his complaints of residual symptoms to be reasonable and within the expected range given the severity of the accident. My impression is that, while all of his symptoms do impact on his everyday life, it is probably his back symptoms that undermine his quality of life and are the fundamental cause of his continuing disability. In my opinion, his restrictions are attributable to the accident and I do not consider it likely that he would have experienced any of these restrictions in the absence of the accident.

6.2.4   Questions about Percentages

In particular circumstances, the court may choose to apportion damages between two or more defendants on a percentage basis. This may be done where two or more defendants are responsible for the same injury or where the court cannot distinguish which specific accident or adverse event has caused what specific damage. This is normally done without the input of medical experts.

Some examples of such apportionment are:

A claimant suffers a psychiatric injury as a result of the combined effects of a vicious assault in which he suffered damage to his eye - for which assault his employer was liable - and a subsequent clinical negligence, which resulted in the loss of vision in that eye. Aspects of the damages recovered were apportioned between the defendants to reflect their relative contributions to the condition.

As the different aspects of his subsequent mental problems could not be readily attributed to the 2 separate incidents (the assault and the surgical operation) an apportionment was made based on the rough and ready assessment of their likely contribution. Neither defendant was found to have caused the whole injury, some being caused mainly by one, some mainly by the other, and some by their combined effect, so that neither could properly have been held liable for the whole.

A claimant suffered three road traffic accidents, in each of which a whip-lash injury was suffered. After the third accident, the claimant was forced to retire.

The two medical experts giving evidence at the trial agreed that the effects of the accidents were cumulative and were responsible for the chronic pain state from which the claimant subsequently suffered. The judge held that it was this 'cumulative effect' that resulted in the retirement and the court apportioned damages resulting from the retirement and for the long term consequences between the three defendants. (The first two defendants had sought to argue that it was the third accident that caused the retirement and without it the claimant would not have retired.)

In both of these situations[4], the medical expert's role was to describe the consequences of the accident or injury in relation to which he/she is instructed – i.e. the effect of the assault or of the clinical negligence or the effect of the first, second, third or all three of the road traffic accidents. The expert will only address the proportions by which each breach of duty is responsible for the whole after first considering the effects of each individual breach and then only if specifically instructed to do so.

6.3 Industrial Disease Claims and 'Material Contribution'

In limited circumstances, the law permits the claimant to establish causation of damage to a lower standard, on the basis that the breach of duty made a 'material contribution' to the injury suffered by the claimant. In these cases, it is not possible to establish that 'but for' the negligence or other breach of duty of the defendant, the injury (including within the term 'injury' both medical conditions and diseases) would not have occurred. The most common application of this material contribution principle is in industrial disease claims in which the claimant is exposed to a harmful substance or agent, although it has also been applied in other fields including clinical negligence.[5]

In this difficult area of law, the expert should always seek clear instructions from the instructing solicitor as to which of the tests of causation needs to be applied. However, it is useful for experts to understand the important distinguishing factors in all cases where the material contribution causation test should be applied.

---

4   From *Rahman v Arearose* [2001] QB 251 and *Pearce v Lindfield* [2003] EWCA Civ 647

5   See for example *Bailey v Ministry of Defence* [2009] 1 WLR 1062 and Section 8.7 below

There are three factors that distinguish these cases:

1. the agent responsible for causing the disease or condition is the same in each of several periods of exposure;

2. the mechanism by which that agent is applied to the claimant is the same; and

3. medical science cannot prove which period of exposure caused the injury.

So for example, the material contribution test would be applied in a case where a claimant demonstrates symptoms of noise induced hearing loss having been exposed to excessive noise by each of a number of employers as well as in his pastime of clay pigeon shooting. Or in the case of a claimant who used hand vibrating tools in several periods of employment – some as a self-employed contractor – who now suffers from vibration white finger.

However, where the agent that may have caused the condition could be one of several different agents – i.e. there are competing causes for the condition – the claimant will still have to establish which of the agents did, on the balance of probabilities, cause the condition and the lawyers will seek evidence from the medical experts on the 'but for' basis. For example, smoking and certain chemicals are major risk factors for bladder cancer. So, a claimant who smokes and who develops bladder cancer after exposure to aromatic amines from dyes will have to prove that this latter exposure more than doubled his risk of developing such a cancer as a result of smoking in order to demonstrate that the aromatic amines were the more likely cause.[6]

6.3.1 Application of Material Contribution Test to Complex Factual Situations

There are a variety of complex factual situations that create difficulty for lawyers and experts alike when seeking to address causation using the material contribution test. We discuss these difficult situations below and then explain how the medical expert must deal with these issues in the report.

Scientific Impossibility or Factual Difficulty

The law distinguishes between cases where the difficulty or impossibility of proof is as a result of an inability on the part of medical science to answer the causation question and those cases where it is as a result of a problem in establishing what the facts are (or were). The medical expert must therefore be able to distinguish between these two situations.

---

6   *Novartis Grimsby Ltd v Cookson* [2007] EWCA Civ 1261

Only in the situation where there is an inability on the part of medical science to answer the causation question on the 'but for' basis is the material contribution test applicable:

> A turkey plucker, who was provided with gloves and an apron, contracted campylobacter enteritis. She alleged that she had been infected as a result of her employer's failure to protect her from the risk of infection from handling dead poultry. The judge hearing the case held that the employer was negligent and in breach of statutory duty in failing to warn her of the risk of exposure to the bacterium and to advise her as to the precautions she should take to minimise the risk of infection. He went on to find that it was not possible to establish if those breaches had caused the infection, that is, that the infection would not have occurred had there been no such breaches. Therefore, he went on, the 'but for' test was not applicable and the claim succeeded because the breaches had materially increased the risk of infection.
>
> On appeal, it was pointed out that the judge's difficulties with the 'but for' test were the result of a failure by him to make crucial findings of fact, for example, as to whether if properly warned the claimant would have avoided touching her face, or would not have discarded her gloves, or whether the risk of contact with the bacterium from contact with door handles would have been reduced or avoided. Had such findings been made it would have been open to him to hold that on the balance of probabilities the claimant would not have been infected if the employer had fulfilled its obligations. Therefore, it was not impossible for the claimant to prove causation on the usual 'but for' basis and it was not appropriate to apply the material contribution test instead. This was not a case where medical science was unable to establish the probability that the claimant would suffer the injury as a result of the employer's breaches of duty.[7]

Some Exposure Culpable/Some Non-Culpable

A claimant may be able to prove that he/she has suffered injury as the result of cumulative exposure to a substance that is now known to be hazardous. Although all of the exposure may have been during employment with one employer, some of the exposure was culpable (i.e. negligent exposure or in breach of duty) and some was not. This situation arises where, for example, the state of knowledge about a substance has advanced, so that its hazardous nature is discovered or the level of what was previously regarded as safe exposure is reconsidered at a time when employees had previously been exposed to it without such knowledge. The situation also arises where there are statutory regulations that prohibit one activity that would result in such exposure, but not another activity that would also result in exposure.

---

7   *Sanderson v Hull* [2008] EWCA Civ 1211

In these cases, it is impossible to prove whether it was the culpable, or so-called "guilty" exposure, or the non-culpable or "innocent" exposure that caused the injury. The claimant may then establish liability arising from the employer's culpable exposure if it can be proved that this exposure made a material contribution to the cause of the injury:

> A claimant contracted pneumoconiosis from being exposed to harmful silica dust at work with one employer. Some of the dust came from using swing grinders, and some from use of a pneumatic hammer. Owing to the regulations that applied at the time, the former was exposure for which liability arose (it was culpable), the latter was not. In the absence of detailed evidence as to the relative proportions of dust inhaled by the claimant arising from those 2 processes, the employer was held liable as the 'guilty' dust – that for which the employer was legally liable – had made a material contribution to the causation of the disease.[8]

Cumulative Exposure where the Mechanism of Exposure is Unclear

The material contribution test also applies in claims where there is cumulative exposure to a substance capable of causing injury, but where medical science cannot prove the precise mechanism by which the injury was caused and therefore which period of exposure was responsible for the injury:

> An employee contracted dermatitis from brick dust. He was exposed to brick dust while working in pipe kilns but also was exposed to the dust when he went home in his dusty work clothes. The employer was not liable for exposure in the pipe kilns but was under a duty to provide facilities to enable the employee to wash off the dust before going home. The precise mechanism by which the dermatitis was caused could not be proved by medical science at that time and it could not be proved whether it was the dust in the kilns or the dust on the clothes taken home that caused the dermatitis. However, the claimant was permitted to recover in full for his condition against his employer on proof that there was a significant increase in the risk of contracting that disease as a result of the 'guilty' exposure.[9]

Cumulative Exposure: Two or More Culpable Exposers

The material contribution test is also applied to claims in which there are 2 (or more) potential defendants liable to the claimant for cumulative exposure to a substance that is capable of causing injury, but where medical science cannot prove which of the defendants has in fact caused the injury.

---

8   *Bonnington Castings v Wardlaw* [1956] AC 613
9   *McGhee v National Coal Board* [1973] 1 WLR 1

Where the condition is dose-related, so that the greater the exposure, the worse the condition will be (as might be the case with pneumoconiosis, asbestosis or noise induced hearing loss), then the condition will probably have arisen to some extent as a result of each period of exposure, and each period of exposure can be said to have materially contributed to the final condition. Each employer responsible for a 'more than minimal exposure' will be liable to the claimant for causing the condition.

Where it is not possible scientifically to say which of the periods of exposure by the successive employers resulted in the disease (as for example in the development of mesothelioma from exposure to asbestos) then any of the employers who had been responsible for 'materially increasing the risk' of contracting the disease will be liable.[10] Therefore, in this limited category of cases, liability will be established where it is proved that exposure by one defendant resulted in a material increase in the risk of the injury being caused.

Cumulative Exposure: 'But For' Test Applicable

In contrast to the above situations, it may be that the claimant has been exposed to a single substance or agent capable of causing harm by several employers, but that it is still possible to address causation on the usual 'but for' basis.

For example, it may be proved that in the absence of the exposure by the last employer, the claimant would not have developed the condition at all. This could be argued where the threshold for the development of symptoms had not been reached until the exposure by the last employer, in which case, the other employers may be able to avoid liability on the usual 'but for' basis. Typically, this situation may arise in relation to a cumulative condition such as vibration white finger where, had the claimant's exposure to vibration ceased with the penultimate employer, the condition would not, on the balance of probabilities, have developed.

6.3.2   Apportionment of Damages

A further issue that arises in claims involving concurrent and cumulative causes is the extent to which a defendant should be liable for the total damage and loss suffered by the claimant. If 3 employers exposed the claimant to asbestos and he subsequently contracts asbestosis or mesothelioma, with damages assessed at say £100,000, how is that liability to be divided between the employers? Further, where one of those employers was not culpable (for example, owing to the state of knowledge during that period of employment as to the dangers involved from the asbestos) or cannot now be identified or has no insurance or assets, how then is the liability divided?

---

10   *Barker v Corus Plc* [2006] UKHL 20

'Divisible' and 'Non-Divisible' Conditions

Where the condition that the claimant contracts or develops is dose-related, such as with noise induced hearing loss or asbestosis, then each defendant is liable for its contribution towards the condition. Lawyers call such injury 'divisible', meaning that the seriousness of the medical condition is related to the degree of exposure to the agent causing it. The defendant is only liable for the part of the overall injury that its culpable exposure caused. Where there is a period of exposure that does not result in liability being established against anyone (for example because of non-culpable exposure) that contribution is also taken into account in such a 'divisible' injury claim, reducing the liability of the liable employers. Also, where there is a period of exposure for which the claimant him/herself is responsible, for example during a period of self-employment, then this contribution is also taken into account, reducing the amount of damages to be paid by the liable employers.

If the injury is not dose-related and is therefore 'indivisible', so that it is not possible on the basis of medical science to say how much contribution the exposure by any one defendant has made to the injury or condition (other than that it is more than minimal), then the traditional approach has been that it is inappropriate to apportion the damages between the defendants and non-culpable exposers. Each defendant will be liable to the claimant for the whole (although entitled to a contribution from each of the other defendants).[11]

Where the condition is not dose-related but liability is established on the basis of a material contribution to an increase in the risk of the injury occurring, for example in the case of the development of mesothelioma from exposure to asbestos, the law is that the liability is shared according to 'the contribution to the risk' of contracting the disease.[12] However, in the specific case of mesothelioma (and only in this case) the law has been changed by statute to provide that each of the culpable employers is liable for the whole of the damages, although each is entitled to seek a contribution from each of the other culpable employers.[13]

Where apportionment of damage is required, to avoid a complicated and time-consuming process of assessment of the contributions made, the court will often fall back on a time-exposed basis to assess the contributions. Each liable party will pay as its share of damages that proportion which the period of exposure for which that party is liable bears to the total period of exposure.

Where, for example, a claimant is exposed to asbestos dust by several employers and subsequently develops asbestosis, each employer will be liable to contribute to the damages recoverable for that condition to the extent of their contribution to the condition by exposure to the dust. The apportionment is a question of assessment of time exposure by the defendants or possibly by the intensity of such exposure, but this is a matter for assessment by an engineering expert rather than a medical expert.[14]

---

11   *Dickins v O2 Plc* [2008] EWCA Civ 1144; *Bailey v MOD* [2009] 1 WLR 1062

12   *Barker v Corus Plc* [2006] UKHL 20

13   Section 3(2) Compensation Act 2006

14   See *Holtby v Brigham & Cowan* [2000] 3 All ER 421

6.3.3   Approach to the Evidence

When faced with a claim in which the material contribution test needs to be applied, it is important for the expert to adopt a logical approach in assessing the evidence to ensure that the material contribution test is applied appropriately to the issues in dispute.

Culpable and Non-Culpable Exposure

Where there is a single period of both culpable and non-culpable exposure, the medical expert should address two questions.

1. Would the injury probably have occurred as a result of the non-culpable exposure in any event?

If the answer is that the injury would have occurred in any event, then 'but for' the culpable exposure, the injury would still have occurred. Therefore, the claimant would fail to prove causation of injury as a result of the culpable exposure. Where the answer is that it would not have occurred in any event, then 'but for' the culpable exposure, the injury would probably not have occurred. Therefore, the claimant would succeed in proving causation of injury as a result of the culpable exposure.

2. If the medical expert is unable to answer the above question because medical science cannot establish the probability that 'but for' the contribution of the culpable exposure the injury would not have occurred, then the second question for the expert to address is, was the contribution of the culpable exposure more than minimal?

Where the answer is that the contribution of the culpable exposure was more than minimal, the 'but for' test is modified to the assessment of 'material contribution'. Therefore, the claimant would succeed in proving causation from the culpable exposure. Where the answer is that the contribution was not more than minimal, causation would not be established and the claimant would fail.

Periods of Culpable Exposure

Where there are periods of culpable exposure by more than one potential defendant, the medical expert should assist by addressing two questions, which would need to be considered in relation to each potential defendant.

1. Would the injury in its totality probably have occurred as a result of the exposure by one, some, or all of the other potential defendants in any event?

If the answer is that the injury in its totality would probably have occurred in any event, then 'but for' the potential defendant's exposure the injury would still have occurred. Therefore, the claimant would fail to prove causation of injury against that potential defendant. Where the answer is that the injury in its totality would probably not have occurred 'but for' the exposure by that defendant, the claimant would succeed against that defendant. However, if the medical expert is unable to answer the question because medical science cannot establish the probability that 'but for' the contribution of the defendant the injury would or would not have occurred, then the expert must then consider the second question.

2. Can medical science establish that the contribution of the culpable exposure by that defendant was more than minimal?

If the answer is that the contribution of the culpable exposure was more than minimal, then the 'but for' test is modified. Therefore, the claimant would succeed against that potential defendant. Where the answer is that the contribution is not more than minimal, causation would not be established and the claimant would fail to prove the claim against that defendant.

Therefore, where it is impossible medically to say which of the several defendants' actions or failures caused the injury, but that in each case the mechanism of exposure would have been the same, then the medical expert should express an opinion as to whether each defendant's actions or failures made a material contribution to the risk of developing the injury.

Apportionment

Having expressed an opinion that the defendant has made a material contribution to the cause of a dose-related injury or a material increase in the risk of an injury (except in the case of mesothelioma), the expert should express an opinion as to the extent of the contribution made by that defendant to the resulting injury. Where to do so would be outside the expert's field of expertise, then he/she should indicate this in the report and signpost for the lawyers the need to instruct a suitable expert to address the question.

6.4 'Acceleration' and 'Exacerbation' (a classic case of 'Foot-Wearing')[15]

The terms 'Acceleration' and 'Exacerbation' are not strictly medical or legal terms of art. These terms exist in the medico-legal sphere as a shorthand description of the relationship between the situation since an accident when compared to the likely progression of a pre-existing condition (i.e. the top and bottom line on the causation graph). Experts and lawyers alike talk about "a 3-year acceleration case" as one where the level of symptoms the claimant is now suffering has been brought forward in time by three years. Similarly, experts and lawyers will discuss an increase in symptoms following an injury as "an exacerbation of a pre-existing condition".

---

15   For an explanation of 'Foot-Wearing' see Authors' Note

Although well established as medico-legal terms, the medical basis for opinions based on the underlying principles these terms signify is beginning to be challenged by some medical experts. Indeed, for some experts and lawyers, these terms are simply a fiction to enable an award of damages to be calculated and have no basis in science at all. For others, the use of these terms represents the best approach available for predicting what would have happened to the claimant in the absence of the accident and so represents the only sensible way of calculating an award of damages.

For a few experts, however, the use of these terms appears to be a way to humour lawyers and their obsession with quantification:

> We have come to slightly differing opinions with regard to the period of advancement of symptoms as a result of the index event. I suggest 9 – 12 months; Mr S suggests a somewhat wider range of 12 – 24 months.
>
> However, given that the whole concept of advancement or acceleration is an artificial one that cannot be accurately quantified and is a concept that we introduce in cases of this nature to try to help the legal profession in the quantification of damages, we should simply produce these figures as a guide for the court and would not see them as an area of significant disagreement.

Whatever an expert's professional opinion on the conceptual validity of these terms – and it seems that this argument may become more contentious in the next several years – there is no doubt that in most cases these terms are either used inappropriately or without an appropriate level of explanation, to the point where the accuracy of the evidence is lost. A very serious problem arises when experts in their reports use these terms as a shorthand description, because experts and lawyers alike have forgotten (or never knew) what the terms actually mean and so use the terms without making clear what in fact they mean by them.

What the law requires is a comparison of the likely situation as it would have been but for the accident and the situation as it now is and is likely to be in the future. The expert is required to assist in that exercise by applying his/her expertise to the evidence to provide an opinion, on the balance of probabilities, as to the difference(s) of onset – both temporal and qualitative – of the symptoms as the result of the accident and the differences in consequences for the claimant as the result of the accident. (We first introduced this issue in Section 5.4 above in the discussion of 'Proof'.)

Even though medical experts generally find this approach to be artificial and not based in medical science, for lawyers this is a pragmatic approach to calculating the appropriate level of compensation. In many cases where acceleration and exacerbation are relevant issues, medical experts often reach very different opinions without a strong basis from which an opposing opinion can be challenged.

Such differences of opinion would have to be discussed at an experts' meeting and the basis of the difference explained. The outcome of the discussion then allows the lawyers or the court to reach a judgement on the matter. For the valuation of the claim, these differences of opinion can be extremely important, so the more help experts can offer in relation to the likely progression of a pre-existing condition, the more helpful the evidence will be to the lawyers and the court.

Let us turn once more to the causation graph to understand precisely what the terms 'acceleration' and 'exacerbation' mean:

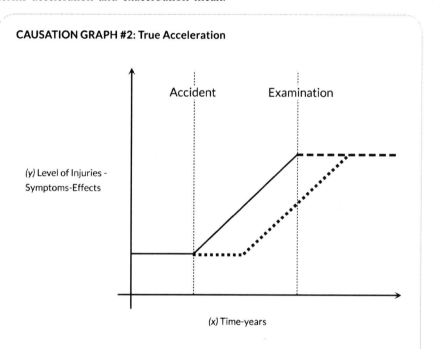

CAUSATION GRAPH #2: True Acceleration

Accident

Examination

(y) Level of Injuries - Symptoms-Effects

(x) Time-years

The accurate use of the term acceleration would require that the injuries, symptoms and effects that the claimant suffered as a result of the accident are *exactly the same* as those that the claimant would have suffered in the absence of the accident, but are experienced earlier as a result of the accident. On the causation graph, this means that the line moves to the left on the X-axis (i.e. brought forward in time) but its shape does not change.

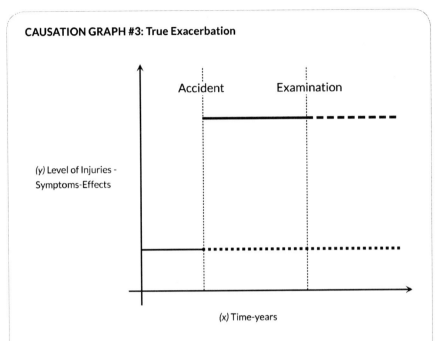

CAUSATION GRAPH #3: True Exacerbation

(y) Level of Injuries - Symptoms-Effects

Accident   Examination

(x) Time-years

The accurate use of the term exacerbation would require that the injuries, symptoms and effects that the claimant suffered as a result of the accident are of *exactly the same type* as those that the claimant would have suffered in the absence of the accident, but are now more severe as a result of the accident. On the causation graph, this means that the injuries/symptoms/ effects line moves upwards on the Y-axis (i.e. increasing the severity) but its relation to time does not change.

Therefore, where the onset of a condition caused by an accident is different to what would have otherwise been the case, this is not "an acceleration case". Where more injuries have been suffered than would otherwise been the case, this is not "an exacerbation case". If an expert chooses to use the shorthand terms acceleration or exacerbation, then it is essential to also explain what is meant in terms of the injuries, symptoms, effects and consequences for the claimant. Otherwise, there is the considerable danger that the expert will not communicate to the lawyer with any accuracy what he/she in fact means.

The use of the terms acceleration and exacerbation alone is not sufficient or precise enough to communicate clearly the situation to the court. The expert must, therefore, avoid the terms altogether or use them only as the starting point for a clear description of the situation. It may be appropriate to indicate that there has been an acceleration of the onset of symptoms, but it is then necessary to describe (and if appropriate to contrast) the differing onsets: the actual and the hypothetical onset but for the accident.

Therefore, a lawyer would find the following opinions **unhelpful** because the evidence does not address whether the symptoms are identical to those that would have been suffered in any event, whether the onset of symptoms is identical or what the rationale is for the opinion (a guess in the first example and unstated empirical evidence in the second being unacceptable):

> It must be emphasised that the issue of acceleration in a case such as this is essentially speculative. It is quite possible that different colleagues might take significantly different views regarding the length of time of the acceleration periods, some preferring a longer period and others a shorter period. My guess, and it can be no more than that, is an acceleration period of 3 years.

> He is a 59 year old man with evidence of degenerative change in his spine and a reasonable suggestion is that he would be experiencing symptoms probably within 2 to 3 years of this material incident. This is a purely speculative suggestion based on no valid scientific evidence and is very much empirical in nature.

NO FOOT-WEARING!

A lawyer would find the following opinions **helpful** as the evidence deals effectively with both the recovery from the accident and the 'but for' the accident situation:

> The back and neck symptoms and pain that Mr X suffered following the accident were initially severe and incapacitating. These began to diminish gradually in the weeks following the accident, so that six weeks on from the accident, Mr X was able to spend short periods out of bed and to move short distances around the ward. He returned home after 10 weeks in hospital. His neck pain and stiffness gradually resolved within 12 months of the accident, leaving him with residual back symptoms and pain that continued to settle over the next 6 months (i.e. 18 months post-accident). At that time, he was able to begin part time work in office based employment, though he continues to suffer pain and stiffness that requires analgesics and occasional days off work.

> In the absence of the accident, Mr X would probably have suffered a gradual increase in back symptoms and pain as a result of the natural progression of the pre-existing deterioration in his lumbar spine. It is my opinion that, in the absence of the accident, the pain and restriction that he would have experienced within a period of 3-6 years in any event would have been commensurate with the level of residual symptoms that remain 18 months after the accident.

However, there is a both a qualitative and quantitative difference between a sudden onset of symptoms and pain as a result of trauma and the gradual onset of symptoms and pain as a result of the deterioration of a pre-existing condition. First, a sudden onset of symptoms as the result of a trauma removes any possibility that the injured person can make adjustments to ameliorate the effects resulting from the symptoms and pain. Second, the injured person, once recovered (to the fullest extent possible) usually feels more vulnerable to further injury and tends to be more risk averse in his day-to-day activities. This leads to a greater level of restriction than would be the case with similar symptoms from a pre-existing condition.

In the case of Mr X, it is probable that in the absence of the accident, with appropriate treatment and reasonable adjustments, he would have been able to continue in his full time manual employment until about…

The issue of acceleration inevitably requires a degree of speculation. In forming an opinion on the acceleration of his pre-existing condition, I have taken into account the following factors:

1. the nature of the accident and the injuries he sustained;

2. his age and previous medical history;

3. his working and recreational activities over of the last 20 years; and

4. the nature and extent of degenerative changes shown on X-ray and MRI.

I am of the opinion that whilst it is probable that Mr Q would have developed similar symptoms in any event in due course, such symptoms almost certainly would not have commenced before his 50th birthday and probably not until his mid-fifties, which is some 10-15 years after the accident. I am therefore of the opinion that the accident has probably resulted in his suffering symptoms some 10 to 15 years earlier than would otherwise have been the case. So far as the nature and effect of those symptoms is concerned…

6.4.1   Differences in Valuation

In an "acceleration case", where the accident has brought forward symptoms from a pre-existing condition, the lawyers need to know, on the balance of probabilities, when it would have been that the claimant would have suffered such symptoms and restrictions in activities in any event in the absence of the accident and therefore by how many years the accident has brought forward those symptoms. The lawyers also need to know the relative onsets of the consequences arising from both the accident and the projected onset of the pre-existing condition.   The lawyers require that the expert addresses causation of injury in this way so that they can calculate the loss caused by the injury.

As an example, let us take what may initially have been described as a 4 to 6 year acceleration case that could, following a more detailed description of the onset of symptoms, lead to an unexpected outcome:

Following the accident, a 54-year old claimant (with a normal retirement age of 65) was unable to return to work. Therefore, the accident led to his medical retirement within 6 months of the accident when he was 55. The medical expert's opinion is that, but for the accident, the symptoms from a pre-existing previously asymptomatic degenerative condition would probably have developed 4 to 6 years later.

Based on this evidence of a '4-6 year acceleration case' the lawyers may value the loss of earnings in the case as follows:

Limited to say 5 years: (i.e. at age 60, his situation would have been as it is now). Therefore loss of earnings = 5 x annual net earnings.

Say:

£15,000 x 5 = £75,000

Had the medical expert reported in more detail on the gradual onset of symptoms after 4-6 years, the consequences for the claimant may have altered. The expert may actually consider that a gradual onset of symptoms from his pre-existing condition would have allowed the claimant to adapt to his back condition more successfully - the gradual onset of symptoms allowing the claimant time to adapt to the requirements of his work, to take appropriate medication, to receive physiotherapy when necessary and to take short periods off work when his symptoms were at their worst.

If this were to be the situation, then the claimant would probably have been able to continue in employment perhaps until his normal retirement age after another 5 years. Therefore, on the balance of probabilities, the claimant has not lost 4 to 6 years' earnings (the period of acceleration of symptoms) but has in fact lost 9 to 10 years' earnings (the period of acceleration, plus the 5 years he would probably have managed to continue working during the gradual onset of the symptoms) together with the additional pension he would have earned in that time.

Based on this assessment the valuation for loss of earnings alone would be:

Limited to 10 years: (i.e. at age 65, his situation would be as it is now). Therefore loss of earnings = 10 x annual net earnings.

Say:

£15,000 x 10 = £150,000

In reality, most cases in which pre-existing conditions (whether symptomatic or asymptomatic) are relevant contain both an element of acceleration and an element of exacerbation of symptoms. Symptoms are usually worse in the initial period following the accident than they would have been with a gradual onset. Also, the effects and consequences are often more severe because of the trauma that precipitates the sudden onset. These are important issues that the expert must consider when expressing opinions on causation.

Take another look at causation graph #1[16] for a typical injury situation and compare it to the acceleration and exacerbation graphs. These graphs have fundamentally different shapes and therefore would probably result in markedly different consequences for the claimant and markedly different assessments of financial award for the injury.

> To return briefly to the sign outside the temple in Mandalay, if what the expert intends to communicate is the equivalent of 'Wear nothing on your feet', then the expert should avoid using the phrase 'No Foot-Wearing'. If symptoms have been brought on earlier by the accident and have been made worse for some or all of the time as a result, describe the situation – do not simply state that the symptoms have been accelerated.

NO FOOT-WEARING!

6.5   Prognosis and Future Risk

In relation to a claim, lawyers are only interested in the future for one purpose – to value the damages recoverable. The questions that the lawyers want answered are (typically):

1. will the claimant be able to continue in his current employment, or in any employment, until normal retirement age?

2. what assistance is the claimant likely to need in the future? and

3. will further costs be incurred?

Lawyers do not ask these questions in order to be able to empathise with the claimant's plight, but rather in order to calculate the total value of damages claimed. The law seeks to provide suitable compensation for the future in order to put the claimant in the same position that he/she would have been in but for the accident, so far as it is possible to do so in monetary terms.

---

16   See Section 6.2.1 above. Please remember, the causation graphs we have discussed in this section are an aid to clear thinking; such graphs have no place within the expert report itself - a medical expert's opinion should be expressed in words not illustrated with graphs.

6.5.1   Use of Percentages

Lawyers deal with the future in terms of the degree of risk of something occurring over a time period. This is because damages will be awarded as a proportion of the full value, to reflect the degree of risk and when the loss related to that risk is likely to occur. The best way to express the degree of risk is by the use of percentages.

For the court to award damages for a future complication or deterioration it must be established, on the balance of probabilities:

1.   that as a consequence of the accident or adverse event, a risk now exists of a future complication or deterioration (a risk that would not otherwise have existed); and

2.   what degree of risk the claimant now has of suffering such a complication or deterioration that leads to a future financial loss or of incurring future expense.

The risk should be assessed, so far as it is possible to do so, in terms of a percentage (or a range of percentages) and the point in time at which (or the period within which) the risk is likely to occur. Therefore, the medical expert has first to consider whether the injury has resulted in there probably being a risk of some kind of degeneration of the current condition. If, on the balance of probabilities, there is such a risk, then the medical expert has to go on to assess the degree of risk.

Where, for example, a fracture has marginally affected a joint, the expert may conclude that it does, more likely than not, give rise to a risk of deterioration:

There is a 20-30% chance that he will need a hip replacement within 4 to 6 years.

If the injury did not involve the joint, then the expert may conclude that it is unlikely that there exists any risk and will not need therefore to consider the degree of risk:

It is unlikely that this injury will have any effect on the hip joint in the future.

Prognosis can be presented on an injury by injury basis, with a separate prognosis given for each injury in turn, or a prognosis for all the injuries can be presented after causation for each of the injuries has been addressed. The approach of giving a prognosis for each injury in turn encourages the expert to provide a detailed prognosis on each of the injuries – nothing is left out. However, it may be necessary to consider an injury in relation to other injuries that the claimant has suffered and so writing the prognosis for all the injuries together may be more appropriate in some cases.

Whichever approach is adopted, the prognosis must deal clearly with the medical and the medico-legal issues: the likely progression of the injuries/symptoms/effects in the future and what the likely situation would have been without the accident, particularly as we have seen in respect of the onset of symptoms from a pre-existing condition.[17] The prognosis of injuries is essential for helping the lawyers to establish the end point of the claim. All calculations of future loss are calibrated by the timeline established in the prognosis.

Once the opinion is clear, the lawyers will be able to value the loss:

> The claimant's lawyers are provided with the cost today of joint replacement surgery. Adding this to loss of earnings prior to and following the surgery gives a total loss of £30,000. In the opinion of the expert, the risk of the claimant needing this surgery is around 25% and the date the surgery will be required will be in about 5 years.
>
> The claimant expert's opinion establishes that a risk of requiring this surgery consequent upon the injury exists. The damages recovered will be proportionate to the degree of risk of needing the surgery as assessed by reference to the medical expert's opinion. The expert's opinion is that there is a risk of around 25% that the claimant will require the surgery. On that basis the loss is reduced to approximately £7,500 (25% of £30,000). A further adjustment will be made to reflect the fact that the sum is to be paid now and will not be required (if at all) for around 5 years. Therefore, the sum is discounted in accordance with actuarial tables by a factor of 0.8839 to £6,629 (or thereabouts).

It will, therefore, make a considerable difference in the damages recovered whether the risk is 'small', so that only a small fraction of the full potential value will be awarded, or if the risk is 'substantial', in which case most of the full potential value will be awarded. We return to this issue in Section 6.5.4 below.

6.5.2   Use of Dates

An issue that often arises is when the expert offers a prognosis without making clear which date the prognosis is to be calculated from – the examination date or the accident date:

> In my opinion, it is likely that Mr S's back pain is due to damage to the soft tissues and ligaments of his lower lumbar spine. I expect his pain to settle in around 18 months and that he will be pain free within two years.

---

17   See the discussion of Acceleration and Exacerbation in Section 6.4

It is important that the expert makes clear which date is being used as the baseline and the expert can make the report even clearer by giving the date or range of dates in the future which the time period indicates:

> In my opinion, his pain will settle in around 18 months from the accident date, after which time he will be able to carry out all of his normal daily activities, with only occasional episodes of mild back pain. I expect that he will be pain free within two years of the accident date, that is, by about April 2010.

6.5.3   Clinician's Approach to the Future

The medical mind approaches the future in a very different way to the legal mind. There is often a sensible reluctance to fill a patient's mind with problems, which may develop but also may not. Clinicians seek to avoid causing unnecessary worry and potentially causing a patient to interpret symptoms in an exaggerated manner and so undermine his/her chances of making a full recovery. Having completed complex treatment or therapy to a standard that clinicians would normally regard as successful, the treating clinician may also be reluctant to sit down with the patient to spell out everything that could now go wrong and the possible time scales for such potential problems.

The 'tactful honesty' and optimism of a doctor in the role of treating clinician and the assessment of a medical expert are often at odds with each other. It is not good enough for the purposes of a medical expert report to provide the following as a prognosis, however true it may be as a statement:

> All that can be said about prognosis is that symptoms may last indefinitely. That is not the same as saying that symptoms may last forever, but rather that it is impossible to give a meaningful prognosis. Some patients may improve by 2 years from the index event, others may take longer.

Lawyers will, in this context, tend to treat 'indefinitely' as meaning 'forever'. The issue that the lawyers want to have addressed is "what the prognosis is for this particular claimant". What the lawyers require is a reasoned opinion based on the medical expertise and experience of the expert:

> In assessing the prognosis for the symptoms Mr T is currently experiencing, there are no relevant scientific studies that I can rely upon. In clinical practice, approximately 10% of patients continue to experience symptoms of neck and back pain that do not improve with time. However, given the gradual improvement and settling in Mr T's symptoms over the last 12 months, his recent return to work and his obvious determination to get his

life 'back to normal', my prognosis is that his symptoms will continue to improve in the future, achieving an almost full recovery within 2-3 years. During this period, I expect he will benefit from 6 sessions of physiotherapy per year, and will require treatment with analgesics and a few days of bed rest, up to four times per year.

After this 2-3 year recovery period, he will probably continue to suffer with intermittent residual symptoms of neck and shoulder stiffness, which would probably need to be treated with analgesics, a few days of bed rest, and occasional physiotherapy - perhaps 2-3 sessions per year. I expect such episodes of residual symptoms probably to happen once or twice per year, for 5-7 years after the initial recovery period of 2-3 years.

Most medical experts do not like to quantify risks in terms of percentages over time. Forming opinions about the future, on the balance of probabilities, often causes the medical mind to experience an elevated level of anxiety. The obvious lack of a scientific basis for the opinion leaves the expert feeling exposed and vulnerable. What good medical experts realise is that they are the ones best placed to identify the level of risk and the likely period of time within which any such risks would manifest and so they are not afraid to provide a reasoned estimate of the risk.

6.5.4   Using Percentages in Opinions on Prognosis

As we have seen, the clearest way of describing future risk is by giving a percentage risk within an appropriate time period. We set out in the table below expressions typically used by medical experts when describing future risk. Try completing the 'percentage' column for each expression, and then ask some of your colleagues (in no particular order and without showing them the table or your own quantification for each expression) what percentage they would assign to each of these expressions:

EXPRESSION	PERCENTAGE
a small risk	%
some risk	%
a risk	%
a real risk	%
a substantial risk	%
a high risk	%
a very high risk	%

If we consider what is meant by these expressions, in terms of the percentage degree of risk, it becomes clear that no single or consistent interpretation exists. Therefore, no single interpretation will be agreed by the parties, their lawyers, the medical experts or the judge at trial. Each person hearing these expressions will form his/her own interpretation. The interpretation will vary in different contexts: doctors with their natural reluctance to worry a patient unduly, lawyers seeking the best outcome for their clients, and the common use of understatement in British English ("it's a bit hot"; "the traffic is none too good"; "it wasn't a great weekend").

Without a quantified description of the risk, there is a real danger that many of these phrases will fail to convey to the listener or reader the assessment of risk made by the expert. The words will convey no objective measure of risk and so the claim cannot be properly and appropriately valued.

It may not sound, at first read, unreasonable to give a prognosis as follows:

> Mr B sustained a whiplash injury to his neck. The residual symptoms are likely to improve with physiotherapy. However, he may be left with some symptoms of pain and stiffness which could occur permanently on an intermittent basis.

However, if we assume that the symptoms are interfering with the claimant's ability to manage his employment, how can the value of his claim be assessed on the basis of this description? Leaving aside issues as to how intermittent the symptoms may be and what interference with employment may result from symptoms of inconvenience, the question still remains as to how likely it is that the symptoms will persist – what is the risk?

The difficulty in communicating what is meant when describing the risk can only be overcome by the expert's use of a clear and understandable scale and then communicating the percentage risk associated with that scale in the report. Inevitably, there will usually be a range of possible percentages to describe the risk, so it is generally more appropriate to indicate a range of percentages in the report:

- 'there is a 10-15% risk'
- 'there is a 70-80% risk'.

There is then no possibility that the lawyers will fail to understand the indicated level of risk or have to seek clarification of it. The expert's opinion is clear, and the lawyer can value that risk appropriately.

This approach also applies if there is a chance of improvement, as this would justify a reduction in damages to reflect that possibility. In circumstances where a claimant's symptoms are improving, the lawyers will apply an appropriate discount to reflect the situation. To say that the claimant 'might improve with time' gives little indication of the likelihood of the improvement taking place and over what period of time, and does little to assist in valuing the claim.

To say 'There is a real risk that further major surgery will be necessary' is equivalent to 'No Foot-Wearing'. To stop the reader guessing as to the meaning, the expert should state unambiguously what he/she really means by 'a real risk'.

NO FOOT-WEARING!

6.5.5   Life Expectancy[18]

In contrast with future complications, life expectancy is decided 'on the balance of probabilities'. The issue to be answered is to what age, or for what period, is the claimant more likely than not to survive. This is established as a present fact, not as a future risk. Life expectancy is based on the present known facts – there is in fact no risk of death, only a certainty of death. The only issue is when it will occur.

To a lawyer, if on the balance of probabilities death is likely in 5 years, then that date of death is treated as a fact. This period of life expectancy will almost certainly be wrong – the claimant will either die sooner or later, but this lack of certainty is of no concern to the lawyers. It is for this reason that the court, in compensating for continuing future loss, can now award periodical payments instead of lump sum damages in certain circumstances, so that the damages in fact paid will continue until the death of the claimant and will be the correct amount for that period of life. However, periodical payments are not always awarded and calculations of lump sum payments continue to be made on the basis of the probable life expectancy of the claimant.

In some cases, establishing the life expectancy of a claimant is an essential part of the assessment of future loss as part of the damages to be awarded. It may have most significance in clinical negligence claims, such as those involving serious birth injury - because of the ongoing substantial cost of care – but will also arise in claims for a failure to diagnose or treat a condition as a result of which life expectancy is significantly reduced. Issues of life expectancy do arise in personal injury cases as well, for example, because of catastrophic injuries or in claims for a cancer resulting from exposure to substances in breach of duty.

In many cases, published 'life tables' can be used to establish a figure for life expectancy, or sources such as *Brackenridge's Medical Selection of Life Risks* (now in its 5th edition published in 2006), with appropriate adjustments, as necessary, for particular factors such as smoking or cardiac history. However, if the claimant is outside the cohort for whom the life tables are applicable, then the question for the expert to address is 'to what age or for what period will 50% of the claimant's cohort survive'. It is at this point that it cannot be said that the claimant is more likely than not to

---

18   See also the earlier discussion in relation to the balance of probabilities at Section 5.3 above

survive and therefore the claimant cannot prove on the balance of probabilities that he would live that long (or any longer). Life expectancy in cases involving cancers (whether caused by breach of duty or missed through negligence or poor manage- ment) can often be assisted from references to published papers on survival rates.

By applying medical expertise and knowledge to the particular facts of the case, a medical expert should be able to identify a range of opinion as to probable life expectancy and narrow that range down by reference to the particular facts of the case. This is not and is not thought by the lawyers to be anything more than an opinion reached on the balance of probabilities.

In some cases, it is not only the life expectancy of the claimant that is important. If the claimant is married then it may be necessary to know for how long it is probable that he/she would have continued to support the spouse in the absence of the breach of duty and resulting shortened life expectancy, and therefore which of them would have had the longer life expectancy must also be proved.

6.6   Consequences of Injuries

Many experts are unaware of the importance of addressing in detail the conse- quences of the claimant's injuries. The medical expert report provides the basis for the assessment of the damages claimed by the claimant and therefore has an essential role in helping the lawyers to value cases appropriately. It is essential that the medical expert gives opinions on all of the consequences of an accident. This includes all the consequences that arise along the accident timeline, beginning at the accident date and continuing until the claimant makes a full recovery or reach- es the point where no further improvement or deterioration is likely to occur.

6.6.1   Addressing Consequential Loss

CPR 35.3(1) requires an expert only to comment on matters within his/her expertise. This requirement guides us to the approach that the expert needs to adopt when assessing the consequences of an injury to the claimant. Most medical experts are aware that they are in no way qualified to comment on the type of job that an injured claimant unable to return to his previous employment would be able to manage. Nor would many claim any expertise in assessing how many hours of help with housework would be required if a claimant can no longer do the cleaning. These questions would perhaps require the expertise of an employment expert or care consultant.

However, employment experts and care consultants will be instructed only where the cost of doing so is proportionate to the value of the claim; otherwise, the parties will have to manage as best they can based on a medical expert's opinion. Where employment experts and care consultants are instructed, they usually have little or no medical expertise and so will also base their assessment of the claim- ant's likely restrictions upon the medical expert's opinion.

Essentially, the expert needs to address whether, on the balance of probabilities:

1. the consequences claimed are medically supportable given the levels of injuries/symptoms/effects, and are therefore 'attributable' to the accident; and

2. the consequences claimed are within the expected range given the levels of injuries/symptoms/effects, and are therefore 'reasonable'.

The key to addressing whether a consequence is attributable and reasonable, while staying within medical expertise, is to concentrate on identifying the restrictions on activities that the claimant now has or will be likely to experience in the future. Specifically, the court needs to know the nature of tasks that are now likely to be impossible or difficult as a consequence of the accident.

Medical experts can avoid the temptation of becoming pseudo-employment or care consultant by expressing opinions only upon the type and level of restriction the claimant is likely to have in the future, rather than the types of job the claimant will be able to do.

Work

Since the accident, Mr J says he has been unable to do any work activity that requires heavy lifting, stretching or repeated bending. He says that at work his role has been limited to light duties such as fixing fuses and sockets and excludes re-wiring and the fitting of appliances. In my opinion, his level of ongoing restriction is likely to be permanent and is both reasonable and attributable to the accident.

The disc-prolapse operation in Sep 08 has meant that he has less pain, but Mr J tells me that it did not improve his capacity to do heavy work. At present, he tells me that he has an agreement with his employers to continue with light duties at work. As I do not consider that any improvement in his condition is likely, in my opinion, were this agreement to be discontinued, he would be limited in the open labour market to maintenance roles that did not require him to do heavy lifting, stretching or repeated bending.

Domestic

Between the accident and the operation in Sep 08, Mr J says he was restricted in carrying out household duties. In my opinion, this is reasonable and attributable to the accident. During this period, any task that would have required him to use more than minimal force, such as is required when vacuuming or cleaning, would have been too difficult for him.

Transportation

[...]

Notice that in this example the expert uses mundane description of the restrictions that the claimant is facing, '…that did not require him to do heavy lifting, stretching or repeated bending.' Any form of abstract description of restriction, such as using percentages when describing restrictions, is not helpful.

6.6.2   Consequences to Assess

The best evidence as to whether the consequences of an injury claimed by the claimant are attributable to the accident and reasonable given the level of injuries sustained will come from the medical expert. The evidence of a medical expert carries much greater weight than anything that the claimant can say, owing to the medical expert's expertise and independence. As an independent expert, with a duty to assist the court with matters within his/her expertise, the medical expert is not seen as benefiting from (and therefore not influenced by) the litigation.

Consequences relevant to a personal injury claim may be found in some or all of the following heads of claim arising from the injury:[19]

- pain and suffering, and loss of amenity;
- medical or therapeutic treatment;
- care and assistance;
- current employment;
- future employment;
- life expectancy;
- additional housing, mobility or transportation needs;
- restrictions on activities of daily living; and
- restrictions on domestic, recreational, social or sporting activities.

If any of these heads of claim are clearly not relevant to the case, then there is no need for the expert to comment on them. Otherwise the expert should deal with all the consequences that arise in the relevant categories.

6.6.3   Pain and Suffering, and Loss of Amenity

The judge will look closely at the medical expert report in assessing damages for the injury itself (i.e. damages for 'pain and suffering and loss of amenity'). The medical expert report should therefore:

- summarise the likely continuing effects of an injury, in terms of disability, pain and suffering;
- predict whether this situation is likely to change over time, in terms of deterioration or recovery, and the consequential level of disability; and
- provide a comparison of the situation that would have existed but for the accident and the situation following the accident, identifying what difference the accident has made.

---

19   See Section 2.6 and 2.7 above for further discussion of heads of claim

6.6.4   Medical or Therapeutic Treatment

If there has been medical or therapeutic treatment, or if there is likely to be such treatment in the future, then the medical expert report should:

- identify what treatment there has been;
- where past treatment has been outside the NHS[20], address whether it was reasonable and attributable to the accident;
- identify the likelihood of the need for treatment in the future, giving some indication of the percentage risk of that need (if at all possible), and provide an indication of when in the future it will be needed;
- give some indication of the likely cost of such future treatment if carried out privately - at today's values - and give some indication of any other material implications of such treatment: e.g. the need to take time off work or the need for significant quantities of post-operation care or domestic assistance; and
- provide a comparison of the situation that would have existed but for the accident with the situation following the accident, identifying what difference the accident has made.

As a claimant is under a duty to take reasonable steps to mitigate his/her loss or damage, if there is treatment that the claimant is reluctant to undergo or if potential treatment is risky or may have adverse consequences, the nature of any such risk that might reasonably affect the claimant's decision to undergo the treatment should be addressed in the report. This may also be relevant to whether there has been a break in the chain of causation (see Section 7.8 below).

6.6.5   Care and Assistance

Medical experts are not care experts. A medical expert will not generally be expected to assess the amount of care and assistance necessary to enable the claimant to live a normal (pre-accident) life. However, the medical expert is often in a much better position than the lawyers or the judge (or even the care expert) to indicate what level of restriction is relevant to the need for care and assistance that a claimant has or is likely to suffer in the future, as a consequence of his/her injuries.

If there has been a claimed need for care and assistance, or if there is likely to be such a need in the future, then the medical expert report should:

- express an opinion as to the nature of help that it would have been reasonable to need, or continues to be needed, or which the claimant will be likely to need in future – e.g. help with dressing or washing, applying dressings, general housework, heavier domestic tasks, home maintenance and DIY or gardening; and

---

20   The cost of such treatment, whether funded by the claimant or by his medical insurers, will form part of the damages claimed. A claimant is entitled to choose to be treated privately – Section 2(4) Law Reform (Personal Injuries) Act 1948

- provide a comparison of the situation that would have existed but for the accident with the situation that exists following the accident, identifying what difference the accident has made.

6.6.6   Current Employment

The effect of an accident on a claimant's earning capacity is likely to be a significant aspect of the damages claimed. Frequently, it is the largest item of claim. Whilst a medical expert is not an employment expert or an occupational therapist, the medical expert report should assist in identifying:

- the ability of the claimant to continue in his pre-accident employment since the accident and in the future;
- the time for which it was reasonable to be off work;
- the general nature of the work that the claimant is now incapable of doing;
- any limitations or restrictions on future working by reference, for example, to activities which could or could not reasonably be managed until the intended retirement age; and
- provide a comparison of the situation that would have existed but for the accident with the situation following the accident, identifying what difference the accident has made.

A lawyer would find each of the following opinions **unhelpful** because the evidence does not address the practical restrictions arising from the injuries:

Ms T will be at a disadvantage in finding suitable employment in future because of the effects of the accident on her.

He is 56 years of age, and his opportunities on the open labour market are essentially non-existent.

Mr G is not at a significant disadvantage on the employment market.

His psychiatric status is not altogether incompatible with the acceptance of the responsibilities of employment.

NO FOOT-WEARING!

A lawyer would find the following opinions **helpful** because the evidence addresses the practical restrictions that the claimant will have:

> Mr G can no longer lift or carry heavy weights or bend repeatedly, and therefore will be unable to return to manual work such as he was performing prior to the accident. There is however no reason why he should not continue in work such as that in which he is currently employed and which he has described to me as a factory storeman role.

> Given these restrictions it is unlikely that in his present psychiatric state he would be capable of returning to full time work in any office environment. With a graduated return to work in 12 – 24 months' time he could probably manage to work part time in a less demanding and less stressful environment, but he would be prone to further periods of stress-related absences from time to time.

> He would not now be capable of employment that required him to walk any more than very short distances, to stand or sit for protracted periods, and lift or carry anything of any significant weight. The effect of the injuries and the continuing symptoms and restrictions is that he could not now return to his previous work as a school caretaker.

> Given the restrictions in activities set out above, were Ms T to seek to return to the employment market in future she would no longer be able to manage a job that required her to spend much of the working day at a keyboard or in any employment requiring repetitive movements of the fingers or wrists. However, subject to those limitations, there is no reason why she would not be able to manage more general and varied office work or light manual work.

> Miss C is currently employed within the local authority's education department in an advisory role. She has no contact with young people at work and is not required to partake in or observe classroom activities. She appears to be managing this role well. She has made good progress since the index event and would no longer fulfil the criteria for diagnosis of Major Depressive Episode or Panic Disorder. However, despite the treatment she has received, in future she is very unlikely to be able to cope with any situation in which she would be exposed to large numbers of people and therefore she is most unlikely ever to be able to return to the classroom setting. I expect that a return to working in a classroom would initiate further panic attacks.

6.6.7   Future Employment and 'Ogden 6'

Where an injury affects the claimant's ability to secure future employment, this can form part of the claim. Where the claimant is likely to face a disadvantage in looking for further work, then the medical expert report should assist the lawyers in identifying:

- any disadvantage the claimant may suffer in the future on the open labour market by reference, for example, to relevant restrictions in activities that would otherwise reasonably be expected; and
- provide a comparison of the situation that would have existed but for the accident with the situation following the accident, identifying what difference the accident has made.

Where a claimant is disabled as a result of the accident, the lawyers may seek to assess the value of the future impact on employment using the 'Ogden Tables', actuarial tables provided for the assessment of future loss.[21] In what lawyers informally refer to as an 'Ogden 6 calculation'[22], it is possible to compare, on an actuarial basis, the likely future earnings of someone with and without disability. For this purpose, it is necessary to establish whether or not the claimant is 'disabled' and the extent of such disability. The medical expert is therefore likely to be asked to assist in this assessment.

The notes to the Ogden Tables contain the following guidance as to when a claimant is to be regarded as 'disabled':

Disabled:

A person is classified as being disabled if all three of the following conditions in relation to the ill-health or disability are met:

(i)   has either a progressive illness or an illness which has lasted or is expected to last for over a year,

(ii) satisfies the Disability Discrimination Act definition that the impact of the disability substantially limits the person's ability to carry out normal day-to-day activities, and

(iii) their condition affects either the kind or the amount of paid work they can do.

Normal day-to-day activities are those which are carried out by most people on a daily basis, and we are interested in disabilities/health problems which have a substantial adverse effect on the respondent's ability to carry out these activities.

---

21   See Section 2.7.3 above

22   This basis of calculation first appeared in the 6th edition of the Ogden Tables in March 2007

There are several ways in which a disability or health problem may affect the respondent's day-to-day activities:

Mobility - for example, unable to travel short journeys as a passenger in a car, unable to walk other than at a slow pace or with jerky movements, difficulty in negotiating stairs, unable to use one or more forms of public transport, unable to go out of doors unaccompanied.

Manual dexterity - for example, loss of functioning in one or both hands, inability to use a knife or fork at the same time, or difficulty in pressing buttons on a keyboard.

Physical co-ordination - for example, the inability to feed or dress oneself, or to pour liquid from one vessel to another except with unusual slowness or concentration.

Problems with bowel/bladder control - for example, frequent or regular loss of control of the bladder or bowel. Occasional bedwetting is not considered a disability.

Ability to lift, carry or otherwise move everyday objects (for example, books, kettles, light furniture) - for example, inability to pick up a weight with one hand but not the other, or to carry a tray steadily.

Speech - for example, unable to communicate (clearly) orally with others, taking significantly longer to say things. A minor stutter, difficulty in speaking in front of an audience, or inability to speak a foreign language would not be considered impairments.

Hearing - for example, not being able to hear without the use of a hearing aid, the inability to understand speech under normal conditions or over the telephone.

Eyesight - for example, while wearing spectacles or contact lenses - being unable to pass the standard driving eyesight test, total inability to distinguish colours (excluding ordinary red/green colour blindness), or inability to read newsprint.

Memory or ability to concentrate, learn or understand - for example, intermittent loss of consciousness or confused behaviour, inability to remember names of family or friends, unable to write a cheque without assistance, or an inability to follow a recipe.

Perception of risk of physical danger - for example, reckless behaviour putting oneself or others at risk, mobility to cross the road safely. This excludes (significant) fear of heights or underestimating risk of dangerous hobbies.

Condition (i) is not normally controversial. To enable the lawyers to establish whether or not the claimant is disabled for these purposes the medical expert will need to express an opinion, within his/her area of expertise, as to whether:

1.   there is a substantial adverse effect on the claimant's ability to carry out normal daily activities; and

2.   there is an effect on the kind of paid work the claimant can do.

To do this the expert will need to address the restrictions in relevant activities that the claimant has presently and will reasonably experience as a result of the injury sustained.

6.6.8   Life Expectancy

Where the claimant's life expectancy has reduced as a consequence of the accident, then the claimant, or the claimant's estate or dependants, can claim for consequential losses resulting from the probable shortening of his/her life. The potential losses that arise as a consequence of losing many years of a working life may make the assessment of life expectancy an important one. The medical expert report should either address the issue directly or where this assessment is beyond the area of expertise of the expert should indicate the need for an appropriate expert to consider the issue.

6.6.9   Additional Housing, Mobility or Transportation Needs

Where a claimant is likely to suffer mobility restrictions, the medical expert report should assist in terms of likely restrictions relevant to housing, mobility or transportation needs. This may involve matters such as:

- the walking distance of which the claimant is reasonably capable;
- the ability reasonably to use public transport;
- the need for adaptations to a car;
- difficulty with stairs and therefore the need for single floor accommodation, adaptations to the home or a stair lift;
- difficulty with bathing or the need to install a shower; and
- the need for residential adaptations.

The medical evidence will deal with the nature of the likely restrictions and the impact on housing, mobility or transportation. A suitably qualified expert will then be used, if it is considered appropriate by the lawyers, to advise as to the details and cost of the adaptations required.

6.6.10 Restrictions on Activities of Daily Living

In a case involving serious disability, a suitably qualified care expert will be instructed to assess the restrictions on daily self-care activities and the need for care and assistance. The care expert will benefit from an assessment of the restrictions as assessed by the medical expert. In less serious cases, the assessment of the degree of impact on activities of daily living and the cost of assisting the claimant will be based on the lawyers' and the judge's assessment of the impact, which will in turn be based on the medical expert report and the evidence of the claimant and his/her witnesses.

Therefore it is important to address in the medical expert report:

- the extent to which any continuing restrictions are likely to affect the claimant's ability to manage activities of daily living, such as dressing, undressing, washing/bathing/showering, using the toilet and preparing and eating meals; and
- how these restrictions compare with restrictions which would have existed in the absence of the accident.

6.6.11 Restrictions on Domestic, Recreational, Social or Sporting Activities

To the extent that these are not covered in an assessment of restrictions on activities of daily living, the medical expert should describe the restrictions likely and reasonably to impact on other everyday activities. This will include:

- housework (from dusting to spring cleaning);
- window cleaning;
- home decoration inside and outside;
- other home maintenance tasks specific to the claimant's pre-accident life (from changing light bulbs to building house extensions);
- gardening (from pruning roses to laying a patio and hedge trimming);
- shopping;
- dog walking, jam making and sexual activity;[23] and
- sporting and other physical activities such as dancing, football or swimming.

The assessment of damages for such loss of activity will, where appropriate, be based on the cost of getting others to perform these activities for the claimant. The loss of an ability to participate in social or sporting activities will not generally be compensated for by an award based on financial loss or financial costs. Any compensation will form part of the award for general damages for pain, suffering and loss of amenity.

---

23 Medical experts are often concerned with how to deal with claimant's restrictions in respect of sexual activity. With the exception of loss of fertility and for professionals in the sex industry, this will not result in significant damages being awarded and is best dealt with briefly in a sentence or two.

Conclusion

Writing clear and supported expert opinion is essential if an expert is to perform his/her required duties to an acceptable standard. The opinions that the lawyers require medical experts to address move beyond those that are ordinarily required to be addressed in medical practice. A medical expert must express opinions on all medico-legal issues that fall within his/her area of expertise – specifically these relate to causation, prognosis and future risk, and the consequences arising from a claimant's injuries.

Key-Point Summary

1.   It is important to differentiate the use of the terms 'injury', 'symptoms', 'effects' and 'consequences' when addressing causation.

2.   Lawyers do not generally appreciate the difference between the medical use of the terms 'signs' and 'symptoms', so it is important that the expert makes clear what the sign is and what it shows, and how it supports or does not support particular aspects of the claimant's claim.

3.   Expressing opinions on causation involves a two-stage analysis: on the balance of probabilities, were the claimed injuries caused by the accident or negligence of the defendant? And in the absence of the accident or negligence, what would the situation have been in any event?

4.   Causation graphs are a useful tool for analysing cases, especially so in more difficult cases – these graphs should not however be used in the report itself.

5.   The cases in which 'material contribution' needs to be assessed – most often relating to industrial disease – are those where there is more than one relevant period of exposure to an agent responsible for the disease or injury and medical science cannot establish causation on the 'but for' basis.

6.   'Acceleration' and 'exacerbation' are terms that are both misused and misinterpreted by experts and lawyers alike. Experts should only use these terms in conjunction with a clear explanation of the underlying factual/ opinion matters. The sudden versus gradual onset of symptoms following an accident is a crucial issue that medical experts, and as a consequence their instructing lawyers, often fail to consider.

7.   Expressing opinion on prognosis and future risk involves a two-stage analysis: on the balance of probabilities, is there likely to be a deterioration or improvement in the claimant's condition? And having described this likely deterioration or improvement, what is the likelihood of this occurring and within what period?

8.   Wherever possible, prognosis and future risk should be expressed as percentages (or a range of percentages) over a specific number of years or a specific time period.

9.   Medical experts play an important role in identifying the consequences of an injury, both to the date of the report and for the future. This requires the expert to ask appropriate questions of the claimant to ascertain what consequences are being asserted as part of the claim.

10. Where future treatment is likely to improve the claimant's condition and prognosis, the expert should indicate this in his/her report. The claimant is under a duty to mitigate his/her loss.

11. Expressing opinions on the consequences of the injuries claimed involves considering two related issues: are the consequences claimed 'attributable' to the accident and are they 'reasonable' given the severity of the injuries/symptoms/effects caused by the accident.

Next Steps

In the next chapter, we will explore complex claims, where experts and lawyers alike face difficulties in dealing with the issues in dispute.

Developing Your Medico-Legal Mind (6)

Based on your understanding of writing opinion, please consider the following scenario and answer the questions that follow:

C.T. v Ever-So-Quick Deliveries Ltd

Case Outline

On 1 April 2008, C.T. (a 45 year old male) suffered injuries in a road traffic accident. In the accident, a delivery van owned by Ever-So-Quick Deliveries Limited overtook on a bend and collided head-on with the car in which C.T. was a back seat passenger. The van driver was killed instantly, while the driver of the car, Mr P, and his friend Miss S (the front seat passenger) both suffered serious injuries. Details of C.T.'s injuries are set out below.

Proceedings have now (assumed to be April 2010) been commenced against the employer of the deceased van driver who was responsible for the accident. The company's insurer has conceded primary liability (i.e. that the van driver breached his duty of care to the occupants of the car).

The solicitors for C.T. wish to submit medical evidence and details of the value of the claim to the company's insurer, in the hope of achieving a speedy (and appropriate) settlement.

History of the Accident

C.T. was the rear seat passenger in the car and was wearing a seat belt. The car was fitted with headrests for both the front and rear seats. C.T. describes seeing the white van coming out of the bend on the wrong side of the road and realising instantly that there would be a collision. He remembers nothing else about the accident until the moment he was lifted out of the wreckage by paramedics and firemen. C.T. describes feeling "completely numb" and "disconnected from what was happening". He thinks that he was treated by a doctor at the scene, before being taken to hospital by ambulance. He describes his memory of the events as "sketchy".

Personal Details

C.T. is 45 years old and at the time of the accident was a self-employed electrician. For many years, he worked on building sites, but a few months before the accident had found work on temporary contract as a maintenance electrician on a local industrial estate.

Before the accident he was a home improvement fanatic, who had made substantial sums by buying houses in need of renovation, which he carried out himself, before selling them on. He was also a keen referee in the Pilkington Southern League, although since the accident he has been unable to continue to do DIY or referee matches.

Injuries

C.T.'s solicitor has instructed the medical expert that his client has suffered the following injuries and symptoms from the accident:

1. whiplash injury to his neck;

2. lateral disc protrusion at L5/S1;

3. three fractured ribs and extensive bruising to his torso, abdomen and legs;

4. intermittent "sharp" pains in his right knee; and

5. psychological symptoms that include flashbacks, episodes of depression and continuing feelings of low-level anxiety.

Treatment and Progress

Immediately after the accident C.T. was admitted to hospital and remained there for four days, before being allowed home to be cared for by his wife. He was in pain from his injuries and needed full-time care for the first three weeks after his discharge from hospital. As his symptoms began to settle, C.T. was able to do more for himself, though with some tasks such as bathing he still required assistance.

C.T. returned to work in July 08, three months after the accident. His employer made substantial adjustments to his workload to enable him to get back to work. C.T. describes his work at that time as "light duties" such as replacing fuses and replacing switches. He was unable to do any lifting or carrying.

By December 08, it became clear that C.T.'s persistent back symptoms, with sciatica, were not improving and so he underwent a discectomy. No significant improvement in his symptoms was achieved - if anything, his symptoms are now more frequent and disabling than before the operation.

C.T. stayed off work for 4 months after the discectomy, requiring physiotherapy and extensive attention and care from his wife. He has once more returned to work (May 09) on light duties and still requires occasional days off on account of his back pain.

C.T. claims that he has tried to control his back pain using support belts, heat packs and a TENS machine. He is no longer able to cope with the work involved in doing up houses. Since the accident, in addition to entries about back pain, the

GP records indicate a number of appointments referring to diarrhoea and unexplained stomach and digestive problems, "general malaise" and "insomnia".

Because of an understanding employer and the low demands of his work at present, C.T. has been able to perform his role. However, the demand for his work remains low and he is concerned that his contract work may come to an end in the next few months.

Presenting Condition

C.T. now has symptoms of continuous aching and intermittent pain in his low back, unless he avoids all but the lightest of lifting. MRI shows evidence of some degenerative disc disease at L4/5 with disc dehydration and disc space narrowing, and a significant lateral disc prolapse at L5/S1.

Past Medical History

C.T. has a previous medical history of having had occasional low back symptoms. These symptoms did not interfere with his ability to work, save for needing occasional days off. Three years before the present accident, C.T. had a week off work and a course of physiotherapy when he injured his low back in an accident at work. He describes the injury as being a "back strain" which was caused by he and a work colleague lifting a large fuse box. His colleague suddenly "let go" of the fuse box and C.T. had to bear far more of its weight himself.

Prior to the accident, C.T. had not been to see his GP about his back for 2 years, but consulted his GP twice in October and November 2008 complaining of difficulty sleeping and "work and money problems".

1. In an orthopaedic or a psychiatric expert report on C.T., what would be the main issues that the instructing solicitor would need the expert to address?

2. In respect of C.T.'s claimed injuries, what sources of evidence would the expert use when addressing whether the claimed injuries/symptoms/effects were caused by the accident?

3. What is the importance of C.T.'s pre-accident physical condition and mental state when considering C.T's claimed injuries?

4. In order to deal with financial loss in this case, what are the issues that the solicitor would need the expert to address?

5. What other consequences (aside from financial loss) arise from the accident?

6. What future treatment, if any, would be helpful to C.T.?

7

Opinion Evidence in Complex Claims

7.1   Difficulties in Diagnosis
7.2   Linking the Injury to its Cause
7.3   Competing Factual Scenarios
7.4   Exaggeration and Malingering
7.5   Surveillance Evidence
7.6   Seat Belts and Contributory Negligence
7.7   Multi-Accident Claims
7.8   Breaking the Chain of Causation
7.9   Criticism of Medical Treatment in a Personal Injury Claim
7.10   Cases that Rely on Expertise

Introduction

Once the basic principles underlying medical expert evidence have been understood, the vast majority of personal injury claims are straightforward and do not pose fundamental difficulties. However, there are complex claims that are intrinsically difficult for everyone who is concerned with achieving settlement or preparing for trial. In such claims, the expert has to show a greater level of awareness and skill in applying his/her medical expertise within the medico-legal context. In these complex claims, the expert must truly engage his/her medico-legal mind to give coherent opinion on what are often extremely difficult issues.

Chapter Outline

In this chapter, we will discuss ten categories of complex claim. In each category, there are specific approaches that will help the expert to provide coherent expert evidence when reporting. The ten categories are as follows:

1. difficulties in diagnosis;

2. linking the injury to its cause;

3. competing factual scenarios;

4. exaggeration and malingering;

5. surveillance evidence;

6. seat belts and contributory negligence;

7. multi-accident claims;

8. breaking the chain of causation;

9. criticism of medical treatment in a personal injury claim; and

10. cases that rely on expertise.

In claims falling into any of these categories, the medical expert must apply exactly the same medico-legal principles that we have already discussed, in order to achieve a consistent and coherent approach to all the issues that arise. However, the care and skill with which these principles need to be applied create a qualitative difference in the evidence.

7.1   Difficulties in Diagnosis

In some claims, claimants present with complex or even paradoxical complaints on which the medical expert has to report. It may be that a single area of expertise, be this in a physical or a psychological field, cannot on its own fully explain the situation. Further, a minority of claimants seem to suffer worse symptoms and effects than the vast majority of claimants who present with similar injuries. This may be a by-product of the litigation itself, the particular circumstances or nature of the accident or solely as a result of the claimant's physiological or psychological makeup.

It is easy to assign the motive of financial gain to these claimants – and without doubt for some claimants this is entirely justified. However, as with all opinion evidence, care must be taken to assess all possible causes for the complaints and to give reasons for any conclusion reached, not least because abnormal illness behaviour is commonly seen in surgeries and consulting rooms across the country in the absence of any claim for damages.

7.1.1   Approach to the Evidence

When dealing with such cases, while staying within his/her area of expertise, the expert should seek to explain the situation as far as is possible and in so doing assist the lawyers in understanding the key medical issues in the case:

1.   what is probably wrong with the claimant, if anything?

2.   what probably caused this condition?

3.   what would the situation probably have been in the absence of the accident?

4.   what is likely to happen to this claimant in the future? and

5.   what are the probable consequences for this claimant?

These issues are the same as for any other claim; what changes is the level of certainty that the expert has when expressing opinions. It is entirely appropriate for the expert to express the difficulty of the case openly in the Opinion section of the report:

> The range and severity of symptoms that Mrs J is experiencing are not commensurate with the injuries she sustained in the accident. I can find no physiological basis for the ongoing pain and physical restrictions with which she presents. However, in my opinion, on the balance of probabilities Mrs J does have a genuine restriction in her ability to twist, bend and stretch and is genuinely in pain.

The expert can then discuss the range of possible causes for these symptoms and give opinion on the likelihood of each being caused by the accident. The need for an assessment from another expert can also be indicated in the report, for example, by recommending a referral to a psychiatrist or pain consultant. This may enable progress towards a diagnosis to be made. Alternatively, where another expert report has already been obtained, an expert is entitled to rely on this opinion evidence, suitably referenced, in reaching his/her own opinion.

Experts, when faced with paradoxical symptoms that no single area of expertise seems capable of explaining, are sometimes faced with having to give an opinion as to whether the accident has caused the claimant's symptoms, whilst acknowledging that the diagnosis for the injury itself remains uncertain:

Given the findings on MRI, I am uncertain as to why Mrs D has such severe leg pain with signs of nerve root irritation. It may be that Mrs D sustained nerve root damage at the time that her disc tear occurred in March 2006 and this might be the cause of ongoing neuropathic pain. I would not however expect her to have the very reduced straight leg raising that she has on the basis of her MRI scan, and indeed I would not expect her to have such restrictive back movements given the extent of her degenerative disc disease and her only moderate paravertebral spasm.

The absence of anatomical abnormality commensurate with the symptoms she is reporting does not imply that her complaints of pain and disability are disingenuous but may reflect the fact that our understanding of the mechanisms of the initiation and perpetuation of pain are poorly understood and that our techniques of investigation are limited. Although her pain symptoms seem out of proportion to the MRI finding, the GP records contain no indication that she experienced pain or psychological problems prior to the accident…

Therefore I identify the following possible causes for her continuing pain and disability:

1.   conscious exaggeration;

2.   unidentified damage to structures causing pain;

3.   unconscious exaggeration (psychological or psychiatric component).

In respect of conscious exaggeration, testing of Mrs D by myself and other practitioners has been consistent and no practitioner has raised doubts about Mrs D's veracity. While recognising that this is a matter for the court to decide, given the assessments by myself and others, I consider it unlikely that Mrs D is consciously exaggerating her symptoms.

Unidentified additional damage to structures causing ongoing pain and disability is a possible explanation. Any such damage would almost certainly have been caused by injury sustained in the accident given the absence of any previous history of pain in the medical records. However, given the current state of medical understanding I am unable to say that such damage probably exists – this is a possible explanation.

In my opinion, the most likely explanation is psychological or psychiatric factors, which are wholly responsible for, or contributing to, an exaggerated sense of pain and disability. However, it would require the opinion of a medical expert of the appropriate expertise to address this issue.

In these difficult claims, experts must pay particular attention to the boundaries of their expertise. For example, if chronic pain comes within the particular expertise of an orthopaedic surgeon or rheumatologist, then he/she can give opinion relating to chronic pain. However, the expert's qualifications and relevant experience set out at the beginning of the report should give details of this particular expertise, so that the lawyers understand the basis on which the opinion is given. If such expertise is beyond the expertise of the expert, then defining the limits of expertise and suggesting a referral is the appropriate approach.

7.2 Linking the Injury to its Cause

In the vast majority of claims, it is obvious that the accident caused the injury of which the claimant complains, even if the full extent of that injury may not be so clear. However, in some claims, the connection is less clear and the medical expert can and should express an opinion on the 'attribution' of the injury to the accident or adverse event. In such cases, the expert has to identify factors that may or may not connect the claimant's presenting condition with the accident.

The following are examples of situations in which an expert should express an opinion on the attribution of the injury to its alleged cause, and give reasons for that opinion whether for or against the attribution:

1. complaints of symptoms or of loss of function that cannot readily be attributed to the accident;

2. symptoms, effects and consequences that are on a scale larger than might normally be expected from such an accident;

3. work related upper limb disorders or other 'repetitive strain' type of claims;

4. industrial disease claims; or

5. stress related or other psychiatric injury claims.

7.2.1 Approach to the Evidence

In 1 above, the claimant may complain of symptoms such as pain or of some loss of function that cannot readily be causally linked to the accident or adverse event. The expert must consider whether there is any other possible cause to which these complaints can be attributed, whether in the claimant's make-up or pre-accident condition or in the treatment that the claimant has received because of the accident. The elimination of alternative causes is as important to the lawyers as the identification of a cause.

In 2, symptoms, effects and consequences may be on a scale larger than might normally be expected. These claims may arise, for example, out of a low-impact collision or a relatively minor lifting incident. The expert must consider whether the symptoms complained of are beyond the possible range of injuries and symptoms that could be caused by the forces involved in the accident or whether the symptoms might be explained by, and be consistent with, those forces given what is known about the claimant's previous medical history or condition. Findings on examination may be consistent with the expected range of injuries and symptoms that could be caused by the forces in the accident, even though the general description of symptoms and limitations given by the claimant appears to be of an apparently more serious nature than would be expected. The medical expert needs to explain the rationale underlying his/her opinion on these matters.

In 3, when reporting on cases involving work-related upper limb disorders or 'repetitive strain' type cases, the expert should express an opinion as to whether the particular condition that has developed can be attributed to the precipitating activity described or the movements or position of the claimant's body as reported to the expert, and if there are other possible causes of the condition, whether it is possible to express an opinion as to which is the more likely cause.

In 4, in industrial disease claims involving, for example, complaints of noise induced hearing loss or the development of a condition (such as dermatitis or asthma) as a result of exposure to a substance at work, the expert should be able to express an opinion as to whether the findings in relation to the condition are supportive of a connection with the alleged causative agent. Other possible causes should be considered and if possible an opinion expressed as to the more likely cause.

In 5, the development of a recognised psychiatric condition (whether claimed to be as a result of exposure to the trauma of an accident or the effects of an accident or stress at work) may be multi-factorial and may be related to the nature of the precipitating event or the claimant's previous psychiatric history. The expert should address whether the development of the condition is consistent with, and capable of being attributed to, the precipitating event. This may require consideration of more than one account of the factual context in which the condition developed. Again other possible causes should be considered and where possible an opinion expressed as to the more likely cause.

In each of these 5 types of claim, it is essential that the expert only expresses an opinion consistent with the his/her own area of expertise, and if that is not possible, then provides a signpost to the appropriate expert to address the issue. The last 3 are also examples of situations where the expert should express an opinion as to whether the injury sustained by the claimant is of a type, if not an extent, reasonably to be foreseen from a medical point of view in such a situation.

A lawyer would find the following evidence **helpful** because the experts delineate possible causes and provide a rationale for the opinions expressed:

Miss Q, who is left hand dominant and uses a computer mouse in her left hand, has developed both left carpal tunnel syndrome and de Quervain's syndrome at the left wrist. Both of these conditions arise spontaneously throughout the population, but it is widely acknowledged by specialists that both can on occasions be caused by excessive or inappropriate use of the hands. As a result, these conditions can be caused by activities at work.

In Miss Q's case, despite a probable pre-existing vulnerability, she appears to have had no difficulties with her keyboard work for about 3 years. She reports that her problems began when the intensity of her work increased in March 2008. She describes a clear association between her work and her symptoms, with an improvement when not at work, deterioration later in the working day, and deterioration with increased intensity of work. Despite a work station assessment and various adjustments to her workstation, the symptoms persisted.

Based on the facts before me, I am of the opinion that should it be found that there is a close association between her symptoms and the increased intensity of her work, both de Quervain's syndrome and carpal tunnel syndrome were in her case probably caused by her work and did not develop spontaneously.

There are two possible causes of Mr H's condition. The first is long term low level exposure to di-isocyanates. The second is a history of heavy smoking. In this case, Mr H's work history of low level exposure to di-isocyanates would not commonly result in his developing the severe condition from which he now suffers. However, the medical literature referred to above supports a causal link between low-level exposure over a long period of time and severe presentations of the condition.

There is uncertainty about Mr H's smoking history. If he were found to have a history of heavy smoking, then I consider the more likely cause of his condition would be his smoking rather than his occupational exposure. However, if he were found to be a light smoker, then it is unlikely that his smoking has any causal link with his condition. In the latter case, in the absence of evidence of any other non-occupational exposures to irritants, on the balance of probabilities, his condition was the result of his occupational exposure to di-isocyanates.

Mr J gives a clear and consistent account of the accident in August 2008. The current symptoms as described to me by Mr J are spread across the neurotic spectrum, involving obsessional thinking, depression and anxiety. He describes ruminations about death, anxiety and depressive symptoms and also flashbacks to the accident.

The accident was understandably a very traumatic experience and given his pre-existing vulnerability, it is unsurprising that he coped badly in the months that followed. His relationship and work difficulties that then emerged resulted in a significant deterioration in his mental state some 12 months after the accident.

In my opinion, Mr J is currently suffering ongoing symptoms of PTSD as a result of the accident. These symptoms have begun to diminish and will continue to do so over the next 12 to 18 months. In addition, he is suffering from continuing depression with anxiety of moderate severity. In the absence of the accident, my opinion is that he would probably have suffered similarly with depression and anxiety as a result of his pre-existing vulnerability and the difficulties in his work and marital relationship and that the accident has therefore made only a minor contribution to his depressive condition.

7.3   Competing Factual Scenarios

An expert opinion will often depend on which facts are accepted by the expert as being probably correct (see for instance the example relating to Mr H in Section 7.2.1 above). It is for this reason that the expert is required to make clear in reaching the opinion:

- the facts that have been relied upon;
- the facts that the expert knows to be true and those which the expert assumes to be true; and
- any asserted facts that the expert has rejected as improbable and why the expert has rejected them as improbable.[1]

However, there is more than one side to every claim, so if the expert expresses an opinion based on one of two sets of inconsistent facts, and this set of facts is rejected by the judge, the expert is effectively left expressing no relevant opinion. It is therefore necessary, and required, for the expert to express an alternative opinion on each alternative set of facts:

Protocol   13.11   Where there are material facts in dispute experts should express separate opinions on each hypothesis put forward.

---

1   Protocol 13.10 and 13.11 and see Sections 4.2.7 and 4.2.10 above

7.3.1   Approach to the Evidence

Where the expert does not express an opinion in favour of one or other set of facts, the expert simply sets out the factual dispute and gives an opinion on each set of facts:

> If Mr D is correct and the past shoulder problems had resolved completely prior to the accident, then the accident caused a further episode of impingement syndrome which continues. However, for the reasons set out above, significant symptomatic impingement syndrome would probably have commenced in any event within about 2 years of the date of the accident, reaching the level of symptoms he experienced after the accident within a few months. At this point, 30 months on from the accident, the situation is most probably as it would have been in the absence of the accident, with the need for treatment and finally surgery being brought forward by a similar period.
>
> However, if, as the GP records suggest, the court finds that Mr D had not recovered from the past shoulder pain at the time of the accident then it is probable that the accident caused an exacerbation for a few months of the symptoms already present but that otherwise the course of the shoulder symptoms and the treatment has not been affected by the accident.

Where the expert is able to express an opinion in favour of one or other disputed set of facts, as a result of his/her particular expertise, the expert is permitted to express an opinion that one set of facts is 'improbable or less probable'.[2] Once again, if the expert expresses such an opinion, then he/she should still express an opinion on the other set of facts.[3]

In some areas of expertise, the diagnosis rests on a finding of fact in the absence of which there would be no satisfactory evidence of injury, as in the following example:

> During my examination of the claimant, he stated that he has severe and continuing tinnitus. In contrast to what he told me, there is no reference to tinnitus in any previous assessment or in the medical records. This condition is not susceptible to objective assessment. If the court finds that the description given to me by him is correct, then in my opinion, his condition is probably caused by exposure to excessive noise at work and his condition is likely to be permanent. This opinion on causation is however dependent upon the court's finding that he does indeed suffer tinnitus as described. Conversely, if the court does not accept his evidence, then there is no other evidence to substantiate that he does in fact suffer from tinnitus.

---

2   Protocol 13.11

3   We discuss competing factual scenarios in the context of clinical negligence claims in Section 8.5 and 9.3.3

7.4   Exaggeration and Malingering

When dealing with cases where there is a suspicion of 'Exaggeration' or 'Malingering', an expert should first define how these terms are being used in the report or avoid their use altogether, as neither term has a legal definition.

7.4.1   Exaggeration

Exaggeration suggests that complaints, descriptions of symptoms, behaviour or apparent restrictions have been enlarged or altered beyond what is normal or expected, or to an extent that is out of proportion in some manner to the injuries sustained.

From the medico-legal perspective, the significance of exaggeration is whether it is conscious or not. The claimant is entitled to recover for all of the genuine injuries, symptoms and effects of the accident and for the genuine consequences. If the exaggeration is probably not conscious, then the claimant will recover damages for all the additional symptoms, effects and consequences experienced beyond what would objectively be expected given the organic findings. Although the claimant can recover damages for the actual impact of the injury as perceived by him/herself, the fact that there is an element of non-conscious exaggeration may be relevant to prognosis and therefore to assessing damages for future loss.

7.4.2   Malingering

If exaggeration is conscious then it is considered by the courts to be malingering. The definition of malingering used in DSM-IV-TR[4] is a useful one for our purposes:

> 'Malingering is intentional production of false or exaggerated symptoms motivated by external incentives, such as obtaining compensation...'

The emphasis is on intentional falsehood and external motivation. The malingering claimant is trying to extract money from the defendant through false (and therefore dishonest) pretences – a criminal offence. If there is probably conscious exaggeration, then that exaggeration is taken out of consideration in assessing damages, but the claimant is still entitled to damages for the genuine effects and consequences of the injury. However, the claimant, having lost credibility as a witness, may well have difficulty proving the probable (and genuine) impact of the injury.

Some experts identify different categories of conscious exaggeration. Sometimes a claimant will exaggerate when motivated by a desire to be taken seriously as someone with pain or disability. Although this is probably in the conscious category of exaggeration, experts often see such claimants in a different light to the 'malingerer'.

---

4   *DSM-IV-TR: Diagnostic and Statistical Manual of Mental Disorders - 4th edition* (2000). Washington DC: American Psychiatric Association

Lawyers and experts alike often use exaggeration and malingering to mean different things, resulting in miscommunication and confusion. The medical expert must describe accurately what he/she actually means when using these expressions and not merely use these expressions as a shorthand description.

> To state that the claimant 'is clearly exaggerating' is an example of Foot-Wearing. The expert must make clear if such exaggeration is in the expert's opinion conscious or unconscious and give reasons.

NO FOOT-WEARING!

7.4.3   Approach to the Evidence

The medical expert may consider that there is exaggeration of symptoms, or that the claimant is altogether fabricating them. However, whether or not there is conscious fabrication by the claimant is strictly a matter for the judge to determine, not the medical expert. The honesty or dishonesty of witnesses is a legal matter not a medical matter. The medical expert may be able, as a result of particular expertise, to provide factual or opinion evidence that can assist the judge in coming to a decision. However, there are likely to be few occasions when the medical expert can properly express an opinion, based on medical expertise alone, that a claimant is lying about his condition.

Interestingly, experts often put all difficulties relating to the previous medical history down to the claimant's attempt to manipulate the situation and give scant regard to any other issue, including the expert's own ability to communicate effectively. Claimants report that they are often unclear about what information the expert actually wants to be told.

> One expert told us that he had asked a claimant if he had ever had any "spinal problem", to which the claimant gave an emphatic, "No". Later looking through the medical records, the expert found a 20-year history of back pain and so wrote in his report that the claimant had attempted to present a misleading previous medical history. Three days after issuing the report, the expert received a call from the instructing solicitor requesting that the report be amended, because the claimant had not realised that the expert's question about his "spinal problems" meant that he should tell the expert about his periodic back ache.

Whether this claimant misunderstood the expert or used the claimed misunderstanding to try to cover up for a lack of frankness, the medical expert must ensure that in communication with the claimant there is no room for any such misunderstandings. Similar issues arise when a claimant may not connect a question about "previous mental health issues" with having been prescribed tablets "to help" during a messy divorce.

For these reasons, we recommend that medical records are read before interview, so that any factual conflicts can be explored with the claimant before the report is written. If during such exploration the claimant refuses to deal honestly with his/her previous medical history, then the expert is under an obligation to express an opinion on the conduct of the claimant in the Opinion and Prognosis section of the report.

7.4.4   Observations Outside the Medical Examination

The medical expert may make observations outside the formal medical examination, which he/she considers relevant to the question of the genuineness of the claimant's presentation or reported symptoms or observed restrictions:

> From my consulting room window, I witnessed Mr R get out of his car without any apparent discomfort or difficulty, walk quickly to the boot and take out his crutches. He then proceeded to use his crutches to slowly cross the car park with an expression of intense discomfort on his face.
>
> On examination, Mr R was unable to perform physical movements that I had already witnessed him performing without difficulty in the car park. This complete change in physical function I attribute to a conscious exaggeration of his symptoms (malingering).

Other less dramatic examples of such observations would include observations as to the wear on shoes or of the rubber ferrules on crutches or walking sticks (which might be considered inconsistent with the claimant's reported disability or use of aids), or the state of a splint (one reported to be needed "all of the time" but which appears in a pristine condition) or the state of a claimant's hands (where there is a complaint of being unable to carry out various tasks but the state of the claimant's hands appears to suggest otherwise). Such observations can also be potentially supportive of the claimant's case (for example wear on shoes or ferrules consistent with a limp, a well-worn splint or soft clean hands and nails).

In these situations, the medical expert must appreciate that he/she has become a witness of fact in relation to such observations, in the same way as an undercover surveillance operative would be. Where such observations are disputed (in their entirety or even just in certain relevant details) the expert will be submitted to cross-examination in relation to the precise circumstances of the observations and precisely what was seen.

The observations could also be the subject of detailed written questions.[5] A detailed contemporaneous note recording the observations and the circumstances in which they were made is therefore essential. Those notes should record such matters as:

1. precisely what was seen and when;

2. from where the observations were made;

3. at what distance;

4. what light conditions were; and

5. the period of such observations.

In the case of subtler observations, it is usually appropriate, having recorded the claimant's account, to put the apparent inconsistency to the claimant for comment and possible explanation (for example, the claimant may have worn new shoes for the trip to the medical expert or the old splint has fallen apart and has just been replaced).

Should the medical expert's observations successfully be put into doubt under cross-examination, or in the light of other contradictory evidence, then it is likely that the medical expert's evidence as a whole – including the medical opinions within it – would also be thrown into doubt.

7.4.5   Observations Within the Medical Examination

It may be that as a result of an expert's particular expertise or experience he/she is able to say that facts put forward by the claimant are improbable, for example, as to the nature of the claimant's symptoms or restriction in activity or loss of faculty:

> In the course of examination of Mr V, I elicited pain on axial loading, pain on simulated rotation and straight-leg raising of 90° when extending the knee when Mr V was seated, in contrast to the 60° when he was lying supine on the couch. These findings do not have an organic cause or explanation. These positive responses to 3 of the so-called Waddell signs indicate a non-organic component to his complaints. Such findings could be explained by Mr V's heightened emotional state as demonstrated by his crying as he described to me the effects of the accident on his daily life. An alternative explanation is conscious exaggeration.
>
> Waddell himself emphasised that psychological factors needed to be considered when positive signs are elicited, and that on their own such

---

5   Under CPR 35.6 – see Section 4.4 above

findings were not a test of credibility or faking. Given the consistency of Mr V's presentation during my examination and in previous examinations by other medical practitioners not involved in the litigation, at this stage I consider it probable that Mr V is genuine in his complaints. I recommend that a psychological assessment should be obtained to explore possible psychological factors contributing to his presentation.

The results of the psychometric tests suggest that Mr B has pronounced intellectual deficits, significant memory problems, poor naming skills and impaired executive and visuospatial functions. However, it is unlikely that the results accurately represent his true abilities for the following reasons:

1. His working memory for digits was unusually short, a result pointing to the operation of functional factors.

2. When cued to facilitate recall, his performance deteriorated significantly, whereas performance usually is maintained or improves with prompting.

3. Mr B performed normally on one symptom's validity task, but his performance on another was worse than found among those with conditions such as Alzheimer's or vascular dementia, indicating that he did not apply proper effort.

4. The results are inconsistent with Mr B's everyday level of functioning as related by himself and his mother, which indicates independence in activities of daily living.

5. When assessed by Dr N in 2009 using many of the same tests, his performance was within normal limits. Such deterioration does not fit with the sequelae of a head injury.

6. On a visual recognition memory test Mr B's performance fell significantly below chance. Such a result is inconsistent with a genuine memory disorder and represents unambiguous evidence of dissimulation.

It is therefore highly probable that the results of the tests are invalid and non-credible and that they represent dissimulation.

The expert should only express an opinion as to the improbability of what the claimant says or does where such opinion is based on the expert's particular expertise. If, therefore, the claimed loss of movement or the claimed distribution of a loss of sensation is inconsistent with any physiological or neurological explanation, then this is a matter on which an expert in the appropriate speciality should comment. If pain is apparently experienced during examination as a result of tests that should not induce such pain – such as Waddell's signs on an orthopaedic examination – then this too should be explained clearly.

Such inconsistency in signs on its own need not be evidence of conscious or intentional exaggeration, so the medical expert should report on the inconsistency and list the possible explanations. Waddell himself wrote that 'Isolated signs should not be over-interpreted. Multiple signs suggest that the patient does not have (only) a straightforward physical problem, but that psychological factors also need to be considered […] Behavioural signs are not on their own a test of credibility or faking.'[6]

The medical expert will be more effective if he/she lists those matters that give rise to questions about appropriate responses, consistency or honesty. Only in the clearest of cases should the expert go further to express his/her opinion on the credibility of the claimant, as it is beyond the role of the expert in reporting to the court. It is best to leave it to the judge (or the lawyers) to form a conclusion on the basis of all of the available evidence.

> Mr W sustained an injury to the cervical spine. Given the nature of the accident and the investigations detailed above this is the kind of accident which would be expected to result in some neck symptoms but would generally be expected to resolve in 6 to 12 months.
>
> Mr W presents in an exaggerated fashion. The examination and presentation do not fit the clinical picture. He demonstrates virtually no range of movements of his neck or right shoulder girdle but despite this apparent disability is able to wash and dress himself (including putting on shoes, socks and trousers), shave and maintain his appearance. He is showing gross signs of inappropriate illness behaviour and is either consciously or unconsciously magnifying his symptoms.
>
> His behaviour as observed by me and his general demeanour are such that I believe it probable that he is unconsciously exaggerating and that his main disability is therefore psychological. I recommend that Mr W undergoes formal psychological and psychiatric assessment and that he be admitted into a multi-disciplinary rehabilitation programme.

---

6   Main, C.J. & Waddell, G. (1998) 'Behavioural responses to examination. A reappraisal of the interpretation of "nonorganic signs"' *Spine* 23(21):2367-71; Waddell, G., McCulloch, J.A., Kummel E., & Venner R.M., (1980) 'Nonorganic physical signs in low-back pain.' *Spine* 5(2):117-25.

The inconsistencies between the history given to me by Mr A in relation to previous spinal problems and what was disclosed in the medical records and the inconsistency on examination in respect of his ability to dress raise questions as to his reliability as a witness. In particular, the ease with which he picked up his shoes and put on his socks after the examination and ran the fingers of his right hand through his hair after dressing lead me to suspect conscious exaggeration of his symptoms, and those instructing me might well wish to carry out further investigations as to Mr A's true level of disability.

The medical expert's observations of the claimant are extremely important, so these must be accurately described and their potential significance explained in simple terms.

7.5   Surveillance Evidence

When defendant insurers suspect that an exaggerated or false claim is being made, surveillance of the claimant is one approach to disproving the claim. Typically, a claimant is followed for several days or weeks (on occasions, over a period of years) in an attempt to video behaviour that is at odds with the account given to the medical experts on examination. This surveillance usually results in an edited video recording, and mostly showing mundane and inconsequential behaviour. This is normally supplied to the expert on DVD.

When shown surveillance evidence that appears to contradict the evidence obtained during the medical examination, medical experts should avoid reacting to feelings of betrayal or professional embarrassment at having apparently been misled by the claimant. It is essential to move beyond such emotions before considering the issues from the independent and impartial standpoint required of the medical expert.

Let us consider a claim where a claimant reports at interview that he has a significant degree of disability, consistent with an inability to carry out various activities. The expert's findings support the claimant's account and the medical expert reports on these findings in the usual way. Several weeks later, surveillance video is produced showing the claimant partaking freely in such activities that he previously claimed were impossible for him to do.

This video is clearly evidence upon which the medical expert must give an opinion. However, before giving such an opinion the questions the medical expert needs to consider are:

1.   is the person in the video actually the claimant?

2.   when and in what context was the video taken? and

3. has any other information (such as a commentary or report) been provided that may influence any interpretation of the video?

The expert should be sure that the person in the video is actually the claimant, and not, for example, a family member. Before making any assessment of the relative abilities of the claimant as reported to the medical experts and as shown in the video, it is important to take proper account of the period during which observations were made and the date in relation to any medical examinations, therapy or other treatment in the case. The expert should also consider if the abilities of the claimant are within an expected range, especially in cases where symptoms may vary in their intensity and where symptoms and restrictions might reasonably vary from time to time.

If the person featured in the video is clearly the claimant and the activities shown on the dates indicated are clearly outside the range of activities that can be reconciled with the history given or the findings on examination, then the expert may give a clear opinion of conscious exaggeration. However, it is sensible to be cautious in less clear-cut cases, remembering that it is the role of the judge to decide on the honesty of witnesses.

When commenting on the surveillance evidence, an expert should consider the following:

1. are the observations for a few minutes, or several hours, on consecutive days or spaced out?

2. are the observations mixed in that some are consistent and some inconsistent with the previous complaints, observations or descriptions of restriction, or are all inconsistent?

3. is the weather, the time of year, the time of day, the nature of activity or any other factor of potential relevance to an assessment of the relevance of the video?

Where part of the expert's assessment of the video is dependent on a report or commentary provided with it by the investigators, it is essential that the expert makes clear whether it is what is shown in the video or what is described in the accompanying report or commentary that is being relied upon in making the assessment. As is always required under CPR 35, the medical expert must make clear the facts upon which the opinion as to the significance of the surveillance evidence is based.

If the expert is informed that there is a dispute as to the significance of potentially relevant observations of the claimant – for example, that the claimant says that the video shows a "good day" and not a "typical day" or that it was the day after a particularly beneficial therapy or that the observations were only for a short period during the "best part of the day" – then it may be necessary for the expert to express separate opinions on the significance of the evidence on each of the potential versions of the facts.

Taking sufficient care to analyse the video in this manner will ensure that the expert's opinion as to its significance can be justified, even under cross-examination, and that the opinion can be evaluated properly by the lawyers involved in the claim.

7.6   Seat Belts and Contributory Negligence

A failure to wear a seat belt in a car may result in the passenger or driver suffering injury that could have been avoided or that is more severe or is of a different kind to that which probably would have been suffered had the seat belt been worn. This failure is regarded in law as 'contributory negligence' on the part of the claimant, which in the most serious case will reduce the damages that would otherwise have been recovered by 25%. This reduction is to reflect the degree of 'blameworthiness' of the claimant for his/her own injuries. The leading judgment, in addressing the judge's task in such cases, gives the following guidance:

> 'Whenever there is an accident, the negligent driver must bear by far the greater share of responsibility. It was his negligence which caused the accident. It also was a prime cause of the whole of the damage. But insofar as the damage might have been avoided or lessened by wearing a seat belt, the injured person must bear some share. But how much should this be? ... This question should not be prolonged by an expensive enquiry into the degree of blameworthiness on either side, which would be hotly disputed. Suffice it to assess a share of responsibility which will be just and equitable in the great majority of cases.
>
> Sometimes the evidence will show that the failure made no difference. The damage would have been the same, even if a seat belt had been worn. In such cases, the damages should not be reduced at all. At other times the evidence will show that the failure made all the difference. The damage would have been prevented altogether if a seat belt had been worn. In such cases, I would suggest that the damages should be reduced by 25 per cent. But often enough the evidence will only show that the failure made a considerable difference. Some injuries to the head, for instance, would have been a good deal less severe if a seat belt had been worn, but there would still have been some injury to the head. In such cases, I would suggest that the damages attributable to the failure to wear a seat belt should be reduced by 15 per cent.'[7]

The medical expert should not, unless instructed to do so, proffer an opinion on the consequences of such failure to wear a seat belt even where it is apparent that a seat belt has not been worn by the claimant or where there is an issue as to

---

7   *Froom v Butcher* [1976] QB 286

whether or not a seat belt was worn. There are circumstances when the law does not require a seat belt to be worn and therefore in which there will not be criticism of the claimant for not wearing a seat belt (for example taxi drivers and pregnant women). The expert, however, could quite properly signpost in the report the fact that the failure to wear a seat belt may have had an impact on the injuries sustained and await further instructions.

When instructed to provide an opinion, the medical expert in such cases will need to express an opinion on questions related to the 'but for' scenario. Typically, experts will be asked to address questions about what the situation would have been had a seat belt been worn:

1.   what injuries would probably have been sustained?

2.   what injuries in fact sustained would probably have been avoided?

3.   what injuries in fact sustained would probably have been significantly different (and describe the difference)?

4.   what injuries would probably have been sustained which in fact were not?

Based on the above, did the absence of wearing a seat belt probably make a significant difference to the injuries sustained, and in general terms, what was that difference?

The law is only interested in a significant or 'considerable' difference.[8] The more grave the injuries and the larger the sums in issue in the claim, the more detailed an examination will be called for. In a high value claim, engineering as well as medical expert evidence may well be called for and the expertise of the appropriate medical expert to deal with the issues may be investigated in detail by the parties and the court. In a low value claim, the court is likely to take a more 'broad brush' approach to the assessment on the basis of such expert evidence as is available in preference to carrying out a detailed and costly investigation.

The medical expert must, therefore, be able to justify logically any opinion expressed as to the likely differences in injury and must ensure that sufficient factual information is available (such as accident photos of the vehicle) in order to express such opinion. As with all opinion evidence, the expert should make clear in the report any reservations or qualifications he/she may have in expressing such opinion.

The medical expert will need to make sure that there is an adequate factual basis for expressing such opinion. Information necessary before expressing an opinion would be likely to include, in addition to the medical records, evidence as to the general circumstances of the accident, collision speed and angle, and the damage to the vehicles (or other objects) involved. The expert is likely to want to see the

---

8   *Stanton v Collinson* [2010] EWCA Civ 81

police accident report (if any), witness statements, plans and photographs or other detailed description of the state of the vehicle(s) after the accident.

In some cases, there may be a factual dispute as to whether or not a seat belt was worn. In such cases, the medical expert should express an opinion as above on the probable consequences of any failure to wear a seat belt. In addition, if the expert, as a result of his/her particular expertise or experience, considers it more likely that either the seat belt was or was not being worn, then the expert should express an opinion in favour of one or other proposition, explaining and justifying the basis of that opinion.[9] For example, the expert may be guided by the nature of the injuries sustained.

7.7   Multi-Accident Claims

Reporting on multiple accident claims often causes experts confusion. Although we term these cases 'multi-accident', the same principles apply where one or more, or indeed all, of the 'accidents' are the result of clinical negligence.

The need to instruct a medical expert to deal with a multi-accident claim usually arises in one of three situations:

1.   a claimant has suffered injuries in two accidents and the total loss from both accidents needs to be assessed;[10]

2.   legal liability attaches to a defendant in only one of two accidents, and the loss attributable to that defendant needs to be assessed; or

3.   two defendants are in dispute as to what proportion of the damages each is liable for.

In 1 above, the medical expert has to report on what has occurred after both accidents, compared with what would probably have occurred without both accidents.

In 2, the medical expert has to report on what has occurred as a result of the accident to which legal liability attaches compared with what probably would have occurred without that accident.

In 3, the medical expert has to report in two stages: first, on the difference that the first accident has made to the claimant, compared with what would probably have occurred without the 1st and 2nd accidents; secondly, the expert has to report on the difference that the 2nd accident has made when compared to the probable recovery of the claimant from the 1st accident.

---

9   Protocol para 13.11

10   In such cases, the claim would be against the same defendant, such as an employer or the same insurance company where different motorists were insured by the same insurer.

7.7.1   Applying Causation Graphs

A useful tool for preparing reports on multi-accident cases is to adapt the causation graph, which we introduced in Chapter 6, to reflect these more complex issues.

(1) Two Accidents - Report on Both (Cumulative Effects)

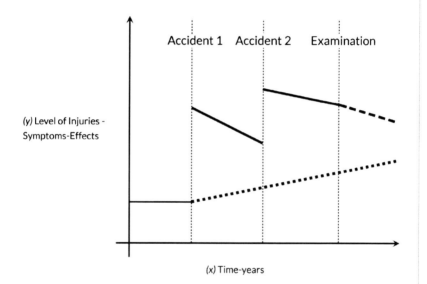

CAUSATION GRAPH #4: Two Accidents - Report on Both (Cumulative Effects)

Accident 1   Accident 2   Examination

(y) Level of Injuries -
Symptoms-Effects

(x) Time-years

The expert reports on the cumulative effect of both accidents by describing the situation represented by the solid lines (and the dashes representing the future), then the situation represented by the lower dotted line, and then describing the injuries, symptoms, effects and consequences that create the area between these lines. The situation in the absence of either one of the accidents is irrelevant.

(2a) Two Accidents - Report on First

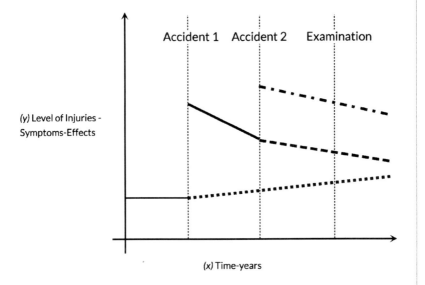

CAUSATION GRAPH #5: Two Accidents - Report on First Accident Only

Accident 1   Accident 2   Examination

(y) Level of Injuries -
Symptoms-Effects

(x) Time-years

When reporting on the first of two accidents, the expert has to describe the situation represented by the solid line (and the dashes representing the projected first accident recovery), the situation represented by the lower dotted line, and the injuries, symptoms, effects and consequences that create the area between these lines. The upper dot-dashed line, the impact of the second accident, is irrelevant.

(2b) Two Accidents - Report on Second

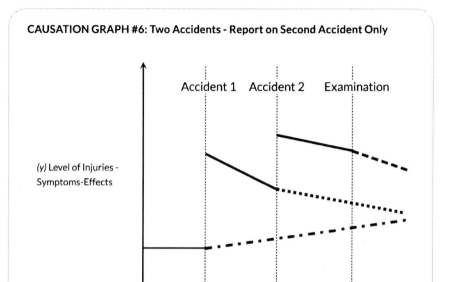

CAUSATION GRAPH #6: Two Accidents - Report on Second Accident Only

Accident 1   Accident 2   Examination

(y) Level of Injuries - Symptoms-Effects

(x) Time-years

When reporting on the second of two accidents, the expert has to describe the situation represented by the solid line (and the dashed line for the future), the situation represented by the dotted line (the projected first accident recovery) and finally describe the injuries, symptoms, effects and consequences that are represented by the area between the these lines. The situation in the absence of both accidents represented by the dot-dashed line is irrelevant.

(3) Two Accidents - Report on Both (Differentiating Effects)

When the expert has to report on the separate impact of each of two accidents, the expert has first to report on the first accident, in the absence of the second accident. This means that the expert has to project what recovery the claimant would probably have made had the second accident not occurred and contrast this with the without both accidents baseline. Then the expert has to report on the additional loss caused by the second accident beyond the projected recovery from the first accident.

Once again, the expert must address these issues in terms of the additional injuries, symptoms, effects and consequences probably caused by each accident. Causation Graph #6 above can be readily adapted to illustrate this type of report.

In multiple accident claims, the medical expert may find difficulty in establishing an accurate factual basis – namely, the condition of the claimant after the first accident and the recovery that was (or was not) taking place when the second accident occurred. The medical situation that the expert must give opinion upon is also more difficult, with little help from the medical literature available on victims of multiple accidents.

7.7.2   Approach to the Evidence

The expanded long-form opinion structure[11] can be developed to cope with these multi-accident cases, whether the expert is asked to report on the cumulative effect of both accidents, the first accident only, the second accident only, or on the differentiated effects of both accidents. We will take each of these situations in turn:

Report on Both Accidents (Cumulative Effects)

Opinion and Prognosis

1.   Acknowledge the complexity/difficulty

2.   Identify the claimant's present medical situation

3.   Identify the specific injuries sustained in the 1st accident and the resulting symptoms/effects and any recovery prior to the 2nd accident

4.   Identify the additional injuries sustained in the 2nd accident and the resulting symptoms/effects and any recovery prior to the examination date and for the future

5.   Identify the claimant's medical situation without both accidents to the examination date and for the future

6.   Express opinion on causation for the present situation (on the difference in injuries/symptoms/effects between the present situation and the situation as it would have been without both accidents)

7.   Contrast the prognosis for the present injuries/symptoms/effects and the projected situation as it would have been without both accidents

8.   Deal with the likely consequences now and for the future[12] (the restrictions in activities of daily living arising from the injuries/symptoms/effects suffered in both accidents and the situation as it would have been without both accidents)

---

11   See Sections 7.10.1 and 10.4.1 below

12   We recommend that the consequences of injuries be dealt with in a separate section of the report. We include the consequences of injury here to show the underlying logic for the order of the opinion.

Report on 1st of 2 Accidents

Opinion and Prognosis

1. Acknowledge the complexity/difficulty

2. Identify the claimant's present medical situation

3. Identify the specific injuries sustained in the 1st accident and the resulting symptoms/effects and any recovery prior to the 2nd accident

4. Identify the likely progression of the 1st accident injuries/symptoms/effects (without the intervention of the 2nd accident) to the examination date and if necessary into the future (i.e. if the 1st accident injuries/symptoms would not have resolved by the examination date)

5. Establish the 'but for' 1st accident baseline to the examination date and if required projected into the future (and discounting the 2nd accident)

6. Express opinion on causation as at the examination date (on the difference in injuries/symptoms/effects between the projected recovery from the first accident and the situation as it would have been without both accidents) and where possible give medical justification for discounting injuries/symptoms the expert attributes to the 2nd accident

7. Contrast the prognosis (if required) for the injuries/symptoms/effects from the projected recovery from the 1st accident beyond the examination date and the projected situation as it would have been without both accidents

8. Deal with the likely consequences now and for the future (the restrictions in activities of daily living arising from the injuries/symptoms/effects suffered in the 1st accident and the situation as it would have been without both accidents)

Report on 2nd of 2 Accidents

Opinion and Prognosis

1. Acknowledge the complexity/difficulty

2. Identify the claimant's present medical situation

3. Identify the specific injuries sustained in the 1st accident and the resulting symptoms/effects and any recovery prior to the 2nd accident

4. Identify the additional injuries sustained in the 2nd accident and the resulting symptoms/effects and any recovery prior to the examination date and for the future

5. Identify the likely progression of the 1st accident injuries/symptoms/effects (without the intervention of the 2nd accident) to the examination date and if necessary into the future (i.e. if the 1st accident injuries and symptoms would not have resolved by the examination date)

6. Express opinion on causation as at the examination date (on the difference in injuries/symptoms/effects between the situation as it is now and the projected recovery from the 1st accident) and where possible give medical justification for discounting injuries and symptoms that the expert attributes to the 1st accident

7. Contrast the prognosis for the present injuries/symptoms/effects and the situation as it would have been without the second accident

8. Deal with the likely consequences now and for the future (the restrictions in activities of daily living arising now and for the future from the present injuries/symptoms/effects and the situation as it would have been without the second accident)

Report on Both Accidents (Differentiating Effects)

Opinion and Prognosis

1. Acknowledge the complexity/difficulty

2. Identify the claimant's present medical situation

3. Identify the specific injuries sustained in the 1st accident and the resulting symptoms/effects and any recovery prior to the 2nd accident

4. Identify the additional injuries sustained in the 2nd accident and the resulting symptoms/effects and any recovery prior to the examination date and for the future

5. Identify the likely progression of the 1st accident injuries/symptoms/effects (without the intervention of the 2nd accident) to the examination date and if necessary into the future (i.e. if the 1st accident injuries and symptoms would not have resolved by the examination date)

6. Identify the claimant's medical situation without the 1st accident to the examination date and if necessary for the future

7. Express opinion on causation for the 1st accident as at the examination date (on the difference in injuries/symptoms/ effects between the projected recovery from the 1st accident and the situation as it would have been without both accidents) and where possible give medical justification for discounting injuries and symptoms that the expert attributes to the 2nd accident

8. Contrast the prognosis (if required) for the injuries/symptoms/ effects from the projected recovery from the 1st accident beyond the examination date and the projected situation as it would have been without both accidents

9. Deal with the likely consequences now and for the future (the restrictions in activities of daily living arising from the injuries/symptoms/effects suffered in the 1st accident and the situation as it would have been without both accidents)

10. Express opinion on causation for the 2nd accident as at the examination date (on the difference in injuries/symptoms/effects between the situation as it is now and the projected recovery from the 1st accident)

11. Contrast the prognosis for the present injuries/symptoms/effects and the situation as it would have been without the second accident

12. Deal with the likely consequences now and for the future (the restrictions in activities of daily living arising now and for the future from the present injuries/symptoms/effects and the situation as it would have been without the 2nd accident)

A lawyer would find the following evidence **unhelpful** as the expert makes no attempt to differentiate the two injuries and the symptoms, effects and consequences arising from them. This opinion will almost certainly lead to questions from the lawyers to the expert so that the claim(s) can be valued:

> It is very difficult to attribute the proportion by which each of these two accidents contributed to the current condition of the ankle. There was not a full recovery following the first accident and I am not sure that one can put everything down to the second accident. I believe therefore that the first accident primed the ankle but the main injury was in the second accident and I would put it in the region of 30% to the first and 70% to the second.

A lawyer would find the following evidence **helpful** as the expert describes the difference that the accident has made both in medical and in practical terms, thereby helping the lawyers to value the claim:

> As the result of the first accident, he suffered a soft tissue injury of the right ankle giving rise to acute pain for about a week and thereafter frequent episodes of aching and stiffness, which interfered only minimally with his activities of daily living. These symptoms were gradually resolving in the 3 months before the second accident.

In the absence of the second accident it is probable that these remaining symptoms from the first accident would have continued to resolve gradually so that by 12 months on from the first accident it is probable that he would have made a full symptomatic recovery.

As the result of the second accident 4 months after the first accident, when he again suffered a soft tissue injury of the right ankle, the level of symptoms he was experiencing was exacerbated so that he had difficulty walking and required strong painkillers and a prolonged course of physiotherapy. The current symptoms, as described above, are likely to resolve slowly over the next 2 to 3 years from the date of my examination.

Given that the circumstances of the second accident and that the mechanism of injury in the 2 accidents were different, in my opinion the first accident did not contribute to or increase the severity of the subsequent injury and the resulting symptoms and restrictions.

For the first 8 months after the second accident, the first accident contributed a small and reducing element to his symptoms, which was of little or no functional significance. In the absence of either accident there was no reason for him to suffer any symptoms in his ankle.

In this example, the expert would also have to deal with the consequences arising from the injuries, symptoms and effects from the second accident and would need to contrast these with the consequences that the claimant would have been likely to experience without the second accident. In this extract, the expert has not dealt with the consequences of the injury, only its effects.

More Than Two Accidents

In the examples above, we have set out graphs for cases where the claimant has suffered two accidents. Unfortunately, some claimants become serial accidentees and suffer more than two accidents. We hope that by now the reader will be able to extend the X-axis of a causation graph to account for additional accidents and will be able to draw the relevant lines to indicate how causation needs to be addressed.

7.7.3 Cumulative Effects Cases

The most difficult expression of a multi-accident case is when it is impossible, even on the balance of probabilities, to differentiate between the injuries, symptoms and effects of each of the accidents and the loss attributable to each. In this situation, the lawyers need the expert to be as helpful as possible.

The question as to whether the presenting condition since the last accident is attributable to the cumulative effect of both (or all) of the accidents is the essential question that the lawyers need the expert to address. If so, the lawyers will simply divide up the loss between the defendants based on a percentage estimate of the contribution of each accident.

This approach, as far as the medical expert is concerned, should be adopted only when a more detailed approach is simply impossible or where instructions are expressly given to the medical expert not to seek to differentiate between the effects of each accident.

7.8 Breaking the Chain of Causation

We have seen that damages are only recovered for the injuries and loss resulting from the breach of duty on which the claim is based. Therefore, as illustrated by the causation graph, damages are for the difference between what would have been in the absence of (or 'but for') the accident or adverse event and the situation as it now is.

Damages may in certain circumstances also be limited if something happens after the accident that adversely affects the claimant. It is a matter of law whether a subsequent event 'breaks the chain of causation'.[13] The question is whether the law holds that the subsequent event can be regarded as breaking the causal connection between the breach of duty and the damage suffered. If it does, then the original wrongdoer will not be liable for any subsequent damage.

The subsequent event must have such an impact that it is regarded as obliterating the original wrongdoing, and it may take the form of:

- some natural event independent of any human agency;
- the act or omission of someone other than the claimant and the original wrongdoer; or
- the conduct of the claimant him/herself.

In the following 5 examples, the chain of causation could become an issue in the claim:

1. One year after the accident, and while recovering from it, a claimant suffers a heart attack and dies for reasons totally unconnected with the accident.

In this situation, the heart attack breaks the chain of causation and damages cease on death. Damages for pain and suffering are assessed on the basis of the period of one year. Care needs and loss of income are limited to that same period.

---

13   Lawyers often refer to an act that breaks the chain of causation as a 'novus actus interveniens' (a new act intervening).

2. One year after suffering severe injury to a leg in an accident, a claimant is involved in a subsequent accident for which no one else is blamed. In this accident he suffers a traumatic amputation of the same leg.

In this situation, the second accident breaks the chain of causation. Pain and suffering arising from the first accident is assessed on the basis of the period of one year and care needs and loss of income are limited to that period.

3. One year after the accident, while still recovering from a severe leg injury, a claimant trips and falls down stairs while carrying something in both hands, sustaining further serious injury.

In this situation, whether or not the chain of causation is broken may be contentious. The resolution of the issue will depend on whether the original breach of duty and injury contributed to the fall.

4. A claimant refuses to undergo or to continue treatment, which is necessary to assist in the recovery from the original injuries sustained.

Whether or not the chain of causation is broken, relieving the original wrongdoer of liability for an extended period of recovery caused by the absence of treatment, is likely to focus upon the reasonableness of the claimant refusing such treatment.

5. A claimant is treated in hospital following an accident, but receives substandard care as a result of which his condition is aggravated.

In this situation, whether the original wrongdoer avoids liability for the impact of the substandard care depends on the nature and degree of the breach of duty in hospital. We consider this issue further in Section 7.9 below.

7.8.1   Approach to the Evidence

It is not appropriate for the medical expert to refer to such intervening events as breaking, or not breaking, the chain of causation. However, the expert should be aware of the potential issue for the lawyers and, if appropriate, and from within the medical expert's area of expertise, address this subsequent event and how it relates to the original injury. If the subsequent event is outside an expert's area of expertise, then the medical expert should indicate in the report the need for another appropriate medical expert to deal with the issue.

The matters that a medical expert should address would therefore include:

- whether the claimant's subsequent death was related or in some way connected to the accident;
- whether a subsequent medical complication was related to the accident or its consequences;
- whether a subsequent accident might have been caused or contributed to by the effects of the original accident;
- whether there is an explanation for the claimant's refusal to undergo or complete treatment or whether there are reasons why such refusal might be regarded as reasonable generally or in the particular circumstances of the claimant; and
- whether the claimant's condition has been aggravated by his treatment at the hands of the medical profession subsequent to the accident.

It is enough for the medical expert in the first instance to indicate only briefly an opinion on such matters, unless specifically instructed to address the issue. Should issues concerning a possible break in the chain of causation prove to be an important aspect of the case, then it would be for the lawyers to return to the medical expert for greater clarification.

7.9 Criticism of Medical Treatment in a Personal Injury Claim

In preparing a report in a personal injury claim, the medical expert may be critical of the treatment that a claimant received in hospital following the injury. If the treatment to be criticised has resulted in the claimant suffering additional or unnecessary injury, then the claimant may be able to bring a clinical negligence claim in relation to that additional injury and the defendant in the personal injury claim may be able to avoid paying compensation for that additional injury by blaming the healthcare provider.

In a personal injury claim, most claimants and their advisers do not consider it a desirable course of action to add an additional defendant to the claim – the healthcare provider – and to have to launch a concurrent clinical negligence claim. If a concurrent action is launched, the initial claim immediately becomes complicated by the addition of parties and issues. The claim will also become considerably more expensive to run and will take longer, with a less certain outcome. To the defendant, whilst recognising such effects, it may be a way to reduce the financial exposure in the personal injury claim by passing it on to the healthcare provider. However, even investigating the matter will inevitably incur additional costs, which one of the parties will have to bear.

Where medical treatment subsequent to an accident does give rise to a claim in clinical negligence for the additional injury resulting to the claimant, lawyers describe the intervening clinical negligence as "breaking the chain of causation".

The injury that has been caused (or part of it) has not been caused by the original wrongdoer's breach of duty and so the original wrongdoer is not liable for it.

Although the basic principle is straightforward, applying the principle to the facts of a case is a difficult area of law. This is because not all negligent treatment that causes a worsening of an injured claimant's condition will give rise to a separate (and additional) claim for clinical negligence against the healthcare provider. To do so within an existing personal injury claim, the medical treatment must be 'grossly negligent', so that its effect is to 'eclipse the original wrongdoing'[14] and 'extinguish the causative potency of the earlier tort (or wrong).'[15] After all, it was the original wrongdoer whose actions (or omissions) put the claimant unwillingly into the hands of the medical profession in the first place.

Therefore, even where the medical treatment did fall below an acceptable standard of care, it will not necessarily in law break the chain of causation and make the healthcare provider liable for any resulting damage caused by the unacceptable treatment. Nor necessarily will unacceptable treatment allow the original wrong-doer to avoid paying full compensation to the claimant.

A medical expert is not expected to know when in law treatment comes so far below the appropriate standard of care that the negligence becomes 'gross'. Indeed, it is difficult for a lawyer to identify the line between 'simple negligence' and 'gross negligence'. The expert is expected only to compare the actual care with that reasonably to be expected. In so doing, the expert can probably give some impression as to how far below an appropriate standard the care was, perhaps in a range from 'momentary oversight' to 'inexplicably crass'.

7.9.1   Approach to the Evidence

Personal injury reports are required for the purpose of establishing the causation of injury or damage and in assessing damages. The report will almost certainly address the causation of the injury sustained by the claimant. Where subsequent medical treatment has contributed to the claimant's condition the expert will need to consider the extent to which the situation was worsened by the treatment received from the medical practitioners.

Therefore, where there are issues as to whether the treatment or management of the claimant by the healthcare provider has contributed towards the claimant's current situation or where the expert considers that the claimant would be in a better condition if he/she had received an appropriate standard of care, the opinion on the causation of injury expressed in the report will not be complete without reference to these issues.

---

14   *Webb v Barclays Bank Plc* [2002] PIQR P161

15   *Rahman v Arearose Ltd* [2001] QB 351

The instructions from the lawyers should state 'the purpose of requesting the advice or report'[16] and this will not normally include questions about the standard of medical care in a personal injury claim. Nonetheless, a medical expert minded to be critical of the standard of care given by medical professionals in treating the injury suffered in the accident should consider two important issues:

1. whether his/her opinion given in the report is 'true and complete'[17] and whether the 'duty to assist the court on matters within his expertise'[18] has been complied with; and

2. whether the medical expert is of the appropriate expertise properly to give an opinion critical of the treating clinicians.

In the first instance, the expert will have been chosen in order to assist with identifying the injury, its causation and the assessment of damage. The expert is not instructed to address the standard of care applicable to the subsequent treatment and so may not necessarily be the appropriate expert to do so.

The medical expert must be sure of his/her ground to be making criticisms as to the standard of care provided in hospital subsequent to the accident. The expert must also be confident that he/she has seen all relevant documentation on which to base such opinion. Medical experts must only express an opinion on matters within their expertise[19] and must make it clear 'when a question or issue falls outside their expertise; and when they are not able to reach a definite opinion, for example because they have insufficient information'.[20]

It is often useful for the expert to discuss his/her concerns regarding the subsequent medical treatment with the instructing solicitor to establish what new instructions, if any, need to be given to the expert and to get advice as to the manner in which the issue needs to be addressed within the report. If the expert's instructions do require, whether expressly or by implication, him/her to consider whether the outcome of treatment may have been worsened by the acts of someone other than the initial wrongdoer (the defendant), then it would be appropriate for the expert to make reference to concerns about the standard of care on the part of the healthcare provider.

Even though a medical expert may not be in a position to express a concluded opinion about the standard of care or may not have the expertise to do so, if genuinely concerned the expert should at least signpost this for the lawyers as an area for possible further consideration. It may also be appropriate to identify the relevant area of expertise by which the standard of such care should properly be considered should the instructing party choose to do so.

---

16 Protocol para 8.1(c)

17 See Statement of Truth and PD35 2.4

18 CPR 35.3(1)

19 PD35 2.2

20 PD35 2.4 and Section 4.2.11 above

To state that 'the claimant's current condition has been contributed to by the medical treatment he received following the accident' is an example of Foot-Wearing. The expert must say how and in what way the medical treatment has contributed to the claimant's present condition and distinguish between sub-optimal, sub-standard and inappropriate treatment when expressing the opinion.

NO FOOT-WEARING!

7.10   Cases that Rely on Expertise

Some cases rely more heavily on the opinions of experts because the factual basis is incomplete. The court seeks to hear from the medical expert as to the likely factual position. The problem is that when an opinion is difficult to justify on strictly medical or scientific grounds, most experts are less willing to offer a firm opinion – even an opinion based on the balance of probabilities.

In these difficult cases, the often opaque expressions of opinion found in expert reports are an illustration of the discomfort that the expert feels in applying the civil standard of proof to finely balanced issues. The easy option appears to be for the experts to muddy the waters with artfully impenetrable language and hope the case settles. This is, to say the least, an interesting interpretation of an expert's overriding duty to help the court.

In cases where expressing firm opinions is difficult, experts have to apply their medico-legal minds to the medical issues in dispute. Where scientifically supported opinions are not possible, then the next stage is to consider whether a credible opinion can be given 'on the balance of probabilities'. Clearly, the strength of an expert's opinion, in the face of a contrary opinion, will increase as the expert's level of certainty increases. However, if the expert is confident that his/her opinion is correct 'on the balance of probabilities', then the opinion can be - and should be – clearly expressed in the report.

7.10.1 Structure for a 'Difficult' Opinion

When dealing with a difficult opinion, an expanded long-form opinion structure should be used to explain the basis of the opinion and to deal openly with the difficulties of offering a firm opinion. The following structure allows the expert to deal with the difficulty honestly and openly before expressing clear opinions:

1. acknowledge the difficulty of expressing a firm opinion;

2. discuss whether, given the available evidence, an opinion can be expressed on the balance of probabilities; (and if so)

3. identify the important factors;

4. set out the reasoning process; and

5. give a clear conclusion on the balance of probabilities.

In the example below, the expert begins by acknowledging the difficulty in forming an opinion:

> When considering Mr M's chances of improved long term survival had his lung disease been diagnosed in March 2008, there are no relevant scientific papers on which I can rely in forming an opinion …However, given the nature of the disease and its progression in the months leading up to Mr M's death in December 2008, I do consider that there is sufficient evidence to give an opinion, on the balance of probabilities, on his chances of improved long term survival had the diagnosis been made in March 2008…

Here, the expert has acknowledged the difficulty of the lack of scientific evidence to support the opinion that follows, which is based instead on the expert's expertise and experience:

> … I give substantial weight to the fact that a large tumour had developed (as detailed in 4.7 above) in the claimant's neck by June 2008. In my opinion, this indicates that the disease was probably already present in Mr M's lymphatic system in March 2008 and earlier diagnosis and treatment would not have been likely to prevent the spread of the disease to other lymph nodes as subsequently occurred. Therefore, on the balance of probabilities, I conclude that the failure to diagnose the lung disease in March 2008 made no material difference to the claimant's chances of long term survival.

Acknowledging the inherent difficulty of giving an opinion is likely to draw a challenge to the opinion should the matter reach court. However, such a challenge is going to happen in any event and an acknowledgement of difficulty by the expert demonstrates an open and honest (and therefore, independent) approach to the issues. Beyond this, the expert's willingness to align in the grammar his/her professional credibility with the opinion expressed – by using the first person singular – shows a level of commitment and professional responsibility that a court would be likely to find impressive.

Conclusion

An expert who has developed his/her medico-legal mind understands that the principles to be applied in a complex claim are exactly the same as those that must be applied in all claims. By focussing on these basic principles, the expert will be able to deal with all the issues in the claim appropriately. In many complex claims, the level of proof that the expert needs to apply to his/her opinions is far closer to the civil standard of proof than most medical experts find to be comfortable. But this should not deter the expert from giving clear and concise opinions, explaining clearly the basis on which the opinion is made and the rationale that supports the conclusion reached.

Key-Point Summary

1. Every expert opinion has to be based on a logical and reasoned approach to the evidence. Experts should always take the time to consider all the possible causes for a presentation – it is a mistake to rush to judgement on what are often very difficult issues.

2. Where there is difficulty in linking an injury to its cause, the expert should consider the question as to whether the injury is capable of being attributed to the accident, even though a direct causal link is difficult to establish, and then go on to apply the balance of probabilities to the attribution.

3. Experts should consider factual disputes very carefully and express opinions on both possible sets of facts, unless there is a clear medical justification for preferring one or other set of facts.

4. The terms 'exaggeration' and 'malingering' do not have a legal definition and lawyers and experts apply these terms in different ways. The medical expert should explain what he/she means when using these terms.

5. When reporting on observations outside of the clinical examination, the expert becomes a witness to fact and so should make careful contemporaneous notes of any observations made and the circumstances in which these were made.

6. Surveillance evidence should be considered very carefully and all issues raised should be considered in the light of all the available evidence. Always make sure the person in the video is actually the claimant.

7. Cases involving road traffic accidents where there is an allegation or a real possibility that the claimant was not wearing a seatbelt require the medical expert to consider what the claimant's injuries would have been but for the failure to wear a seatbelt and then to compare the situation as it is with the situation as it would have been but for that failure.

8. Multiple-accident claims often involve the expert in reporting on a projected recovery from an accident in order to properly consider issues of causation. All involved in such cases recognise the difficulty of the task, so a logical and reasoned approach to the issue is essential.

9. Some post-accident events 'break the chain of causation' and experts should be aware of this issue when considering causation.

10. When considering possible clinical negligence within a personal injury report, it is important to consider whether an expert in another discipline would actually be the appropriate expert to consider the matter. It is often useful to seek advice from the instructing solicitor when such issues arise.

11. Experts should not shy away from expressing clear opinions in difficult cases, but should explain clearly the basis of and rationale for the conclusions reached.

Next Steps

In the next chapter, we will explore the law as it relates to clinical negligence and the additional issues that experts have to consider when reporting on clinical negligence claims.

Developing Your Medico-Legal Mind (7)

For this exercise we have altered the history subsequent to C.T.'s April 2008 accident[21] by subjecting him to a second accident, and in the process have introduced some more complex medico-legal issues. Consider these new facts and respond to the questions from the solicitor that follow:

C.T. v Allied and Leicester Insurance Company PLC

In April 2010, friends of C.T. invited him out for a drink 'to lift his spirits' as he had been refusing to socialise and had taken to drinking on his own. As he no longer felt safe as a passenger in the rear of a car and felt very stressed and "imprisoned" by wearing a seat belt, he was the front seat passenger and was not wearing a seat belt.

On the A12 in Essex, while on the way to the pub, the car in which he was a passenger ran into the rear of a car in front, which itself had had to brake heavily as a reaction to other vehicles braking to avoid debris on the road.

In this accident, C.T. suffered a comminuted fracture of the right lower femur into his knee, fractured his lower jaw, lacerated the lower part of his face, and lost 3 teeth. He was also found to have a detached retina. C.T. developed significantly more severe back pain within 72 hours of the accident.

C.T. is left with restricted movement in the right knee and a 1 cm shortening of the right leg. He now spends much of the time lying down, as he says that to stand for more than a few minutes is "excruciating". He has also begun to suffer with episodes of depressive behaviour, typically manifesting as a refusal to communicate or acknowledge the presence of his wife or family, followed by episodes of "raging outbursts" in which he insults whomever he sees.

C.T. is no longer working as an electrician and it is to be doubted that he will find another role. There is now a great deal of tension between C.T. and his family.

Twelve months on from the second accident (April 2011), C.T.'s orthopaedic consultant at the Anywhere General Hospital has noted three inconsistent reports of pain during his examinations of C.T. (on axial loading). He has noted that the level of symptoms C.T. reports has been unvarying over the previous 12 months, even though his orthopaedic and maxillofacial injuries have all healed well. The orthopaedic consultant has discussed the case with the maxillofacial consultant, who has also noted that C.T. seems to have gained little or no relief from his symptoms, despite very good healing of his maxillofacial injuries. The orthopaedic consultant has noted that psychological factors or the ongoing spectre of litigation may be hampering C.T.'s recovery from his injuries.

---

21   See Developing Your Medico-Legal Mind (6)

After receiving an initial medical report from C.T.'s solicitors, the defendant insurance company instructed a private investigator to film C.T.'s activities over a two-week period. On the video, C.T. is seen entering a betting shop on three occasions and seeming to have more mobility than the medical report suggested he would have.

1. An orthopaedic surgeon has been instructed to provide opinion on the impact of the physical injuries that the second accident has had on C.T., so that the financial liability of the driver of the car in which he was travelling can be ascertained.

    The letter of instruction from the solicitor contained the following specific questions in relation to the claim. Consider how you would respond to these questions (as an orthopaedic surgeon), taking into account the factual basis, causation issues, the standard of proof and your duties and responsibilities under the CPR.

    (i)   What injuries did C.T. suffer in this (second) accident?

    (ii) In the absence of the second accident, what would have been the likely outcome in relation to the injuries sustained in the first accident?

    (iii) Is there any medical explanation for C.T.'s continuing and unvarying level of ongoing pain and disability?

    (iv) What are the possible explanations for the inconsistent reports of pain noted by C.T.'s orthopaedic consultant?

    (v)   Mr C.T.'s continuing symptoms of pain and disability have not improved although his physical condition appears to have improved. Is there an explanation for this?

    (vi) Is the level of activity demonstrated by C.T. in the video credible given the level of pain and disability claimed by him?

    (vii) Is any future treatment, or more recovery time, likely to improve C.T.'s condition?

2. Subsequent to the orthopaedic expert's report, the defendant's insurers obtain expert medical opinion that C.T.'s continuing level of pain and disability cannot be attributed to the physical injuries he suffered in the second accident. It also concludes that had C.T. been wearing a seat belt the facial and bony injuries would have been unlikely to have occurred, and the only probable injuries would have been whiplash injuries of moderate severity.

    A psychiatric assessment is now sought of C.T.'s mental state prior to the

April 2010 accident, the impact of the April 2010 accident upon him, and his mental state since the accident, so that the financial liability of the driver of the car in which he was travelling can be ascertained.

The letter of instruction from the solicitor contained the following specific questions in relation to the claim. Consider how you would respond to these questions (as a psychiatrist), taking into account the factual basis, causation issues, the standard of proof and your duties and responsibilities under the CPR.

(i) What is your opinion on C.T.'s mental state prior to the April 2010 accident and was this attributable to the April 2008 accident and its aftermath?

(ii) Was it reasonable for C.T., given his mental state prior to the second accident, to refuse to wear a seatbelt when seated in the front of the car?

(iii) What is your opinion of the impact of the April 2010 accident on C.T.'s mental state?

(iv) In the absence of the second accident, would C.T.'s present mental state be the same as it is now or different? If different, what difference would you have expected?

(v) Orthopaedic and maxillofacial expert opinion indicates a psychological or psychiatric contribution to C.T.'s ongoing level of pain and disability. Do you support this view?

(vi) There is concern in this case that C.T. is exaggerating his level of symptoms and disability. What is your opinion on this question and if you consider there to be exaggeration, is it conscious or unconscious in nature?

(vii) Are there any treatment options that would improve his medical situation or otherwise be of benefit to C.T.?

Clinical Negligence –
Legal Principles

8.1   Legal Principles in Clinical Negligence Claims
8.2   Level of Skill Required – Novices and Specialists
8.3   Consent and Failure to Warn
8.4   Failure to Treat
8.5   Conflicting Opinion on Factual Issues
8.6   Conflicting Opinion on Standard of Care
8.7   Causation and 'Material Contribution'

Introduction

The legal principles applied in clinical negligence claims are exactly the same as the principles applied in all personal injury claims. The court still has to decide issues of breach of duty, causation, damage, and condition and prognosis. This said, there is no doubt that the medical and legal issues in clinical negligence are more complex and require more careful analysis by all the professionals involved in the claim. There are also differences in the legal issues that the medical expert is required to address in the expert report, in particular the question as to whether there has been a breach of the duty of care owed by the treating clinicians to the claimant.

Chapter Outline

In this chapter, we will explore the essential legal principles that are relevant to clinical negligence claims. We will examine the legal tests to be applied in assessing issues of breach of duty and the specific issues relating to consent, failures to warn and failures to treat. We will also address the difference between the court's approach to disputes in factual evidence and disputes as to the appropriate standard of care. Finally, we will consider causation in clinical negligence claims.

8.1   Legal Principles in Clinical Negligence Claims

A claim for damages for the consequences of an adverse event in clinical practice requires proof of 'negligence'. Negligence has been defined by the court as:

> '...the omission to do something which a reasonable man, guided upon those considerations which ordinarily regulate the conduct of human affairs, would do, or doing something which a prudent and reasonable man would not do.'[1]

8.1.1   The 'Bolam Test'

The general definition of negligence is refined where the issue is whether a person with a particular skill - such as a doctor - is guilty of negligence.

In *Bolam v Friern Hospital Management Committee*[2] the judge in summing up to a jury[3] explained negligence in the context of clinical practice as follows:

> 'I must tell you what in law we mean by "negligence". In the ordinary case which does not involve any special skill, negligence in law means this: some failure to do some act which a reasonable man in the circumstances would do, or doing some act which a reasonable man in the circumstances would not do; and if that failure or doing of that act results in injury, then there is a cause of action. How do you test whether this act or failure is negligent? In an ordinary case it is generally said, that you judge that by the action of the man in the street. He is the ordinary man. In one case it has been said that you judge it by the conduct of the man on the top of a Clapham omnibus. He is the ordinary man.
>
> But where you get a situation which involves the use of some special skill or competence, then the test whether there has been negligence or not is not the test of the man on the top of a Clapham omnibus, because he has not got this

---

1   Alderson B in *Blyth v Birmingham Waterworks Co* (1856) 11 Ex Ch 781 at 784

2   [1957] 2 All ER 118. The case concerned the application of ECT to a patient, who had not been given a relaxant drug, who was not restrained, and who had not been warned of the risk of injury from the procedure. During the treatment, the patient fell off the table and sustained bilateral acetabula fractures.

3   In the 1950s, such civil cases were tried by jury.

special skill. The test is the standard of the ordinary skilled man exercising and professing to have that special skill.

A man need not possess the highest expert skill at the risk of being found negligent. It is well established law that it is sufficient if he exercises the ordinary skill of an ordinary competent man exercising that particular art. …A doctor is not guilty of negligence if he has acted in accordance with a practice accepted as proper by a responsible body of medical men skilled in that particular art… Putting it the other way round, a doctor is not negligent, if he is acting in accordance with such a practice, merely because there is a body of opinion that takes a contrary view.

At the same time, that does not mean that a medical man can obstinately and pig-headedly carry on with some old technique if it has been proved to be contrary to what is really substantially the whole of informed medical opinion. Otherwise you might get men today saying: "I don't believe in anaesthetics. I don't believe in antiseptics. I am going to continue to do my surgery in the way it was done in the eighteenth century". That clearly would be wrong.'

Therefore, to establish if a person with any particular expertise has been negligent, it is necessary to measure his/her actions against the standard reasonably to be expected of a reasonably competent practitioner, not against the very best or even the very worst practitioner in that field. It follows that the standard of care to be expected of a reasonably competent practitioner is effectively set by practitioners in that same field, not by the lawyers or by the court. Negligence will only be established in the light of the expert opinion of a practitioner in that same field on the actions (or inaction) of a fellow practitioner. If no practitioner will say that the standard fell below that reasonably to be expected from a reasonably competent practitioner, it is unlikely that liability can be established.

The legal test to be applied, as set out in *Bolam*, can therefore be summarised as follows:

A doctor is not guilty of negligence if he has acted in accordance with a practice accepted as proper by a responsible body of medical men skilled in that particular art…

The judge moved on to explain a finding of non-negligence – an explanation that is particularly helpful, as it places on the expert the duty of explaining the range of opinion across all the responsible bodies of medical opinion, rather than allowing the expert to simply express an opinion based on the practice to which he/she chooses to adhere:

Putting it the other way round, a doctor is not negligent if he is acting in accordance with such a practice, merely because there is a body of opinion that takes a contrary view.[4]

4   *Bolam* (see above) at 122B

8.1.2   Approach to the Evidence – Applying the Bolam Test

The Bolam test has been restated in slightly different ways in subsequent cases[5] and to fit different factual situations, but by its nature the test confirms the need for the expert's evidence to define the acceptable standard and to compare the action of the clinician(s) with the standard as defined.

The following expressions of the Bolam test are all statements of exclusion, in that they identify that the actions (or omissions) of the clinician fell below the standard of care reasonably to be expected of the treating clinician by a responsible body of practitioners.

Other expressions of the Bolam test in a finding of negligence are:

- …the doctor failed to act in accordance with a practice accepted as proper by a responsible body of medical practitioners skilled in that particular field at that time…
- …there was a failure to exercise the ordinary skill of a doctor (in the appropriate speciality) at that time…
- …the actions of the doctor were not in accordance with the practice of a reasonably competent doctor (skilled in that particular field) at that time…
- …what was done would not be acceptable to a responsible body of (such medical practitioners) at that time…
- …he is guilty of such failure as no doctor of ordinary skill (in that particular field) would be guilty of if acting with ordinary skill at that time...

Where the medical expert addresses the standard of care only by addressing what a reasonable body of clinicians at the particular time would have done, rather than by addressing the issue in terms of what no reasonable body of clinicians at the particular time would have done, the expert leaves open the question as to whether a particular practice actually fell below the standard of care of a reasonably competent practitioner. In many disciplines, contrary opinions on treatment exist and different practitioners have different opinions. A successful claim cannot be established on the basis that the action of a clinician was not in accord with the practice of a responsible body of practitioners, rather the claimant must establish that no responsible body of practitioners would accord with the practice adopted.

Therefore, a lawyer would find the following opinion **unhelpful** because the evidence does not address the question as to whether in this case the laparoscopic approach fell below an acceptable standard of practice for a general surgeon at the time:

---

5   In *Maynard v West Midlands Regional Health Authority* [1984] 1 WLR 634 the word 'respectable' is substituted for 'responsible'.

Mr C had a history of bowel surgery, including opening of the bowel, and a subsequent episode of small bowel obstruction requiring laparotomy and symptoms of intermittent small bowel colic. It should therefore have been clear to a surgeon experienced in such surgery that there would be intra-abdominal adhesions at the time of hernia repair and that these would be extensive and would probably have spread to the lower abdomen, so that the risk of injury to the bowel during inguinal hernia repair was significantly increased. …It follows that the preferred technique in this patient would have been the open technique and not the laparoscopic approach in fact used.

NO FOOT-WEARING!

A lawyer would find the following opinion **helpful** because the evidence addresses the surgeon's actions in terms of practice that no general surgeon would regard as proper:

> … In my opinion no reasonably competent general surgeon, in practice at the time of this operation (April 2007), who was presented with a simple, uncomplicated and almost symptom-free hernia in a man with this history of bowel problems, would have failed to recognise that a laparoscopic repair of the hernia involved a high degree of risk. He would therefore have offered the patient an open rather than a laparoscopic repair. In proceeding with a laparoscopic repair, the surgeon failed to act in accordance with a practice that would be accepted as proper by a responsible body of general surgeons. Alternatively, had the surgeon not established the previous history prior to commencing the repair, the surgeon would not have acted in accordance with a practice that would have been accepted as proper by a responsible body of general surgeons.

This opposing opinion would also be **helpful** in delineating the dispute:

> … However, while I personally would have proceeded to carry out the repair by open surgery because of the risk of severe adhesions, and would have criticised any registrar in my team who sought to do otherwise, I have to accept that there are responsible general surgeons who would nonetheless have commenced laparoscopically, recognising that it might become necessary to proceed to an open repair if the anatomical structures were damaged by previous surgery. Therefore, I am of the opinion that the standard of care in this case was such that it would be acceptable to a responsible body of surgeons in practice at the time of this operation.

To give an opinion on breach of duty - i.e. negligence - the expert must apply the Bolam test (or in rare cases the test in *Bolitho* – see Section 8.6 below). The phrases used when applying the Bolam test should accurately reflect the test set out by the court and the phrases properly to be used when applying the test should not be substituted for other less precise phrases.

Using the facts in the example above, compare the following expressions of the Bolam test:

1. No reasonably competent general surgeon in April 2007 would have proceeded with the laparoscopic hernia repair on a patient with a history of abdominal surgery and continuing bowel symptoms.

2. To proceed with the laparoscopic hernia repair on a patient with a history of abdominal surgery and continuing bowel symptoms would not be acceptable to a responsible body of general surgeons in practice in April 2007.

3. In proceeding with laparoscopic hernia repair on a patient with a history of abdominal surgery and continuing bowel symptoms, the general surgeon failed to act in accordance with a practice accepted as proper by a responsible body of general surgeons in April 2007.

4. In proceeding with the laparoscopic hernia repair on a patient with a history of abdominal surgery and continuing bowel symptoms, the general surgeon did not provide an acceptable standard of care.

5. Proceeding with the laparoscopic hernia repair on a patient with a history of abdominal surgery and continuing bowel problems was sub-standard care.

Examples 1-3 accurately apply the Bolam test.

Example 4 would probably be acceptable to most lawyers, but does not address all aspects of the Bolam test. Although the standard of care is identified as 'acceptable' (clearly a reference to Bolam), this example does not include the second part of the test that deals with the 'responsible body of medical practitioners' (skilled in that discipline at that time).

Example 5 would be understood by the lawyers and would probably be acceptable to many, but it provides no reassurance that the expert actually understands the Bolam test or has applied it properly. Many lawyers would seek clarification of this opinion.

8.1.3   Use of the Terms 'Negligent' or 'Negligence'

It is for the court to rule whether or not a medical practitioner has been negligent in law. This ruling will be based on the opinions expressed in the medical expert evidence. The medical expert evidence should apply the Bolam test in one of its forms and express an opinion in relation to it. It is not for the expert to rule whether this amounts to negligence in law and therefore the expert should avoid using the legal terms 'negligent' and 'negligence'.

8.2   Level of Skill Required – Novices and Specialists

As we have seen, the standard by which a medical practitioner is judged is that of the reasonably competent practitioner in the relevant field at the particular time. The law has also considered how the Bolam test should be applied to novices and specialists.

8.2.1   Novices

A newly-qualified doctor is assessed against the same standards reasonably expected of all doctors in that speciality. A lack of experience is no defence. A surgeon who is learning the necessary skills to be a competent surgeon will begin by learning how to perform the more straightforward operations, guided and assisted as appropriate by a competent surgical colleague. This enables the surgeon, although still a novice, to carry out the operation to the standard of a reasonably competent practitioner in that field. The standard is not that of the best and most experienced surgeon, but it is required to be that of a reasonably competent surgeon. To achieve this standard of reasonable competence, the inexperienced surgeon may require guidance from, the assistance of, or even intervention by a competent surgeon.

In *Wilsher v Essex Area Health Authority*[6] it was argued by the defendant that in the case of the medical profession, the nature of the duty owed by a doctor should vary depending on his degree of training or experience. The defence argued that:

> 'Public hospital medicine has always been organised so that young doctors and nurses learn on the job. If the hospitals abstained from using inexperienced people, they could not staff their wards and theatres, and the junior staff could never learn. The longer-term interests of patients as a whole are best served by maintaining the present system, even if this may diminish the legal rights of the individual patient, for, after all, medicine is about curing, not litigation.'

---

6   [1986] 3 All ER 801

However the argument was dealt with in this manner in the Court of Appeal:

> 'I acknowledge the appeal of this argument, and recognise that a young hospital doctor who must get onto the wards in order to qualify without necessarily being able to decide what kind of patient he is going to meet is not in the same position as another professional man who has a real choice whether or not to practice in a particular field. Nevertheless, I cannot accept that there should be a special rule for doctors in public hospitals; I emphasise public, since presumably those employed in private hospitals would be in a different category. Doctors are not the only people who gain their experience, not only from lectures or from watching others perform, but from tackling live clients or customers, and no case was cited to us which suggested that any such variable duty of care was imposed on others in a similar position.
>
> To my mind, it would be a false step to subordinate the legitimate expectation of the patient that he will receive from each person concerned with his care a degree of skill appropriate to the task which he undertakes to an understandable wish to minimise the psychological and financial pressures on hard-pressed young doctors.'[7]

The court therefore placed on doctors the same duty of care that every other professional person has, namely, the degree of skill appropriate to the task being undertaken. An under-resourced, under-trained or overtired junior doctor has to perform to the same standard of competence as a colleague at another hospital who does not experience any such lack of resources or training or the need to work unsocial hours.

An expert instructed to consider a question of medical negligence may find it useful to consider the issue from a departmental perspective:

- were suitably experienced doctors in place or available to assist so that the department could achieve the acceptable standard of care?
- were the correct procedures in place to enable an inexperienced doctor to identify the moment when help from more qualified colleagues should be sought and to obtain such help when required?

If the expert concludes that the treating clinician was inexperienced or out of his/her depth (probably while doing his/her less-than-entirely-competent best), then it is appropriate to point out this fact. However, when addressing whether the standard of care shown in managing the patient fell below the required standard, the medical expert assesses the performance of the department, not merely the inexperienced treating doctor.

Given the difficulties of finding the right expert, the solicitor may instruct an expert who is a leader in the particular field in question, with a senior position in a pre-eminent institution, who must give opinion on the practice of a very young

---

7   [1986] 3 All ER 801 at 813

practitioner in a remote district hospital facing an emergency situation. Perhaps, the reporting expert is a specialist surgeon reviewing the actions of a general surgeon, who still might reasonably be expected to carry out such surgery. In both of these situations, the standard of practice to be applied is that of the reasonably competent practitioner in that speciality in the situation as it unfolded. It is not the standard expected of an expert in that field in a centre of excellence dealing with a referred case to be treated at comparative leisure.

8.2.2   Specialists

Where the doctor is in a specialist field, the practitioner will be expected to show the ordinary skill to be expected in the speciality:

> 'The language of the Bolam test clearly requires a different degree of skill from a specialist in his own special field than from a general practitioner. In the field of neurosurgery it would be necessary to substitute for [the] phrase "no doctor of ordinary skill" the phrase "no neurosurgeon of ordinary skill".'[8]

As a doctor becomes more specialised – but not as he/she becomes more experienced - in a particular area of practice, so the standard of skill that is expected increases. However, the doctor is only required to reach a reasonable level of skill within the higher range appropriate to his/her specialism.

8.3   Consent and Failure to Warn

Unless a patient has consented to contact from a doctor, or such contact is carried out in an emergency, treatment involving physical contact will amount to a trespass to the person – an assault or a battery. All adults with capacity can give voluntary and informed consent. Different rules apply in relation to children and to those unable to understand the nature of the decisions to be made.[9] Once a patient is informed as to the nature of the procedure which is planned in broad terms, and consents to it, the consent is valid so far as to permit contact that would otherwise be a trespass to the person and no claim based on assault or battery can be made.

If a doctor fails to provide information about all possible serious risks, even though information is provided about the nature of the procedure in broad terms, the patient may have a remedy in a claim in negligence where that failure was a failure to act in accordance with the practice accepted as proper by a responsible body of such medical practitioners.[10]

---

8   *Sidaway v Board of Governors of the Bethlem Royal Hospital and Maudsley Hospital* [1985] 2 WLR 480 at 502B

9   We do not seek to address issues relating to children and others lacking capacity to give consent in this book

10   *Chatterton v Gerson* [1981] QB 432

Therefore, in relation to patients who are competent to give consent, claims rarely arise as to whether consent has been given. However, claims do arise as to whether the information given by the clinician in obtaining consent was appropriate.

A consent form will often list a number of known risks and complications of the procedure to be undertaken. Acknowledgment of the risks of the procedure by signing the consent form does not excuse any lack of care in the carrying out of the procedure, even where such lack of care results in the risk that has been acknowledged. Proper consent does not in any way limit the patient's right to competent treatment. Consent is a process for informing the patient of the risks that might occur despite competent treatment so that the patient may reach an informed judgement as to whether to agree to undergo the procedure.

8.3.1   Failure to Warn

A medical practitioner is under a duty to warn a patient in general terms of possible serious risks involved in any proposed course of treatment, although treatment performed without such information is not unlawful (and therefore is not a trespass to the person) where the nature of the procedure in broad terms is explained.[11] The court has described the test in these terms:

> *'If there is a significant risk[12] which would affect the judgement of a reasonable patient, then in the normal course it is the responsibility of a doctor to inform the patient of that significant risk, if the information is needed so that the patient can determine for him or herself as to what course he or she would adopt.'[13]*

The warning that should be given is one that is in accordance with the practice accepted as proper by a responsible body of medical men skilled in that particular field at that particular time (the Bolam Test). This standard is, however, subject to the court being satisfied that the exponents of the body of opinion relied upon can demonstrate, after weighing the comparative risks and benefits, that such opinion has a logical basis and that the opinion is responsible, reasonable or respectable (see the case of *Bolitho* in Section 8.6).

There are two situations in which a claim for negligence can be brought on the basis of a failure to obtain informed consent.

1. Where a patient is not informed of such a serious risk when being consented for an operation and in the course of the operation that risk manifests, the medical practitioner will be liable in damages where the patient can prove (on the balance of probabilities) that if properly warned, then he/she would not have agreed to undergo the treatment.

---

11 See *Chatterton v Gerson* (above)

12 In court judgments relating to consent, the words 'serious' and 'significant' have both been used to describe the risks that need to be acknowledged.

13 *Pearce v United Bristol Healthcare NHS Trust* [1999] PIQR P53

2.   Where the patient would have probably gone ahead with an operation, but once appropriately warned would not have proceeded on that occasion (even though the patient would probably have undergone the operation on a subsequent occasion), the medical practitioner will still be liable for damages if, on the balance of probabilities, on that subsequent occasion the complication of which the patient was not warned would not have occurred.[14]

In *Chester v Afshar* it was found that the surgeon had failed to warn the claimant of a small risk in the proposed spinal surgery. Expert opinion was that no matter how well the surgery was performed, there was a risk inherent in the surgery (1-2%) of developing cauda equina syndrome. The claimant agreed to the surgery, which was duly carried out, but unfortunately she did develop the syndrome. The judge found that the claimant, if properly warned, would have sought a second opinion and would not have undergone the surgery at that time. Had the operation taken place on a subsequent occasion, on the balance of probabilities the complication would not then have arisen, the risk being only 1-2%. The claimant was therefore entitled to recover damages for the consequences of the complication that in fact arose.

Since the injury she sustained was within the scope of the doctor's duty to warn and was the result of the risk of which she was entitled to be warned, the injury was to be regarded as having been caused by the defendant's breach of duty in not informing the patient to the appropriate standard. The court made no finding as to whether or not she would in those circumstances have undergone the surgery on another occasion (with precisely the same degree of risk of the unfortunate outcome on such an occasion).

In cases involving informed consent, the judge will have to resolve on the basis of the evidence presented, whether or not if properly warned the claimant would nonetheless have undergone the treatment at the time it in fact took place. The claimant with the benefit of hindsight may well say, and believe, that if warned of the risk he/she would not have undergone the operation at all or at that time.

Expert opinion may be able to assist the court in assessing the claimant's assertion that he/she would have delayed the operation by addressing the situation where a patient is appropriately warned and dealing with issues such as:

1.   what, on the basis of clinical experience, the expert considers a reasonable patient, properly warned, would have done; and

2.   what patients would be told about the implications of not undergoing the treatment.

---

14   *Chester v Afshar* [2005] 1 AC 134

8.4   Failure to Treat

Commonly, a clinical negligence claim is concerned with whether the positive actions of a doctor were appropriate. Where the matter complained of is an omission – a failure to treat - then expert evidence needs to address three issues:

1. did the failure to act fall below a reasonable standard of care? and if so

2. what would the likely treatment have been had there not been a failure to act? and

3. what would the ultimate outcome have been had the clinician acted in this way?

The first issue requires the medical expert to address the standard of care reasonably to be expected from the practitioner. Once again, the Bolam test needs to be applied: if a doctor of ordinary skill would also have behaved in the same way, then the claim will fail. However, if the failure to act does not meet the expected standard of care, then the second issue is what a doctor of ordinary skill would have done instead. Finally, the expert should consider what the likely outcome would then have been and whether there would have been a difference in the ultimate outcome (i.e. addressing causation).

It may be possible to answer the second question by establishing what a particular identified individual, who would have been the person to act, would probably have done. For example, if there was a failure on the part of nursing staff to call out a doctor, the doctor who would have been on call can give evidence as to what he/she would have done if the call had been made. If this question can only be answered hypothetically, because the person who should have acted cannot be identified or is not available, then the court will apply the Bolam test to the standard of care that would have been applied by a reasonably competent practitioner in the appropriate specialism and therefore assume that the clinician would have acted within the range of acceptable actions.[15] The probable outcome (and therefore causation) would then be assessed on this basis.

8.5   Conflicting Opinion on Factual Issues

Conflicting opinion evidence on factual issues is dealt with on a different basis to conflicting opinion evidence as to the standard of care. Where conflicts of opinion arise on factual issues, the judge is entitled to prefer for good reason, the expert opinion of one expert over that of another expert.

---

15   *Bolitho v City & Hackney Health Authority* [1998] AC 232

For example, an important factual dispute in a case may be:

- whether a claimant would or would not have been pyrexial at a particular examination by the doctor;
- whether an x-ray had it been performed at the time of initial contact with the patient would or would not have demonstrated the presence of a fracture; or
- whether a nerve damaged during the course of an operation was in an atypical anatomical position.

The judge is entitled, with the assistance of expert opinion, to take into account all of the available evidence and to come to a decision, on the balance of probabilities. The evidence that the judge considers most persuasive may be the opinion evidence of a particular expert, so rejecting that of another expert, but may also be the evidence of lay witnesses or information in documents adduced in evidence.

8.6   Conflicting Opinion on Standard of Care

The judge is required to compare the acts or omissions of the treating doctor with what would have happened if a reasonably competent doctor had been faced with similar circumstances. The judge has no relevant expertise as a clinician and in carrying out this comparison is dependent on the expert opinion of an expert similarly qualified to the practitioner being criticised.

When considering conflicting opinion evidence as to the appropriate standard of care, the judge cannot simply prefer the opinion of one competent expert over another. The judge can only reject one expert's opinion and accept an opposing expert's opinion if satisfied that one of the opinions is flawed.

Typical situations where a judge may find an expert's opinion to be flawed would include a finding that an expert lacked appropriate or relevant expertise or lacked credibility as a result of inconsistencies in the evidence or incompetence as an expert witness. However, where the judge is faced with two medical experts of similar expertise and of reasonable competence giving different opinions as to what would have been an acceptable standard of care, two questions arise:

1. can the claimant prove, on the balance of probabilities, that his/her case is more likely to be correct than the defendant's case? and

2. are there any circumstances in which a finding can be made by the court that established practice – a practice that is followed by reasonably competent practitioners as supported by one expert – is nonetheless negligent?

Unless the judge rejects outright the defendant expert's opinion, he/she cannot find for the claimant:

> 'A judge's "preference" for one body of distinguished professional opinion to another also professionally distinguished is not sufficient to establish negligence in a practitioner whose actions have received the seal of approval of those whose opinions, truthfully expressed, honestly held, were not preferred... For in the realm of diagnosis and treatment negligence is not established by preferring one respectable body of professional opinion to another. Failure to exercise the ordinary skill of a doctor (in the appropriate speciality, if he be a specialist) is necessary.'[16]

However, the judge is entitled to require that opinions have a logical basis:

> 'The court is not bound to hold that a defendant doctor escapes liability for negligent treatment or diagnosis just because he leads evidence from a number of medical experts who are genuinely of opinion that the defendant's treatment or diagnosis accorded with sound medical practice. In the Bolam case itself, the judge stated that the defendant had to have acted in accordance with the practice accepted as proper by a "responsible body of medical men." Later he referred to "a standard of practice recognised as proper by a competent reasonable body of opinion." Again, in Maynard's case Lord Scarman refers to a "respectable" body of professional opinion.
>
> The use of these adjectives — responsible, reasonable and respectable — all show that the court has to be satisfied that the exponents of the body of opinion relied upon can demonstrate that such opinion has a logical basis. In particular in cases involving, as they so often do, the weighing of risks against benefits, the judge before accepting a body of opinion as being responsible, reasonable or respectable, will need to be satisfied that, in forming their views, the experts have directed their minds to the question of comparative risks and benefits and have reached a defensible conclusion on the matter.'[17]

Therefore, a judge can reject the practice of respectable practitioners if he/she concludes that that practice does not properly weigh up comparative risks and benefits. This test, from the case of *Bolitho*, would appear to give a judge some freedom to find against one of two conflicting expert opinions as to the expected standard of care. However, it was also said in *Bolitho* that:

> 'If, in a rare case, it can be demonstrated that the professional opinion is not capable of withstanding logical analysis, the judge is entitled to hold that the body of opinion is not reasonable or responsible.

---

16   *Maynard v West Midlands HA* [1984] 1 WLR 634

17   Lord Browne-Wilkinson in *Bolitho v City and Hackney Health Authority* [1997] 3 WLR 1151 at 1158

I emphasise that in my view it will very seldom be right for a judge to reach the conclusion that views genuinely held by a competent medical expert are unreasonable. The assessment of medical risks and benefits is a matter of clinical judgement which a judge would not normally be able to make without expert evidence... it would be wrong to allow such assessment to deteriorate into seeking to persuade the judge to prefer one of two views both of which are capable of being logically supported. It is only where a judge can be satisfied that the body of expert opinion cannot be logically supported at all that such opinion will not provide the benchmark by reference to which the defendant's conduct falls to be assessed.' [18]

Therefore, it will be rare that a judge will find that the opinion of a competent medical expert as to the appropriate standard of care is unreasonable or not logically supported.

An example of this test being applied occurred in *Marriott v West Midlands Regional Health Authority*[19] where the trial judge concluded that if the defence expert's evidence did establish that there was a body of GPs who, on the patient presenting with drowsiness and a headache following a history of a head injury, would not have referred the patient to hospital, then such an approach was 'not reasonably prudent'.

8.7   Causation and 'Material Contribution'

Causation in clinical negligence claims is often extremely difficult to assess. Establishing what injury has resulted from a failure in the standard of treatment is often the main issue between the parties, rather than whether there has been a failure in the standard of care. Breach of duty may or may not have been admitted by the defendant, but the real battleground remains in relation to causation. Indeed, the claimant is likely to have fallen into the hands of medical practitioners because he/she was already ill or injured and was in need of medical attention. The outcome of such treatment may have been uncertain even in the absence of care that fell below an acceptable standard.

Damages are only recoverable for what can be proved, on the balance of probabilities, to be the difference between the outcome in the absence of a failure in the standard of care and the actual outcome. As we have seen in Chapter 6 above, a further difficulty is that the question to be resolved - and on which an expert opinion is to be expressed - is not one that generally arises in clinical practice. The medical practitioner does not regularly ask himself/herself "what would have been the outcome if I had done this instead of doing that, or if I had not done the other?" Research is not frequently directed at the outcome of substandard care, although research comparing different methods of treatment, particularly in different countries, may throw some light on the issue.

---

18   Lord Bridge in *Bolitho v City and Hackney Health Authority* [1997] 3 WLR 1151 at 1160
19   [1999] Lloyd's Rep Med 23

The medical expert, therefore, is once again in an area where the issue that he/she is required to address cannot be addressed directly from clinical practice, but can only be answered by an assessment or even an estimate based on medical expertise. That said, it is probably not too difficult for the expert to identify a likely range of answers or possible outcomes to the causation question: "what would have happened if …?" Once this range of answers or possible outcomes has been identified, it should then be possible for the expert to narrow down the range by reference to the particular facts of the case and their relative importance, and then provide an answer on causation, on the balance of probabilities.

When dealing with a range of opinion, it is necessary to keep in mind the requirements of PD35 3.2(6) and guidance in the Protocol at para 13.12-13[20], which requires the expert to summarise the range of opinion and to give reasons for the opinion the expert holds.

There may also be other possible causes of a claimant's condition, in addition to the negligence on the part of the treating clinicians. In Section 6.1.1, we considered the case of a premature baby who developed retrolental fibroplasia after being negligently exposed to excessive levels of oxygen. There were several 'innocent' or non-negligent explanations for the development of the condition. The claimant failed because he could not prove that on the balance of probabilities 'but for' the negligent cause the injury would not have been suffered, or in other words could not prove that it was the excess oxygen that more likely than not had caused the damage.[21]

---

20   See Section 4.2.12 above

21   *Wilsher v Essex Area Health Authority* [1988] AC 1074

The 'but for' test may be modified in clinical negligence claims in the unusual situation where there are cumulative causes of injury rather than different distinct causes of injury.

> A patient who developed pancreatitis following an ERCP procedure experienced a subsequent negligent lack of care and in her weakened state suffered a cardiac arrest and resulting brain damage. It was not possible to say that the cardiac arrest was caused by one or other of the 2 possible causes (that 'but for' the pancreatitis or the lack of care the cardiac arrest would not have occurred) but it was possible to say that each contributed to the weakness which resulted in the cardiac arrest. As the negligent lack of care had made a material contribution (a more than minimal contribution) to the events resulting in the cardiac arrest, the hospital was liable for all of the damages resulting from the patient's brain damage.[22]

The material contribution test has been applied in several recent claims arising out of clinical negligence.[23] The medical expert should be alert to the possibility of applying this alternative test of causation where there are cumulative causes to injury, but unless specifically instructed to report on this basis, should seek guidance from the instructing solicitor before doing so.

Conclusion

In clinical negligence cases the standard of care reasonably to be expected of the treating clinicians is often a difficult and complex issue to resolve. This difficulty may arise owing to disagreements as to the appropriate standard of care or from an incomplete or contradictory factual picture. However, the main battle ground in clinical negligence actions remains the issue of causation. Even where a breach of duty has been conceded by the defendants, there is often fundamental disagreement about the difference the breach of duty actually made to the outcome for the claimant. Issues of public policy, such as the right to be properly informed before giving consent for a procedure also arise in clinical negligence actions. Ultimately, however, it is medical practitioners themselves who provide the evidence upon which the court will assess the issue of clinical negligence.

---

22   *Bailey v MOD* [2009] 1 WLR 1062

23   *Telles v South West Strategic Health Authority* [2008] All ER (D) 389; *Bousted v North West Strategic Health Authority* [2008] EWHC 2375; *Canning-Kishver v Sandwell & West Birmingham Hospitals NHS Trust* [2008] EWHC 2384

Key-Point Summary

1. The principal legal tests used in clinical negligence are set out in the cases of *Bolam* and *Bolitho*.

2. The Bolam test focuses on a standard of practice that is acceptable to a 'reasonable', 'responsible' or 'respectable' body of professional opinion. The Bolitho test seeks to ensure that any such body of opinion is capable of withstanding logical analysis when considering the benefits and risks inherent in treatment decisions.

3. Patients have a right to make informed choices about medical treatment. A finding of negligence in failing to warn a patient of the possible serious risks of a procedure gives rise to a claim in damages if one of those risks manifests itself and the patient would not have undergone the procedure or would have put it off to another day.

4. A judge is able to decide facts in the face of conflicting professional opinion about those facts, on the balance of probabilities.

5. A judge may only choose to prefer one expert opinion on the appropriate standard of care over another where the judge finds one of the opinions to be flawed. It is not the judge's role to decide which of two reasonable medical practices is to be preferred.

6. The 'but for' test for causation may be modified where there are cumulative, rather than distinct, causes of injury which can be said to have materially contributed to the injury.

Developing Your Medico-Legal Mind (8)

1. What, if any, legal principles are different in a clinical negligence case when compared to a personal injury case?

2. What is the Bolam test and how should it be applied to opinion evidence in a medical expert report?

3. In what circumstances will the court apply anything other than the Bolam test in respect of standard of care?

4. What is the standard of care expected of a novice? And a specialist?

5. How does the court address the issue of whether a patient has given consent to a procedure? If the court makes a finding of a negligent failure to warn of a risk, what issue does the court then go on to consider?

6. What are the issues an expert needs to address when the case involves allegations of a failure to treat?

7. How is a difference of expert opinion on a relevant factual matter decided by the court?

8. How is a difference of opinion on the standard of care owed to a patient decided by the court?

9. How is a difference in expert opinion on causation decided by the court?

10. What are the tests of causation that an expert may be instructed to apply in a clinical negligence case?

Reporting in Clinical Negligence Claims

9.1   Clinical Negligence Marketplace
9.2   Purpose of Expert Reports in Clinical Negligence Cases
9.3   Areas of Potential difficulty in Clinical Negligence

Introduction

In clinical negligence actions, solicitors face a real challenge in identifying and instructing an expert with the appropriate expertise to report on the issues in dispute. In many cases, the solicitor has access to very few choices when instructing an expert, so often instruct experts based on recommendations from other experts or legal colleagues. At the time the instruction is made, it may not be clear to the solicitor which is the best speciality to instruct. This places a responsibility on an expert approached by a solicitor to say whether another speciality or indeed another practitioner within his/her own speciality would be a more suitable expert to instruct. The relationship between the lawyers and the experts in a clinical negligence case is likely to demand far higher levels of communication and engagement than a typical claim for personal injury.

Chapter Outline

In this chapter, we will briefly explore the clinical negligence marketplace and the role of the medical expert in clinical negligence claims. We will then discuss some of the difficult areas in clinical negligence claims that challenge the skills of both experts and lawyers involved in such claims.

9.1   Clinical Negligence Marketplace

An overview of the clinical negligence marketplace can be gleaned from National Health Service Litigation Authority (NHSLA) data. In 2009/10, the NHSLA, which manages claims on behalf of NHS trusts, received 6,652 clinical negligence claims, up from 6,088 in the previous year.[1] However, the number of claims was significantly below the number of adverse incidents reports made within the NHS. Research suggests that approximately 850,000 medical errors occur in NHS hospitals each year resulting in 40,000 deaths.[2] One study recorded that although 17·7% of 1,047 patients in the study experienced serious adverse events that led to longer hospital stays and increased costs to the patients, only 1·2% (13) of the 1,047 patients made claims for compensation.[3]

Claims take an average of 1½ years to be settled. Of the claims received by the NHSLA over the last 10 years, 40% were abandoned by the claimant, 43% were settled, 4% were concluded in court (including approval of settlements of claims on behalf of minors or patients and protected parties) and 13% were outstanding.[4] In 2009/10 the NHSLA paid out £650m in respect of clinical negligence claims against the NHS (in damages and legal costs) and £163m in legal costs in relation to claims concluded that year.[5]

---

1   www.nhsla.com/home.htm

2   Aylin, P et al 'How often are adverse events reported in English hospital statistics?' *BMJ* 2004:329;369

3   Andrews, L.B. et al. 'An alternative strategy for studying adverse events in medical care' *The Lancet*, 349, 9048 pp. 309 - 313

4   The NHS Litigation Authority (2010) *Factsheet 3: information on claims 2009/10*

5   The NHS Litigation Authority (2010) *Annual report and accounts 2009/10*

9.2   Purpose of Expert Reports in Clinical Negligence Cases

Providing medical expert reports in clinical negligence claims is often more challenging, and requires more detailed analysis and assessment than in a typical personal injury claim. Depending on the nature of the case, an expert may be instructed to address issues of:

- breach of duty (i.e. whether the treatment has been negligent);
- causation of injury/damage;
- condition and prognosis.

Such opinions are given in the context of what are often, at least for the non-medically trained lawyer, complicated medical and factual issues. The issues, normally dealt with in more than one report because they are disclosed to the other side at different stages in the claim[6], must be expressed in a manner that assists the lawyers in understanding the issues in the dispute.

The scope of the instructions given to a particular expert will depend upon the nature of the case and the issues that are likely to arise. Sometimes, issues of breach of duty and causation will be dealt with by the same expert, while on other occasions different experts will need to address the different aspects of the claim.

For example, if the criticism is of a hip replacement operation, then it is likely that an orthopaedic surgeon would be able to deal with breach of duty and causation of injury, and (in a separate report) with condition and prognosis. However, a case may require experts to be instructed in several specialities so as to deal effectively with all of the legal issues. Where the events in an A & E department are under scrutiny, it may require an A & E consultant to address the standard of care reasonably to be expected in the first instance, with another expert in a different speciality to deal with the causation issues relating to the outcome of the treatment and to address whether the outcome would have been any different had the actions in A & E been different.

The distinction between the different aspects of a claim for clinical negligence that medical experts have to address can be seen in the example below. This is the conclusion to a report addressing breach of duty and causation, as well as (and a little unusually) the claimant's condition and prognosis.

---

6   A report on condition and prognosis must be served with proceedings [PD16(4.2)] while the reports on breach of duty and causation will normally be exchanged in accordance with directions of the court at a later stage

Conclusions

In failing to identify the extent of Mrs Z's perineal injury after the birth of her first child – that she had a fourth degree perineal tear - the standard of care shown fell below that reasonably to be expected in a reasonably competent maternity department at the material time. [**Breach of duty**]

Had the extent of the perineal injury been correctly identified, then Mrs Z would have undergone repair in an operating theatre under regional anaesthesia by an experienced practitioner. With correct and immediate repair, it is more likely than not that Mrs Z would have avoided the subsequent surgery she underwent, the de-functioning colostomy and the secondary perineal repair. She would have been continent of faeces and would have had normal bowel function. With correct classification and repair of the perineal injury Mrs Z would have been able to undergo further spontaneous vaginal deliveries. [**Causation of injury and damage**]

As the result of the failure in the standard of care, Mrs Z underwent the further treatment and is left with significant continuing and permanent symptoms and has been correctly advised that if she does become pregnant again she would be well advised to deliver by caesarean section. As a result of these events she has expressed great reluctance to consider a further pregnancy, which is a reasonable response given the effects and consequences arising from the original failure to diagnose and treat appropriately. [**Condition and prognosis**]

9.3 Areas of Potential Difficulty in Clinical Negligence

We identify 5 areas of potential difficulty in reporting that have the potential to make producing reports in clinical negligence claims more demanding on the medical expert:

1. dealing with issues of hindsight or outcome bias and focus bias;

2. identifying within the factual basis of the claim whether the key issue is a factual dispute or a dispute about the standard of care;

3. reporting on factual disputes;

4. assessing a series of treatment events over an extended time period; and

5. dealing with complex medical issues.

We address each of these issues in the sections below.

9.3.1 Hindsight and Focus Bias

In assessing and giving opinion on the standard of care shown by other practitioners in treating a patient, the expert must place him/herself so far as is possible in the position of the clinician whose actions or inaction at the time are being criticised.

Maintaining Objectivity

A fundamental issue in clinical negligence claims is to identify an expert who is able to report objectively on the issues in dispute. Consciously or unconsciously, a medical expert may have sympathy for the plight of the claimant or for the clinicians who are the focus of the claim. The expert may be concerned that the claimant should have the funds to be able to receive the care and treatment now required to live a bearable life or conversely that the NHS should not have to use its finances in dealing with such claims rather than in treating patients.

Perhaps an error may have been made in the course of difficult life-saving surgery, where on one view the claimant should be grateful still to be alive at all, but on another view the outcome should have been markedly more beneficial to the claimant. The expert may disapprove of the approach or practice of the clinician and those who still follow it or may have great respect for the hospital or department (or head of department) at which the adverse event occurred. There are many opportunities for the medical expert in a clinical negligence claim to lose an objective mindset when approaching the evidence

Hindsight or Outcome Bias

The expert is always reporting retrospectively on medical treatment. This creates a difficulty in that the expert needs to see the situation as the treating clinician would - or would have been expected to have seen it - at the material time. The expert has to remove from his/her assessment of the evidence the outcome of the actions, which are now known but were not known at the time. The so called 'retrospectoscope' has long been recognised to give a distorted view of the past when applied to the actions of people at the time.

'Hindsight' or 'outcome' bias has been demonstrated to have a significant effect on the objectivity of doctors. Studies have shown that knowledge of an adverse outcome in a case affects the opinions given by medical experts as to the appropriateness of clinical treatment.[7] Having knowledge of a poor outcome may, for example, cause an expert to minimise the management dilemmas facing the doctor at the time and to overlook the uncertainties inherent in diagnosis and treatment.[8] The expert must also avoid the potential pitfalls of reviewing with the present state of

---

7   Hugh, T.B. and Tracy, G.D., 'Hindsight bias in medico-legal expert reports' *MedJ* Aug 2002: 176(6)

8   Cook R.I., Woods D.D. (1994) 'Operating at the sharp end: the complexity of human error', in Bognor M.S. (ed) *Human Error in Medicine*. Hillsdale, NJ: Lawrence Erlbaum Associates, pp. 255-310

knowledge treatment from the past - perhaps from just a few years ago - when practice, knowledge or protocols may have been different.

In the vast majority of cases, it is impractical for the instructing lawyers to attempt to withhold information as to outcome of treatment from the expert. Further, it is impossible to ask an expert for an opinion on past clinical practice in a manner that does not influence, in some way, the expert's perception of the facts he/she must address. Simply asking for an opinion already indicates the need to take a position in a possible dispute, the outcome of which is likely to have considerable importance for the parties involved.

Focus Bias

There may also be difficulties in maintaining appropriate objectivity when reviewing the actions of a clinician following a particular practice that the expert does not favour, but cannot say is (or was at the material time) inappropriate. An expert may have been following a particular practice for many years and indeed may have justified reservations about alternative approaches. An expert may also have had lengthy discussions with other colleagues about the merits of the approach he/she prefers. All of these circumstances mean that the expert has potentially become focussed on a particular way of thinking about issues in relation to this practice. An instruction to give evidence on a claim relating to the alternative approach can become an opportunity for the expert to present, knowingly or unknowingly, an assessment of the evidence that is focussed on the unsound nature of that alternative approach.

Returning to the case concerning the laparoscopic repair, consider the following opinion:

> A reasonable body of surgical opinion would hold that a patient who presents with a single uncomplicated and almost symptom-free hernia, who had had repeated previous abdominal surgery and a history of bowel obstruction, was at a high risk of adhesions and therefore should be offered an open rather than a laparoscopic repair. It follows that the preferred technique in this patient would have been the open and not the laparoscopic approach. It follows that the decision was irrational and not in the patient's best interest.

Drafting such as this creates the opportunity of a challenge to the witness's objectivity. First, the expert has addressed the standard of care incorrectly. By stating what a reasonable body might do, rather than addressing what no reasonable body would do, the expert leaves open the question as to whether this practice actually fell below a reasonable standard of care. Therefore, the opinion that the decision of the surgeon was wrong is not supported by the opinion evidence of the expert as to the appropriate standard of care.

Secondly, the use of the phrases 'irrational' and 'not in the patient's best interest' give the impression of a less than measured - and so less than fully objective - approach to the issue. This is especially so when the treating clinicians' witness statements, which could contain further explanations of the background to the clinical decisions made, may not have been seen by the expert.

Approach to the Evidence

All of these factors, whether conscious or unconscious, which may potentially and adversely affect the validity of the assessment being made of the standard of care, must be recognised by the expert and put aside. This can only happen through self-reflection and the willingness to explore other legitimate points of view.

If a truly valid and objective opinion as to the standard of care and the effects of any failure of standard of care is to be provided, the expert must carefully consider the evidence, following step-by-step the events as they unfolded, and must consider the situation that the clinician(s) faced, having successfully excluded any hindsight, outcome or focus bias. The expert must assess the treatment decisions made against a reasonable standard of care rather than a standard consistent with the expert's own preferred approach and level of expertise.

9.3.2   Establishing the Factual Basis of the Claim

It is not possible for a medical expert to express an opinion on the appropriate standard of care until the facts material to the opinion have been identified. It may not be apparent to the lawyer, with no or limited knowledge or understanding of the medical issues involved, which of the facts are material to the dispute. Without an explanation from the expert of what the material facts are (and in more complicated cases, why these are material), the lawyer may be unable to understand the basis upon which the expert expresses the opinion he/she does and will be unable to assess the strength of the case or the strength of the opposing side's case. The lawyer will also be handicapped in the exercise of seeking to clarify or strengthen the case or to attack the opposing side's case by seeking, for example, further evidence or documentation.

Where the material facts are uncertain or cannot be ascertained from the material before the expert, it is essential that the medical expert makes this clear and where possible indicates the possible means of clarifying or ascertaining the facts. This may involve the expert indicating to the lawyers that there appear to be missing medical records, test results, x-rays or scans and providing sufficient information to enable the lawyer to make proper enquiries as to their whereabouts. Further, it may be important to know whether the hospital concerned used a particular protocol or the expert may need to ask the lawyers to obtain fresh photocopies of medical records that have been badly copied. Sometimes, the medical expert may indicate particular questions that need to be asked of the claimant or a witness or potential witness.

Often, a very large number of medical records are provided to the expert. Frequently these appear to have been jumbled up and placed out of chronological or any other form of order, whether by the health care provider, the person with the task of photocopying the notes or someone else in preparing the claim. Normally, only very few pages are at the heart of the investigation and relevant to the key issue that the expert is seeking to address. The clarity of the report and the ease with which the lawyers are able to understand and engage with the key issues will often be assisted by the expert producing a 'mini-bundle' (or 'core bundle') consisting of just those key pages in the records. These can be attached to the report or provided with it. This mini-bundle can then form the key reference document for the instructing lawyers, in conference with the barrister or at a joint discussion with an opposing expert and at trial. It will also make a subsequent consideration of the case by the expert much easier and will save an immense amount of time (and therefore costs) for all involved thereafter.

9.3.3   Factual Disputes in the Evidence

It is common in clinical negligence claims to find conflicts in the evidence between what the treating clinicians recall that they saw, heard or said and what the claimant and his/her family or friends recall that they saw, heard or said. The factual disputes may, for example, be as to:

- what a doctor said about the risks of the procedure or treatment, or about returning for further treatment or advice;
- what a claimant told a doctor about symptoms or about the timing of symptoms;
- what a doctor observed about how distressed or alert a patient was at a material time; or
- whether a doctor gave particular instructions or whether those instructions were actually carried out.

By this stage, you will be familiar with the medical expert's duty in dealing with conflicts in factual evidence[9]:

Protocol   13.11   Where there are material facts in dispute experts should express separate opinions on each hypothesis put forward. They should not express a view in favour of one or other disputed version of the facts unless, as a result of particular expertise and experience, they consider one set of facts as being improbable or less probable, in which case they may express that view, and should give reasons for holding it.

---

9   See Section 4.2.7 above

Therefore, on each occasion where there is more than one possible factual scenario, the expert should consider:

- whether it is appropriate, based on his/her expertise, to express an opinion as to which set of facts is more probable; and
- what his/her opinion would be, based on each of the factual scenarios in turn.

The expert needs to be very confident of his/her opinion before expressing an opinion on only one of two (or more) competing factual scenarios. In the following example, the expert expresses an opinion on the basis of each of two factual scenarios:

> If the mother's statement about Y's drowsiness is accepted by the court, then I am of the opinion that all reasonably competent paediatricians would have administered Acyclovir to Y soon after her admission to hospital, because with the preceding history there was a significant chance that she had Herpes Simplex Encephalitis. If, however, the court accepts, in keeping with the contemporaneous medical records, that Y was not as drowsy as her mother describes, then I am of the opinion that it would have been reasonable for the clinicians to have diagnosed a self-limiting viral illness and to wait and see how the situation developed before deciding on treatment.

Many clinical negligence claims are in reality disputes about the factual situation at a particular time, rather than being disputes about the appropriate standard of care. Such factual disputes can only be resolved by reference to expert opinion, owing to the technical nature of the dispute. Where, for example, something went wrong in the course of an operation, the essential issue may be a factual issue as to the action by the surgeon that precipitated the operation 'going wrong' rather than any question of the surgeon's standard of operative skill and whether or not it was below the appropriate standard.

This distinction can be illustrated by *Swift v Bexley & Greenwich Health Authority*[10], in which the claimant was blinded in the course of an operation to clip an aneurysm in the brain. The issue was initially approached as being one of whether the operation was carried out negligently, that is, whether the neurosurgeon exercised the skill of a reasonably competent neurosurgeon. However, the experts in the case agreed that the blindness was caused either by a clip damaging the optic nerve or by an ischaemic effect causing catastrophic loss of blood to the optic nerve. If the clip had damaged the optic nerve, then there would have been a failure to exercise the ordinary skill of a neurosurgeon because the clip would not have been placed on the optic nerve had an appropriate level of skill been shown. If the blindness was caused by the ischaemic effect, this was an unavoidable side effect of the operation and not caused by an inadequate level of skill in performing the operation.

---

10   High Court 25th May 2000 (Lawtel 19/12/2001)

The judge was able to prefer the claimant's expert opinion on this point over that of the defendant's expert, as he was entitled to do when faced with conflicting opinions on a factual issue.[11] The judge found that it was the clip being placed on the optic nerve that caused the damage and therefore, as both experts agreed that this action would fall below an acceptable standard of care, the surgeon was found to be in breach of duty.

It is therefore essential for the medical expert to identify whether the principal issue in the case is one of fact, which (as we saw in the last chapter) the judge will resolve on the balance of probabilities or an issue of the standard of care, to which the judge must apply the Bolam test.

Approach to the Evidence

It is essential to accurately establish the facts before going on to consider issues relating to standard of care or causation of damage. The role of the expert is, therefore, first to establish the relevant facts in relation to the dispute and to identify any points at which the factual basis is unclear or disputed. Where the factual basis is clear, the expert can then go on to consider the appropriate standard of care to which those facts give rise and the consequences of any failure in the standard of care.

Where the factual basis is unclear the expert must consider how that lack of factual clarity may be overcome (perhaps by obtaining further documents, further evidence or clarification of factual matters that are presently unclear). Where the factual basis remains unclear, the expert may be able to express an opinion, based on expertise, as to the more likely factual basis. However, if after further inquiry, it does not appear that any greater clarity can be obtained then the expert should go on to consider the standard of care and/or causation on such alternative bases as the facts reasonably give rise to.

9.3.4   Series of Events

A particularly difficult opinion to express clearly is one where there are several medical events in the history (be these acts or omissions by medical staff) that may or may not have made a difference to the ultimate outcome. Such cases require the expert to project what the likely effect of each particular act or omission would have been. Rather than being concerned with a single incident, many clinical negligence claims deal with a failure on the part of a number of clinicians to diagnose a condition or to treat appropriately over a period of time. Such claims may involve a multi-disciplinary or departmental failure, such as against several GPs and successive hospital departments in relation to a failure to diagnose a possible life-threatening condition.

In all such cases, it will almost certainly be necessary to address the situation at a number of different stages in order to express an opinion on the standard of care to be

---

11   See Section 8.5 above

expected (to address the duty that was owed) and on the consequences arising from any treatment that fell below the standard reasonably to be expected (to address causation). At each significant stage of the history, the expert has to identify:

- what happened;
- what was a reasonable standard of care in the circumstances;
- whether or not the treatment given attained this reasonable standard of care (with reasons for the opinion);
- whether any failure in appropriate treatment caused any injury, damage or loss to the claimant; and
- whether any such failure actually made a difference to the outcome.

For example, if an expert criticises a junior doctor for failing to call a more senior colleague to examine a patient, then the expert also has to consider whether the more senior colleague would have acted differently to the junior doctor; if so, whether these actions would have made a difference to the ultimate outcome; and if so, what difference these actions would have made. The expert will then need to address the next stage of the history and follow the same assessment process.

Standard of Care in Multi-Event Clinical Negligence Claims

The following example illustrates an expert's opinion when addressing the standard of care through a series of events and addressing both individual and departmental failures:

Standard of Care

The abnormality on the x-ray, the opacity on the left lung, was of such size and prominence that the failure to identify it by staff in the A&E Department fell below the standard reasonably to be expected of competent A&E clinicians. Once the abnormality was identified, no reasonably competent A&E clinicians would have failed to have considered that it indicated that urgent action was needed.

Had the abnormality been identified, a reasonably competent A&E Department would have contacted the on call medical team and handed Ms T's care over to them. Had Ms T been assessed by the on call medical team then it is probable that she would have been admitted into hospital over the course of the next few days and undergone further appropriate investigations. These investigations would have established, typically within a week of undergoing the investigations, that she had carcinoma of the bronchus. She would then have been transferred to the chest physicians/surgeons who would have decided whether or not it was possible to undertake a surgical procedure.

It commonly takes a day or two for x-ray films taken in an A&E Department to be reviewed and an official report issued. In this case, it took

13 days for the x-ray to be reviewed. This delay amounted to a failure of the A&E Department to act in accordance with a practice that would be acceptable to a responsible body of A&E clinicians.

Having received a 'positive' x-ray report, the A&E Department made no attempt to contact Ms T for 4 weeks. This delay amounted to a failure to act in accordance with a practice that would be acceptable to a responsible body of A&E physicians. When the A&E Department tried to make contact, having failed to get through to Ms T on the phone, they left a single message on her voicemail. This was by now a very serious situation. The failure to take any further measures to attempt to contact Ms T, for example by contacting her GP or her parents whose details were on record, again amounted to a failure of the A&E Department to act in accordance with a practice that would be acceptable to a responsible body of A&E clinicians.

Causation in Multi-Event Clinical Negligence Claims

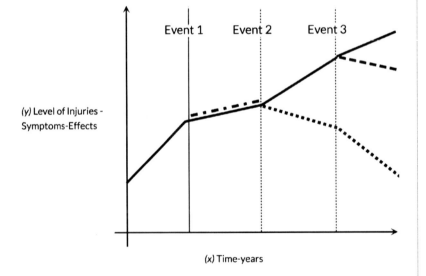

CAUSATION GRAPH #7: Multi-Event Clinical Negligence

Event 1   Event 2   Event 3

(y) Level of Injuries - Symptoms-Effects

(x) Time-years

When dealing with causation in multi-event clinical negligence claims, the expert should follow the same basic approach used when reporting on multiple accident claims.

The facts represented by Causation Graph #7 show that there were three events in the treatment timeline where clinical negligence is alleged by the claimant.

Let us assume that the expert's opinion is that in all three instances the treatment decision made did not meet the Bolam test (i.e. on each occasion the clinicians acted in breach of their duty of care). The expert would then consider what difference each of the treatment decisions made. Here, the first event made no significant difference to the likely progression of the claimant's condition (compare to the dot-dashed line) even had the treatment been of the appropriate standard. The second treatment decision did affect the outcome markedly (compare to the dotted line) and the third decision at a much later stage also affected the outcome, but would have provided a less beneficial outcome than the earlier appropriate treatment decision (compare the dotted and the dashed line).

The expert should provide opinion on all three events, even though he/she may consider that the second event fell below the standard of care to be expected and caused damage. It is for the court to decide whether it accepts the expert's opinion evidence in the light of all the evidence before the court. This could mean that the expert's opinion on the second event is rejected by the court, but his/her opinion on the third event is accepted.

Factual situations can be further complicated by the need for experts in different disciplines to address causation based upon different treatment scenarios. Consider a case where on three occasions over a seven-day period a GP decides not to refer an increasingly lethargic child Y to hospital. When the child is admitted to hospital on day 7, she is found to have an acute viral infection from which with appropriate treatment she makes only a poor recovery. In this case, a GP expert would need to address the issue of breach of duty – the standard of care to be expected of a reasonably competent GP faced with a child exhibiting these symptoms and whether the child should have been referred to hospital sooner. The issue of causation would require that a paediatrician be instructed to address the question: without the delay in referral, what would the likely outcome have been for a child with that viral infection?

The GP expert giving an opinion in this case would need to consider whether it was reasonable on day 1, day 4 and day 5 for the GP in question not to have referred Y to hospital. If the GP expert decides that on any one of these days the answer to this question is 'no' and that the child should have been referred, then the expert gives that opinion and moves on to consider the next date. The GP expert would also need to consider on each occasion what the situation would have been had the hospital discharged the care of Y back to the GP without treatment because no infection had been identified.

A paediatrician would then need to address what would have been the likely situation had Y been referred on any of the dates when the GP would reasonably have been expected to refer the child, dealing with what symptoms Y would likely to have been suffering and the likely treatment that would have been offered and the probable outcome for the child.

We now find ourselves facing the factual situation represented in Causation Graph #7 above. Once the paediatric opinion is that Y would have been started on anti-viral medication as a precaution and that the viral infection would subsequently have been identified, the later failures to refer are only relevant to the extent that another paediatric expert disagrees with the first paediatric expert's opinion. The paediatric expert would therefore address what would the situation for Y have been without the failure to refer and contrast this with the situation as it is now following the referral on day 7. This comparison will be expressed as the difference in terms of the injury, symptoms, effects and consequences that Y now has over what she would have been likely to have had if an earlier referral had been made.

An essential approach to writing well-structured opinion in such cases is to set a clear agenda for each of the possible scenarios that the expert will address:

> In this section, I will give opinion, on the balance of probabilities, as to whether each of the decisions made by the GP not to refer the claimant to hospital was in accordance with medical practice that would be accepted as proper by a responsible body of GPs.
>
> Where I consider that the GP should have referred the child, I will also consider what the position would have been had the hospital failed to diagnose the child's condition and discharged her back into the care of the GP.

9.3.5 Complex Medical Issues

The expert report is the point of communication between the medical and legal experts (both the parties' lawyers and the judge). The report must be capable of being understood as a free-standing document regardless of the complexity of the medical issues it addresses. The expert report does not serve its purpose if it cannot be understood by the non-medically qualified reader, or the first-time reader, with little background knowledge of the case. If the medical issues are not fully understood, then the parties' lawyers cannot prepare the case and assess its prospects and certainly cannot prepare cross-examination of the opposing expert. Similarly, a judge cannot come to a reasoned and logical judgment.

The report must therefore explain the medical issues sufficiently for a non-medically qualified reader to have an understanding of the essential issues in the case. In this respect, the Introduction section to the report is very important. By succinctly setting the scene and identifying the key issues to be addressed, the task of the lawyers seeking to understand the evidence can be made a great deal more straightforward. It is difficult to write a clear introduction until the analysis of the evidence is complete and the key issues in the evidence have been identified. These key issues can also form an agenda for the opinions and conclusions that will follow later in the report.

Approach to the Evidence

It is often extremely helpful to include a subsection offering an overview of the case and the medical context at an early stage of the report. This introduces and where necessary explains the factual and the technical matters that will be addressed in the report. In some clinical negligence cases, the medical issues may be of such complexity that it is more appropriate to provide an appendix to explain the medical context, with a cross-reference to this appendix in the Introduction section of the report.

Case Overview

In March 2007, Y, aged 3 years old, developed an infection. She was seen by her GP on five occasions over the following 7 days, before being found by her mother stiff and unresponsive. She was admitted to Anywhere General Hospital. Tests were carried out in hospital, but the nature of the infection was not identified. Two days later, she was transferred to Somewhere Specialist Hospital where a diagnosis of Herpes Simplex Encephalitis (HSE) was made and treatment commenced. Two years on from the treatment, Y has been assessed as having neurological damage and developmental problems. A clinical negligence claim has been brought against the GP and the Anywhere General Hospital NHS Trust.

Medical Overview

HSE is an acute viral condition. Typically, it produces symptoms of fever, headache and increasing mental confusion but early symptoms and signs may be non-specific. If undiagnosed and untreated the mortality rate is over 70% and many survivors have serious disabilities. Antiviral therapy should be initiated promptly when the diagnosis is suspected and Acyclovir is the preferred therapy. Early antiviral treatment improves the prognosis of patients but even with such therapy just over half of children will have a degree of cognitive impairment. After appropriate treatment, many patients will be left with significant neuro-psychological and neuro-behavioural disorders.

This simple approach can alert the lawyers and the judge reading the report to the important factual and opinion matters that need to be assessed, making the report easier to understand and use. How far it is necessary to go in providing 'bite-size' explanations of the medical issues should be discussed with the instructing lawyers, though the lawyers themselves may initially need such explanations in order to assess what is necessary to prepare for the court.

Below, there is a further example of a technical summary that would be useful to most lawyers:

The traditional 'open' approach to hernia repair necessitates a 10cm incision in the groin, removal of the hernia sac and repair of the posterior wall of the inguinal canal under direct vision. Laparoscopic repair is done from within the abdomen: under general anaesthesia, the abdomen is inflated with carbon dioxide and a 1cm diameter 'port' is introduced in the midline, through which a telescope is inserted. Two smaller ports allow the placement of long dissecting and cutting instruments. The internal orifices of the inguinal hernia or hernias can be visualised and a patch of woven plastic is stapled to the inner abdominal wall to cover all the defects, with care being needed to avoid damaging the adjacent blood vessels, vas deferens and spermatic cord.

A high-quality photograph or diagram (placed in an appendix and cross-referenced in the text) may be extremely useful in helping the lawyers and the court to understand technical issues and also limit the need to provide extended descriptions in the report.

Conclusion

In contrast to most personal injury claims, in clinical negligence the issue of breach of duty is an essential element for the appropriate medical expert to address. The law of negligence is straightforward, but its application to the facts of a particular case involves a careful and objective analysis of the actions of the clinicians involved. The phenomena of hindsight and focus bias make the task of the medical expert extremely challenging. The inherent complexity of dealing with causation in claimants who may already be ill at the time of the claimed negligent treatment only adds to the challenge. The approach of the expert has to be characterised by objectivity, precision and accuracy.

Key-Point Summary

1. One or more experts may be instructed to deal with the issues in a clinical negligence claim: breach of duty, causation of injury or damage, and condition and prognosis.

2. Hindsight and focus bias are important issues when assessing the evidence relating to clinical negligence cases. It is essential that the expert assesses the facts in a logical way, paying close attention to the knowledge that was available to the clinicians at the time of the claimed negligence.

3. Many clinical negligence cases turn on the court's decision in respect of factual issues on which experts disagree.

4.   Where the claimed negligence includes a series of events, the expert must establish the facts at each stage and consider issues of breach of duty and causation, before moving on in the timeline to the next relevant event.

5.   In many cases, the battleground is not the standard of care but causation.

6.   Clinical negligence reports must contain sufficient explanation of the technical medical issues to enable the lawyers to clearly understand the claim.

Next Steps

In the next chapter, we will explore writing skills needed to produce high-quality medical expert reports.

Developing Your Medico-Legal Mind (9)

Consider the following clinical negligence scenario concerning Y, first from the perspective of the clinical records and then taking into account her mother's witness statement.

History

Y was 3 years old in May 2007 when she became unwell. A brief summary of the matter appears from the handwritten medical records:

On 12 May 07, her mother took Y to the GP, Dr M. The GP record notes:

> Cough URTI. Unwell.
> O/E chest crackles L lower zone
> Good A/E elsewhere
> Rx Amoxycillin 250 g   TDS 1/52

On 19 May 07, the GP record notes:

> Saw Dr Standin yesterday and started on Zithromax.
> Still lethargic.
> O/E alert and moving head normally - knees bent.
> Chest clear.
> Plan 1. CXR 2. finish course of abs

On 21 May 07, the GP record notes a home visit in the evening:

> Seen to be having a tantrum
> No rash

On 22 May 07, Y's mother was still very concerned and phoned the surgery for a home visit. The GP record notes:

> Reported still lethargic but fully alert.
> Advised may be brewing up something.
> Mother to report back and will visit as necessary

On 24 May 07, mother found Y apparently unconscious and phoned the GP, who advised her to call an ambulance. The ambulance arrived and Y, accompanied by her mother, was taken to Freetown General Hospital. The hospital record notes:

> 10.30 am Cough/URTI 2/52.
> Seen by GP and given antibiotics, which were subsequently changed, but no better.
> Sent for CXR 5/7 ago.
> Drowsy from about 5th day of illness and vomited twice.
> This a.m. found ?unconscious

The hospital carried out various tests, including a lumbar puncture. Results were reported normal except that the CSF was slightly blood stained and an elevated CSF white cell count was noted. She was pyrexial. During the evening Y had several fits. She was started on anticonvulsants. At about midnight Freetown Regional Hospital for Sick Children was rung. The emergency team were sent out subsequently and Y arrived at FRHSC at about 10 am on 25 May 07.

Herpes simplex encephalitis (HSE) was suspected and she was immediately started on Acyclovir, to which she appeared to respond. However, she had grand mal convulsions. An EEG and MRI scan showed characteristic abnormalities in the temporal region. The diagnosis of HSE was confirmed. Y was returned back to Freetown General Hospital on 28 May 07, and eventually home.

Y has suffered long term neurological damage with severe learning difficulties, epilepsy and behavioural problems.

Background to HSE:

- Lethargy and fever are features of HSE
- Spinal fluid can be normal in HSE
- Acyclovir is an antiviral drug that has very low toxicity - it is the treatment of choice for HSE and should be started as early as possible.

Consider the following questions:

1. In relation to the involvement of the GPs:

   (i) Is there any basis for a claim in negligence against one or other of the GPs?

   (ii) If so, at what stage and on what basis?

   (iii) What was the consequence of any such negligence?

2. In relation to the involvement of the Freetown General Hospital:

   (i) Is there any basis for a claim in negligence against the hospital?

   (ii) If so, at what stage and on what basis?

   (iii) What was the consequence of that negligence?

Y's mother's account from her witness statement is as follows:

1. Y is the youngest of my 3 children. On 12 May 07, I took Y to Dr M because she had been coughing for weeks and it had been particularly nasty for a number of days and she seemed really unwell. He gave her some penicillin.

2.   On 18 May 07, I rang the GP's surgery because Y did not seem to be improving and spoke to a doctor who said he would put out a prescription for collection.

3.   On 19th May 07, I was still worried about Y, who had not improved and who had a temperature. My sister, who lives next door, was worried about Y too and encouraged me to ring the surgery.

4.   Dr M visited after the morning surgery. Y was very sleepy and hardly appeared to notice the presence of Dr M. Dr M was very reassuring and told me to take Y up to the hospital for an X-ray, which I did with the help of my sister. I had to carry Y all of the time, which was unusual for Y, who normally ran everywhere and was normally quite a handful.

5.   I did not see the GP again until the home visit on the evening of 22 May 07, which was the result of my ringing the surgery and insisting that someone came to see Y. Y could hardly be persuaded to have a drink, wouldn't play and was asleep most of the time. My sister was with me when the stand-in doctor called round. He was wearing a dinner jacket and he hardly looked at Y and was only in the house for about 3 minutes.

6.   On 24 May 07, I overslept and when I went into Y's room, Y looked dead – she was cold and was lying in wet bedding. I just panicked. I rang the GP and was told to dial 999.

7.   I am very worried now about Y (now nearly 6 years old) who speaks little, refuses to toilet train, and is very difficult.

Consider the following questions in relation to the case:

1.   What difference does the mother's statement make to the way in which the court will address the issue of the standard of care of the GPs?

2.   How should the expert deal with the factual disputes raised by the mother's statement?

3.   How should the expert now address causation of damage/injury/loss?

10

Writing the Report

10.1   Presentation of the Report
10.2   Expert Report Structures
10.3   Writing Skills
10.4   Writing Opinion

Introduction

High-quality expert reports help lawyers to make better quality decisions about whether to settle or to pursue a claim to court. The settlement of a claim will also be heavily influenced by expert evidence, so the quality of the expert report is fundamental to achieving settlements (and court decisions) that accurately reflect the realities of the claim. High-quality expert reports are also essential to the parties should a case come to trial as judges place great weight upon these reports when deciding cases.

An uncontested medical expert report is often the only expert evidence in a case.[1] As such, it is profoundly important that the expert report deals with all issues relevant to the claim and is written to an appropriate standard of accuracy and precision. Whenever the lawyers handling a claim or a judge at trial cannot clearly understand an expert report, then it will not have served its purpose in the litigation process.

The writing skills set out in this chapter are applicable to all medical expert reports. It is a good investment for experts to spend whatever time is necessary to improve the quality of their reports, as this is an excellent way to build a good reputation amongst instructing solicitors.

---

1   See Section 3.3.2 above and the Pre-Action Protocol for Personal Injury Claims

Chapter Outline

We will give guidance on how the report should be presented and then examine the required structure for an expert report as indicated by the CPR and offer guidance on developing expert report templates. We will also explore some of the practical writing skills that are essential in producing high-quality evidence.

10.1 Presentation of the Report

Producing a well-presented expert report is extremely important. The lawyer's first impression of the report will be the initial frame through which the report is read and the primary aim of the expert should be to produce a report that is easy to read, assimilate and use.

We offer basic guidance below for the presentation of an expert report, although beyond the requirement in the CPR that expert evidence be presented in a report format, there are no formal requirements in respect of report presentation.

We suggest that an expert report has the following elements included in its layout:

1. wide-margins (min 3cm);

2. appropriate font size (11-13pt) depending on the font selected;

3. double-spaced text (1.5 line spacing is acceptable);

4. numbered paragraphs and pages;

5. consistent presentation of section, main and sub-headings;

6. numbered lists (rather than bullet points);

7. appropriate page-header (claimant's name/case reference number/type of report/author/date); and

8. the text is printed single-sided.

Each element of the layout increases the ease with which lawyers can use the report: wide margins mean that when the report is bound, the paragraph numbers are still visible and that there is space for the lawyer's notes; an appropriate font and size such as 'Times New Roman' 12pt is easy to read; double-spacing allows underlining and notes to be made on the text; numbered paragraphs make discussion of (and reference to) the report easier, as does the practice of numbering lists; page headers deal with the problem of pages that become detached from the report, while single-sided text allows extensive notes to be made on the facing blank page of the report and also avoids a myriad of photocopying problems.

10.2   Expert Report Structures

The required form and content of an expert report is set out in CPR 35, PD35 and the Protocol. Experts should familiarise themselves with each of these documents before writing their first (or next!) expert report. The approach indicated by the CPR is consistent with the reporting principles that underlie scientific reports, requiring the author to specify:

1.   clear report objectives;

2.   a defined methodology;

3.   factual accuracy; and

4.   logical and supported conclusions.

10.2.1   Linear Report Structure

In Chapter 4, we discussed in some detail the guidance in respect of the form and content of an expert report, which is set out in PD35 (3.1-3.3). Let us now consider how to produce a high-quality report that embodies these requirements.

The basic elements of an expert report are:

1.   an introduction to the report that identifies the qualifications (and relevant experience) of the expert, sets out the substance of all facts and instructions given to the expert by the instructing solicitor and makes clear where the expert is relying on the work of others in producing the evidence;

2.   a statement setting out the methodology adopted by the expert and the information available to the expert when considering the facts of the case;

3.   a factual basis for the report containing all facts relevant to the issues that the expert has been instructed to address, making clear the sources of those facts and where necessary cross-referencing particular facts to those sources;

4.   a section detailing all the opinions and reasoning of the expert on all relevant issues, with a concise summary of all the expert's conclusions at the end of the report;

5.   the Expert's Declaration and Statement of Truth as required by the CPR.

The report structure can be represented as follows:

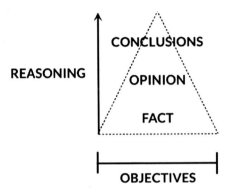

The instructions received from the instructing solicitor by the expert define the report objectives, which in turn define the scope of the report, beyond which the expert should not go. The expert then presents the factual basis relevant to the issues he/she has been instructed to address. There should then be a clear division between the factual basis and the expert's opinions and conclusions on all the issues to be addressed to meet the report objectives. Each opinion should be supported by reference to the factual matters relevant to the opinion and an explanation as to how the expert has applied his/her expertise to those facts to reach a conclusion.

It is very helpful for a report to contain a brief subsection that sets out the order in which evidence will be presented, placed at the end of the Introduction section. In complex reports it may help the court to expand this subsection to explain what issues will be addressed in each section.

> 1.9   I have presented my evidence in the following sections:
>
>   2. History of the Accident and Recovery
>   3. Presenting Condition
>   4. Medical History
>   5. Examination
>   6. Opinion and Prognosis
>   7. Consequences of Injuries

In Appendix 1, we have set out four templates for personal injury, industrial disease and clinical negligence reports based on this linear structure. It may be helpful to look at these templates and the notes to the templates at this point, before moving on to the discussion of the modular report structure set out below.

10.2.2 Modular Report Structure

The linear structure of an expert report will work extremely well where the issues upon which the expert has been instructed to report share a common factual basis. However, where a report has to deal with issues that arise from separate factual bases, the linear structure is not always the most efficient way to present the evidence. For example, consider a personal injury report that has to deal with a series of complex orthopaedic injuries, say to a claimant's spine, chest and right knee.

It may be difficult for the lawyers to follow the evidence if the expert were to set out all the factual information for each of these specific injuries in turn, before returning to express opinions on the first, second and third injuries. This approach would mean that the factual account of the first injury to the spine and the opinion based on that factual account would be separated by the factual account relating to the second (chest) and third (right knee) injuries.

Beyond this, reporting on injuries to different structures in the body may involve different methodologies, in addition to having distinct factual sources for the expert's opinion evidence. Again, attempting to deal with these issues within a linear structure may be difficult for both the lawyers who need to use the report prior to trial and for a judge at trial.

It is often more helpful to write the report using a modular structure:

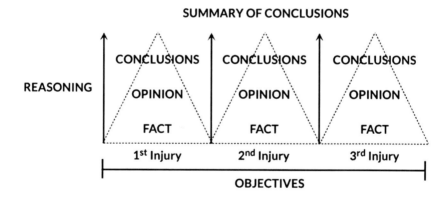

Using this structure, the three separate injuries can be dealt with in separate modules (one section for each module in the structure). The linear template would need to be modified to take account of the modular structure of the evidence:

1. Introduction

2. History of the Accident and Recovery Period (from the claimant)

3. Presenting Condition (from the claimant)

4. Spinal Injuries
   4.1 Methodology
      [...]
   4.2 Medical History (from medical records)
      [...]
   4.3 Examination
      [...]
   4.4 Opinion and Prognosis
      [...]

5. Chest Injuries
   5.1 Methodology
      [...]
   5.2 Medical History (from medical records)
      [...]
   5.3 Examination
      [...]
   5.4 Opinion and Prognosis
      [...]

6. Right Knee Injury
   6.1 Methodology
      [...]
   6.2 Medical History (from medical records)
      [...]
   6.3 Examination
      [...]
   6.4 Opinion and Prognosis
      [...]

7. Consequences of Injuries

8. Summary of Conclusions

The only sections that remain outside the modular structure are: 'History of the Accident', 'Presenting Condition', 'Consequences of Injuries' and 'Summary of Conclusions'. These sections are common to all of the issues in the report. Note also the separation of fact and opinion within each module of the report.

The modular structure may also be particularly useful when dealing with clinical negligence cases. Many clinical negligence cases involve an extended factual basis, involving separate episodes of treatment. It is often much more efficient to set out these separate treatment episodes as separate modules of the report, giving opinion and conclusions on each episode before moving on to the next. The advantage is, once again, keeping the factual basis and the opinion on each issue close together in the report, thereby creating a logical flow, and an ease of interpretation and use.

10.2.3 Report Templates

Report templates should always facilitate the most efficient presentation of the expert's evidence to the court. As such, there is no model template that will deal with every case and it is essential that experts develop the necessary skill and confidence to create a new (or alter an existing) template, if the evidence in a case requires such.

Differentiation of Factual Sources

In creating a personal injury/industrial disease report template, a basic principle is to differentiate the different sources of the evidence that the expert is relying upon in producing the report. In a personal injury report, it is best to set out in separate sections those facts elicited from the claimant during the interview and examination, those facts from medical or other records, and the direct factual evidence from the expert's examination of the claimant. (In the case of mental state examinations, clearly there is no separation between interview and examination.) This enables the expert to consider whether there are any factual conflicts between the different sources that the expert needs to address in the Opinion section. The court is also able to assess the quality of an opinion by considering the credibility and reliability of the source(s) of the factual evidence on which the opinion is based, before going on to consider how the expert has applied his/her mind and expertise to the facts drawn from these sources.

Narrative Approach

In a clinical negligence report template, rather than separating the different sources of information, the expert will set out his/her understanding of the chronology of events in the treatment history. Here, the principle is one of establishing a factual narrative by bringing together facts from different sources of information – e.g. medical records, protocols, and the witness statements of clinicians and family members. The expert should provide the source of the information either in the main text or by using footnotes (or both).

10.2.4 Presenting Evidence in a Logical Order

A logical approach to presenting the factual basis of the evidence will increase the speed and quality of the lawyer's interpretation of the report. Much of the information in a medical expert report will be expressed using chronologies. In personal injury reports, the history of the accident and recovery will be a chronology given to the expert by the claimant, dealing with the period from the accident date to the examination date. Similarly, the claimant's account of his/her medical history will also be presented as a chronology, as will the expert's review of the claimant's medical records. In addition to these chronologies, industrial disease claims may include chronologies of employment history and of the evidence relating to use of, or exposure to, the relevant agent(s).

A past medical history or employment history that is not presented in chronological order is confusing, reflects poorly on the professionalism of the expert and is also very difficult to use should the report come to be used in court. In cases with extensive records, it may be easier to include copies of the relevant entries in an appendix to the report and use the body of the report to provide a commentary on these entries, with appropriate cross-references.

Relevance

The claimant's medical history need only detail issues relevant to the injuries and prognosis that are the subject of the claim, with other matters in the history being either omitted entirely or summarised very briefly:

> The following entries in the GP notes are relevant to my assessment of causation for the claimant's injuries:
>
> 1. 25 March 2004: presented with mild right sciatic pain. He was prescribed painkillers (Ibuprofen) and advised to rest for three days.
>
> 2. 4 Aug 2005: presented with lower backache following a weekend spent decorating. Advised to avoid any heavy lifting and to rest. No prescription given.

There is a benefit in providing an overview of other presentations in the medical history where the expert intends to base opinions upon these presentations. For example, both orthopaedic experts and psychiatrists may wish to give details of a claimant's frequent attendance at his GP with minor health complaints - for the orthopaedic expert this may be a factor in his/her assessment of the likely period of recovery from an injury; for the psychiatrist, this pattern of attendance may indicate pre-existing illness behaviour that is now expressing itself as a failure to recover from an injury. The context of the medical history in both of these examples may be important.

However, where entries in the records have no relevance to the claim, to save time and cost these should be omitted. The only benefit in including such details is to indicate that the expert has actually read the records – it is a matter of individual style as to whether the report includes a paragraph summarising these other presentations.

> Mr S has attended his GP on seven occasions in the last 5 years with minor illnesses. I do not consider these presentations relevant to the claim.

Using Chronologies in Clinical Negligence Reports

In clinical negligence, a 'chronology of events' is the main component of the factual basis and central to the clinical negligence report. Omissions or inaccuracies in the chronology of events can have very serious consequences for a party as such mistakes speak to the care taken by the expert when addressing the issues and may undermine the basis for the opinions reached in the report.

Where there is little or no conflict between different sources of information, the chronology will be set out in date/time order within one section (here assuming a linear report structure/template). The sources of information – the clinical records and the witness statements – can be quoted at the key-moments in the chronology to illustrate the factual account.

Medical experts often have to deal with medical records that are incomplete or poorly written. When considering the case, the first task for the expert is a laborious attempt to interpret each entry in the records. With extensive and poorly written records, this can be both time consuming and irritating, especially when many of the entries may be barely legible or even illegible. And having spent time on this task, there is an understandable temptation for experts to simply reproduce a summary of the entries in the records, rather than producing a concise account of the events that took place. (We discuss producing a 'core-bundle' of important medical records in Section 9.3.2. above.)

For the lawyers and the court, simply translating the records rather than providing a concise account of the events that were taking place is usually unhelpful. The lawyers and the court simply do not have the technical knowledge to be able to understand the importance or relevance of entries in the records, without guidance from the expert about what was actually happening and what these entries actually mean.

The best approach is to give a clear account of the chronology of events that would be accessible to a lawyer, quoting relevant entries from the records at the key moments in the treatment process. This account of the events must be accurate and when relating to contentious matters should include verbatim quotations from the records with explanations of the entries provided as required. It is very helpful to use the date (and where known and relevant to do so, the time) to begin paragraphs in the chronology of events or to use dates and times as subheadings.

For ease of reference, it is also useful to include page numbers from the bundle of medical records where these page numbers exist:

26.9.03	GP: Letter Mr W to GP: "Bypass continues to function well. She has once more resumed smoking."	Page 121
6.12.03	GP: Letter Mr W to GP: "Aorto-femoral bypass graft continues to function well. She is still smoking."	Page 122
15.3.05	GP: Letter Mr W to GP: "All pulses present. Doppler testing showed normal ankle/brachial pressure index. I am disappointed to find she is still smoking. Re-do arterial surgery or further more distal bypasses are always a problem in patients of this sort and may carry a life-threatening potential."	Page 164
	[A Doppler ultrasound test uses reflected sound waves to evaluate blood as it flows through a blood vessel. It helps doctors evaluate blood flow through the major arteries and veins of the arms, legs, and neck. It can show blocked or reduced blood flow caused by narrowing in the arteries.]	

When factual disputes about the chronology of events do occur, the expert has to consider whether these factual disputes can be set out clearly within one section dealing with the chronology of events or whether the sheer number of factual disputes means that evidence from the claimant and defendant witnesses needs to be addressed in separate sections – i.e. two sections dealing with the chronology of events from the evidence of witnesses on each side. The expert's opinion on these factual conflicts should be dealt with in the Opinion section and not inserted in fragments throughout the factual basis of the report.

10.3   Writing Skills

When producing expert evidence, it is essential that experts achieve accuracy and precision in their use of language. We identify five writing disciplines that experts should seek to develop:

1. writing for the court;

2. providing technical explanation;

3. using descriptive language;

4. using modal auxiliary verbs; and

5. addressing the standard of proof and relevant legal tests.

10.3.1 Writing for the Court

Medical expert reports are written for a non-medically qualified legal readership of solicitors, barristers and judges. The claimant will also be shown the report (save in exceptional cases). The medical language that a doctor uses when talking to other doctors will generally be confusing or misleading to a legal readership, unless it is defined and where necessary explained.

A medical expert may assume the level of expertise in the lawyers and the court of an 'informed layperson'. We would characterise this person as being a reasonably intelligent professional, with a good education and mental faculties, but without detailed medical knowledge. A typical lawyer is reasonably well-educated and intelligent (at least, most would like to think so), but cannot be expected to have any medical expertise save that gained from reading a variety of medical expert reports, personal experience of medical matters and from watching medical dramas on television.

10.3.2 Providing Technical Explanations

Where medical issues move beyond the understanding to be expected of a layperson, explanations of such technical matters are usually required. It is essential that the instructing lawyers understand the words on the page, but more important even than this is that they understand the significance of the words on the page in relation to the dispute between the parties.

It is not the expert's role to attempt to provide an extensive medical education for the lawyers, but it is critical to the expert's role to delineate the medical issues relevant to the dispute and to make sure these issues are explained sufficiently that the lawyers can make appropriate settlement decisions or argue their case in court.

The basic approach to giving a medical explanation suitable for the lawyers is to adopt a four-stage structure:

1. introduce the topic;

2. explain the basic medical facts;

3. amplify with essential detail; and

4. explain the relevance of the issue to the facts of the case.

We set out two examples of medical explanations that lawyers would consider useful in an appropriate case:

Explanation: Glasgow Coma Scale

An expert may begin the explanation of the 'Glasgow Coma Scale' by introducing the issue with a 'headline sentence' - a reasonably short sentence that introduces the topic to be explained:

> The 'Glasgow Coma Scale' (GCS) is widely used by clinicians as an assessment tool to make an initial assessment of the severity of a patient's brain dysfunction.

The expert can then move on to explain the basic medical facts that the lawyer will need to grasp to understand the GCS, without introducing any unnecessary detail or complexity:

> A treating clinician when using the GCS will observe the level of responsiveness of the patient after initial resuscitation, by assessing the patient's ability to perform three basic functions:
>
> 1. eye opening
>
> 2. motor response (i.e. ability to move)
>
> 3. verbal response.
>
> The clinician then compares his/her observations of the patient against the criteria set for each of the three functions within the GCS and awards a score for each function. The minimum possible total score is 3 and the maximum is 15. A score below 10 suggests a serious dysfunction, with a score of 7 or lower indicating coma.

Once the basic medical facts have been presented, the expert can then decide whether it is necessary to amplify the medical facts by moving to a greater level of detail:

> The scales for scoring each function are as follows:
>
> 1. eye opening: a maximum of 4 points for spontaneous response and a minimum of 1 for none;

2.   motor response: a maximum of 6 for obeying commands and a minimum of 1 for none;

3.   verbal response: a maximum of 5 for being orientated and a minimum of 1 for no orientation.

Using the GCS allows a rudimentary assessment of outcome to be made at an early stage and enables any improvement or deterioration in the patient's function over time to be monitored more closely by the clinical team.

The expert must then explain the relevance of the explanation to the facts in the case:

In this case, the claimant was scored at 10. This indicates that...

Explanation: Ankylosing Spondylitis

Below, we set out a second example, again using the same approach:

'Ankylosing spondylitis' is an inflammatory and progressive degenerating condition of the spine. [**Headline**]

This condition manifests in two stages. The first stage involves inflammation of the synovial joints, which includes the joint capsules and their attached ligaments and tendons. This inflammatory process is known as 'spondylitis'. In the second stage, a degenerative process leading to the fusion of the vertebrae occurs. This degenerative process is termed 'ankylosis'. The condition can lead to severe deformities of the spine, loss of extension and a bent forward posture. [**Explanation**]

The condition predominantly affects young men. It usually commences in the sacroiliac joints in the lower spine, which are located beneath the lumbar vertebrae and above the coccyx. The condition results in pain and stiffness and treatment is by analgesics, anti-inflammatory drugs and regular daily exercises. In severe cases, where the bent forward posture becomes too great, it may be necessary to perform an 'osteotomy' of the spine, an operation to separate and realign fused joints. [**Amplification**]

In this case, the MRI scan of the claimant's spine indicates that he had a pre-existing condition of ankylosing spondylitis. This means that without the accident, he would in any event have been experiencing pain and stiffness. Since the accident, he reports ... [**Relevance to case**]

Notice that the explanations are sufficient to enable the lawyers to understand the significance of the issue in the case, without going too far into the detail of the condition. It may be that as a case develops, further explanation may be required, particularly where experts disagree as to the diagnosis or its relevance to the dispute. The instructing solicitor will advise the expert should this be required.

Accuracy and Precision

An essential discipline of writing evidence is to ensure that all language in the report is used with accuracy and precision. This includes the use of technical language, quotations from sources, descriptive language and legal tests. The basic discipline is that the expert should write in a style that enables the lawyers and the court to establish an accurate and precise interpretation of the evidence.

Medical expert witnesses can assume that the lawyers reading their reports will be able to understand medical evidence where information is presented logically and with appropriate explanation. We have already quoted the GMC Guidance as to the use of language and terminology that will be readily understood by lawyers and the court.[2] When producing a report, care should be taken not to lose the lawyers by using undefined technical medical language. Such undefined language, in any area of medical expertise, will generally be too difficult for the lawyers unless it is clearly explained in lay terms. Experts often stray from this approach.

When using technical language, the best approach is to define the first use of a technical term in a bracket. If there is a large number of technical terms in the report, bringing these terms together in a glossary may also be useful. The report should identify in the Introduction section where the glossary is to be found; the glossary is usually placed in Appendix 1, although it can be placed after the contents page for ease of use by the reader.

The examples below illustrate language that most lawyers would find **unhelpful** were no explanation of the terms to be given:

This treatment is likely to be associated with less morbidity.

The left eye had an uncorrected visual acuity of 6/9 part improving to 6/5 +2 or 6/4 part with -0.75/+0.25 x 160.

The patient was offered a sub-talar arthrodesis.

---

2   See Section 4.1.2

Her other problems include instability of her INR resulting sometimes in very high levels.

… Mr Q has post-traumatic cerebral arachnoiditis with formation of posttraumatic cysts in both frontal lobes and in the right parietal lobe of the encephalon with stable cephalic, vestibuloatactic, and asthenovegetative syndrome.

In personal injury reports, lawyers are familiar with terms like 'soft tissue injury' or 'muscular ligamentous injury', but defining 'cervical spine' is probably helpful. Some medical experts would simply substitute 'neck' for 'cervical spine'. In other less familiar disciplines, there is a greater need to define terms.

One exception from the general rule about defining terms is the use of technical language in the Examination section of the report. In this section, the expert can simply set out the Examination findings, which can then be summarised at the beginning of the Opinion section as a list of injuries to be addressed, and where necessary, explanation can then be offered of any relevant issues.

Most lawyers would find the following language **helpful** as terms are simply explained:

The surgeon offered the patient an operation to fuse the bones in his foot, known as a sub-talar arthrodesis.

Her other problems include unstable and sometimes very high readings of INR [International Normalised Ratio is a measurement for the effectiveness of anticoagulation of the blood], a high reading being indicative of a high chance of bleeding.

Reviews of the scans and clinical examination showed a Le Fort I/II type pyramidal fracture of the mid-face [broken facial bones including the hard palate, maxilla and cheek bones]

Medical expert reports are technical reports written for a non-medical readership, so a balance has to be struck between simplifying technical language to aid comprehension of the report and using technical language to maintain accuracy. This is a matter of style and experts develop their own approach to reflect their individual stylistic preferences, the difficulty of the technical issues in the report and the likely familiarity of the lawyers with the medical issues.

Particularly in more serious or complex cases, the use of defined technical language is more helpful to the lawyers than attempts at substitution with simplified phrases. Defined technical language helps the lawyers to delineate the medical issues in dispute and facilitates the comparison of reports from different experts in the case. Defined technical language also helps the lawyers to communicate with each other about the medical issues, once they have grasped the essential concepts in the dispute. The key is for the expert to make sure that when using technical language it is easy to understand, by defining technical terms and where necessary explaining technical issues.

Lawyers tend to develop a greater level of technical medical knowledge in the disciplines with which they are most familiar. Owing to their familiarity with road traffic accident claims, lawyers are generally more comfortable with orthopaedic reports on neck and back injuries than with reports in less common disciplines. Where appropriate, it is helpful for experts to provide good-quality visual elements in the appendices to their reports to help the lawyers to understand the evidence. A clear diagram of relevant anatomical structures or a photograph – perhaps dealing with scar tissue - will usually help the lawyers to grasp the importance of what the expert is attempting to communicate in the text.

Some lawyers do specialise in particular areas of injury – for example, brain injury or industrial diseases – where the specific requirements of the claim demand a greater level of medical knowledge and understanding on the part of the lawyers. However, in all disciplines, the standard of knowledge reasonably to be expected of instructing lawyers and the court remains that of 'an informed layperson'.

The lack of awareness amongst medical experts as to the technical abilities of their readership would perhaps be remedied if medical experts had to spend an afternoon interpreting legal text:[3]

> 31.—(1) Except where paragraph (2) applies, a payment of income to which regulation 29 (calculation of earnings derived from employed earner's employment and income other than earnings) applies shall be treated as paid—
>
> (a) in the case of a payment which is due to be paid before the first benefit week pursuant to the claim, on the date on which it is due to be paid;
>
> (b) in any other case, on the first day of the benefit week in which it is due to be paid or the first succeeding benefit week in which it is practicable to take it into account.
>
> (2) Income support, unemployment benefit, sickness or invalidity benefit, or severe disablement allowance under the Social Security Act shall be treated as paid on the day of the benefit week in respect of which it is paid.

---

3   In this case Regulation 31 of the Income Support (General) Regulations 1987

10.3.3 Using Descriptive Language

Any descriptive language in a medical expert report must be capable of being quantified by a lawyer, so that an accurate assessment of loss can be made:

> Mrs H experiences some discomfort in her right wrist.

It is impossible for the lawyer to interpret with any confidence the expert's use of the noun phrase 'some discomfort'. The expert must attempt to make the situation clear by dealing with both the severity and the frequency of the symptoms:

> Mrs H experiences discomfort in her right wrist. She describes this discomfort as "a dull aching sensation", which she experiences several times each day. She says that she particularly feels this sensation when she rotates her wrist rapidly or when she grips heavy items, such as her shopping bags.

Medical experts often adopt negation as a form of description. However, the example below illustrates the difficulties that arise:

> It is not uncommon for patients to experience pain and discomfort for several months following a bony injury to the wrist.

Here the adjective 'uncommon' (to denote the absence of this quality) is negated to form the adjective phrase 'not uncommon'. The lawyer's attempt at interpreting this phrase would likely be that the situation does not occur often enough to be described as common (*def. occurring often*) nor so rarely as to be uncommon (*def. out of the ordinary*) – leaving 'not uncommon' to fall someway between these two extremities.

In reality, the lawyer probably does not have the first idea what frequency of occurrence 'common' or 'uncommon' actually represents, leading to a ragged guess at the interpretation the expert actually intends the lawyer to make. Alternatively, the lawyer may simply draft a letter to the expert to seek clarification. Once again, the description should be quantified either by reference to literature or from professional experience:

In my clinical experience, following a bony injury to the wrist, approximately 10-15% of patients will continue to experience ongoing pain and discomfort for up to 12 months after the removal of the plaster cast. These patients use analgesics, such as Ibuprofen, to relieve their symptoms of pain. In the majority of these patients, symptoms settle with time and they make a full recovery. However, in approximately 5% of all cases, the pain and discomfort does not resolve.

The symptoms described by Mr P seem to me to be consistent with the type and severity of pain and symptoms described to me by patients in my clinical practice whose pain and symptoms do not resolve with time. I therefore consider that Mr P's ongoing complaints of pain are attributable to the accident and are unlikely to resolve.

The need to be precise is also undermined by overly brief descriptions that the medical expert may consider to be correct, but may still mislead the lawyer:

Mr S will now go on to make a gradual recovery.

The lawyer may interpret this to mean that the recovery will be full, even though the word 'full' is omitted. The end point of recovery should be defined or described. It is helpful for the expert to spell out, using simple and pragmatic language, the meaning he/she intends to communicate to the lawyers:

Mr S will go on to make a gradual recovery, but will not return to his pre-accident level of function. It is unlikely that he will be able to return to his former employment as a fitter, involving as it does frequent heavy lifting and walking over rough ground. However, he will be able to carry out most kinds of work of a lighter nature that do not require excessive lifting or repeated bending.

Similarly, the lawyer may have little appreciation of the normal effects of particular injuries or procedures on an individual. Medical expressions may not convey the reality of the condition or injury, meaning that the lawyers may not understand the impact or the potential impact on the claimant, thereby misjudging the value of the claim:

Mr T fractured 5 ribs and felt discomfort from the injury for a month.

This may be better and more fairly described as:

> Mr T fractured 5 ribs. Typically, this results in intense pain for several weeks and interferes with breathing and coughing, hence the need in his case for substantial pain relief. The consequent severe chest infection, for which he was briefly admitted to hospital, would almost certainly not have occurred or have been significant but for the impact of the fractures on his ability to breathe and cough.

The importance of providing a full explanation is also illustrated by the following opinion:

> Mrs J is left with a permanent tracheostomy.

This may be better and more usefully described as:

> Mrs J is left with a permanent tracheostomy. A tracheostomy provides direct access to the trachea [wind pipe] by surgically making an opening in the neck. Once an opening is made, it needs to be maintained by the insertion of a tracheostomy tube. This is a most unpleasant, embarrassing and sociably devastating complication. On a day-to-day basis, the effects that Mrs J will have to deal with are...

Where the expert uses technical scales or technical scoring to quantify the description of a state - such as Pain Rating Scales, Apgar Scoring or Reference Intervals – an explanation of the scale or scoring should be included in the report, either placed in the main text or appended to the report with an appropriate cross-reference.

10.3.4   Using Modal Auxiliary Verbs

In English, modal auxiliary verbs are used to express aspects of 'modality', such as: ability, duty, likelihood, necessity, obligation, permission and volition.

Most native speakers of English are familiar with the distinction between questions such as: "May I get up from the table?" and "Can I get up from the table?" Each question addresses a different aspect of modality: 'may' addresses permission ("Do I have permission to get up from the table?") while 'can' addresses ability ("Am I physically able to get up from the table?"). However, very few native speakers pay much attention to the use of the modal auxiliaries in respect of likelihood. This aspects of modality is fundamental in expert reports, especially so when expressing opinions.

In English, the modal auxiliary verbs are:

- May/Might
- Can/Could
- Will/Would
- Shall/Should
- Must
- Ought.

In respect of likelihood, the modal auxiliary verbs 'may' and 'can' along with the past tense and conditional forms 'might' and 'could' are used to express possible occurrences. The modal auxiliary verb 'will' is used to express a (highly) probable occurrence ('would' being the conditional form); 'shall' and 'must' deal with duty and obligation.

It is essential that experts use the appropriate modal auxiliary to communicate clearly their opinion on likelihood – i.e. possibility and probability. Consider the following extract from a clinical negligence report on the actions of an ENT surgeon. Pay particular attention to the use of the modal auxiliaries:

> To proceed with a surgical procedure without access to such an investigation is negligent. Had the scans been scrutinised prior to the surgery it is possible that the surgeon would have identified the defect within the bony orbital wall. The surgical approach may therefore have been more cautious and the identification of orbital fat may have occurred earlier in the surgical procedure.

The expert describes the actions of the surgeon as 'negligent'. We have already addressed the potential difficulties of medical experts placing themselves in the judge's role, rather than simply applying the Bolam test[4] and this is an illustration of that error. However, it is the clause that begins 'it is possible' and the subsequent use in the next sentence of 'may' that creates an immediate contradiction in the evidence. For, if it is only possible that:

1. the defect within the bony orbital wall would have been identified prior to the surgery;

2. the surgical approach may have been more cautious; and

3. the identification of orbital fat may have occurred earlier;

then, on the balance of probabilities, looking at the CT scan prior to the operation would not have made any difference to the ultimate outcome.

---

4   See Section 8.1.1 above

So, were a court to make its decision based on this expert evidence alone, there could be no finding of negligence (in law) against the surgeon, even though the expert has expressed an opinion that the treatment is in fact negligent. Note also that the expert does not deal fully with the 'but for' situation (i.e. what difference there would have been in the ultimate outcome without this omission on the part of the surgeon).

Another aspect of modality that creates difficulty is 'obligation'. Consider the interpretative difficulties that arise for the lawyers in the following extract from a report on the death of a patient following an operation to realign a fractured femur:

> At this point, Mr B had a low-grade pyrexia, which should have indicated to the treating clinicians the possibility of an embolism and DVT prophylaxis should have been commenced immediately.

Simply using the modal auxiliary 'should' is never sufficient when an expert needs to apply the Bolam test. In medical practice, a lot of things 'should happen', but the court will seek to address the question as to whether the failure to begin DVT prophylaxis represented a standard of care that fell below the level reasonably to be expected of the treating clinicians in those circumstances and at that time. The Bolam test was not applied correctly in this report and so the expert's opinions would have needed to be clarified before it would be useful to the lawyers and the court.

10.3.5 Addressing the Standard of Proof and Relevant Legal Tests

In a civil case, an accurate interpretation of a medical expert's opinion is only possible where the expert applies the civil standard of proof and the appropriate legal test to the opinion. Any medical opinion that does not lead to a clear conclusion from the lawyers' perspective is unusable unless or until it is correctly expressed.

Experts are expected to apply the civil standard of proof and the appropriate legal tests to each of their opinions. Experts should use the standard phrases and should not vary these phrases, as this potentially causes confusion, delay or the need for the lawyers to seek clarification of the report from the expert.

Standard Phrases for Civil Standard of Proof and Legal Tests

Standard of Proof[5]	on the balance of probabilities...
	more probable than not...
	more likely than not...
Causation[6]	the accident/adverse event caused the following injuries...
	without the accident the claimant would/would not have suffered...
	but for the accident the claimant would/would not have suffered...
Causation (material contribution test)	the contribution of the exposure was more than minimal
Consequences of Injuries	The following consequences are reasonable and are attributable to the accident...
	The following restrictions are medically supportable as resulting from injuries sustained in the accident...
Breach of Duty[7]	No reasonably competent practitioner (define expertise/speciality) would have acted in this manner at that time...
	The practitioner did not exercise a level of skill ordinarily to be expected of a... (define the practitioner) at that time...
	The actions of the doctor fell below a standard reasonably to be expected of a... (define the practitioner) at that time...

Some medical experts use the terms 'index accident' or 'index event' in their reports. These are not legal terms, but lawyers understand that the expert is referring to the accident, incident or event that the expert has been instructed to consider. Often the term adds nothing, because there is no other non-index accident or event.

---

5   See Chapter 5

6   See Section 6.1

7   See Section 8.1

10.4   Writing Opinion

Every opinion expressed in the report has to be based upon a detailed analysis of the available facts and must be supported by clear and informed reasoning. It is essential that experts develop the discipline of applying, and then setting out in the report, a logical thought process to support each opinion they express.

To ensure that each opinion is supported by a clear reasoning process that is accessible to the lawyers, experts must develop a way to present their opinions in a structured manner. As experts develop this structured approach to writing opinion, this in turn supports a more careful and logical approach when considering the evidence.

Owning an Opinion

The overriding duty of experts is to 'help the court on the matters within their expertise'.[8] Therefore, expert evidence is always the expression of an individual professional's opinion. This individual responsibility needs to be reflected in the grammar used when writing the opinion, which should be in the first-person singular - 'I' or 'my':

- In my opinion, Mr Jones suffered a soft-tissue injury to his cervical spine caused by...
- I consider that the prior history of bronchitis is not material to prognosis...
- My assessment of the situation is...
- On examination, my findings were...
- I conclude, therefore, that Mrs Jones' ongoing symptoms...

Each of these examples shows in the grammar that the expert has applied his/her professional skill in expressing the opinion. When an expert chooses to use a less direct expression, lawyers often sense that the expert is unwilling to commit him/herself to the opinion.

Compare the following statements of opinion:

- It is considered that the ongoing symptoms are related to the accident.
- I consider that the ongoing symptoms are caused by the accident.

In the first example above, the use of the third person singular short passive construction 'it is considered' and the ambiguous phrase 'are related' when addressing causation indicates that the expert may be backing away from offering a firm opinion. This may or may not be the actual reality, but it is the words on the page upon which the parties and the court have ultimately to base their decisions. In the second example, using the first person singular active construction 'I consider that' and addressing causation with the unambiguous verb phrase 'are caused by' creates a far stronger impression for the lawyers and the court.

---

8   See CPR 35.3(1) and Section 4.1.3

A more subtle way that experts communicate a lack of commitment to an opinion is with the use of the phrase 'In my view...' It is a phrase that often appears in expert reports as soon as there are difficult issues to deal with: the assertive phrase 'in my opinion' makes way for the less assertive 'in my view'. This creates an impression that other views may be equally valid, which in an environment where the standard of proof is 'on the balance of probabilities' can be very concerning for the party relying on the expert's evidence.

Another example of a lack of commitment is an opinion written using negation:

> It would not be unreasonable to say that were it not for the previous injury to the right upper limb, his recovery would have been achieved more quickly.

> If an expert has concerns about giving a firm opinion, these concerns should be clearly explained in the report, rather than being covertly communicated through the expert's inappropriate use of grammar or phraseology.

Phrases for Expressing Opinion

ASSERTIVE PHRASES	WEAK PHRASES
In my opinion	In my view
I consider that	It is considered
I conclude	I think/feel
My findings were	I believe
My assessment is	I contend/submit[9]

Opinion Structures

An expert who does not justify an opinion with reasoning (or reasons) falls short of one of the basic requirements of expert evidence: that the court can assess the basis of an opinion to test its soundness. When faced with such unsupported opinion, the consequence for the lawyers is that they are limited in their ability to properly assess the strengths and weaknesses of the case, which results either in additional correspondence with the expert to request clarification of the evidence or lower-quality decisions being made about progressing the case (i.e. making a Part 36 offer[10], settling the claim, or continuing to trial).

---

9   Bringing forward contentions and making submissions are the actions of counsel in court and these terms should not appear in an expert report.

10   See Section 2.8.2 above

To improve the way opinion evidence is presented, we encourage experts to apply the same structure to every opinion they express. In this way, every opinion will be appropriately supported with the facts relevant to the opinion and the expert's reasoning in moving from those relevant facts to reach a conclusion.

There are two basic structures available when expressing opinions:

10.4.1 Long-Form Opinion

- Topic
- Facts relevant to the opinion
- Reasoning process
- Conclusion

Mr G is a 70-year old man with a history of mild to moderate breathlessness on exertion. Breathlessness is usually either cardiac or respiratory in origin, although there may be a contribution from other causes such as anxiety, obesity and anaemia. I consider the possible diagnoses for his condition below. [**Topic**]

My findings on examination and my review of Mr G's medical notes and records are as follows: [**Facts and Reasoning**]

1) <u>Obesity</u>: he has a BMI of 28 - he is not therefore obese.

2) <u>Cardiac Disease</u>: from his notes and records I can find no evidence of cardiac disease.

3) <u>Smoking</u>: his smoking history, supported from entries in the medical records, is that he smoked occasionally many years ago. I can find no evidence on lung function tests or CT scanning of any tobacco-related lung disease i.e. chronic obstructive pulmonary disease or emphysema.

4) <u>Asthma</u>: this is a disease characterised by intermittent and variable narrowing of the airways - there is no history suggestive of asthma, no doctor who has examined Mr G has ever diagnosed the condition and he has never been on any treatment appropriate for that disease; the lung function tests are not consistent with that diagnosis (with no indication of an abnormally decreased $FEV1/FVC$ Ratio and no improvement in $FEV1$ after bronchodilators, which would indicate the condition).

5) Asbestosis: he has approximately 10 years of what is described as moderate asbestos exposure. He has been recorded as having bilateral basal crackles for which there is no other explanation; lung function tests show the classic features of decrease in transfer factor and decrease in lung volumes; a CT scan, though less than ideal, is reported as supportive of a diagnosis of asbestosis. He therefore satisfies 4 of the major criteria for diagnosing asbestosis.

I therefore conclude that it is more likely than not that the restrictive lung disease from which he now suffers is due to asbestosis, and that all of the employments in which he was exposed to asbestos made a more than minimal contribution to the causation of his condition. [**Conclusion**]

The long-form opinion structure is best suited to presenting any opinion that requires detailed analysis. It is the classic structure for presenting opinion in scientific writing and has the advantage of taking the lawyers stage-by-stage through the reasoning process that the expert has used.

10.4.2 Short-Form Opinion

- Topic
- Statement of Opinion
- Justification (reasons for holding opinion)
- Amplification (any further explanation)

Prognosis

Miss L sustained a musculo-ligamentous strain injury to the cervical spine and shoulder girdle region. [**Topic**]

I consider it probable that within 6 to 9 months her remaining symptoms will have resolved completely. [**Statement of Opinion**]

Miss L presents as a young woman with a positive mindset about recovering from her injuries. She is aged 30 and is physically fit. She has made a very good recovery so far in the short period from the accident to date and I expect this to continue. She has no history of any previous symptoms relating to her cervical spine and shoulders that would impede her recovery. [**Justification**]

On examination, there was a normal shape and contour of the cervical spine and shoulder girdle. Both forward flexion and backward extension are full, but with discomfort at the extreme of movement. Both right and left lateral rotation and right and left lateral flexion are full, but with discomfort at the extreme of movement. There is no evidence of neurological deficit in the upper limbs. [**Amplification**]

The short-form opinion structure is best suited to presenting straightforward opinions and is typically found in low-value claims. It allows the expert to state the reasons for holding an opinion rather than needing to set out the full reasoning and so can be written more quickly – which is extremely important given the low level of fees paid for reports in low value claims.

Conclusion

A medical expert report brings forward both factual and opinion evidence on the medical aspects of the case. The required structure of medical expert reports is based upon the principles of scientific report writing. In personal injury claims a report must address the key medico-legal aspects such as causation of injury, prognosis and the consequences that arise from the accident. In clinical negligence claims, the additional issue of breach of duty must also be addressed by the appropriate expert. The use of chronologies is also an important feature of expert reports. Opinion evidence must be dealt with in its own section(s) and should not be fragmented by placing opinions within the factual basis of the report. It is essential that legal tests are applied with care using the appropriate phrases that correctly express all aspects of the test.

Final Thoughts

Writing high-quality evidence represents a professional challenge and requires a rigorous approach. Adopting the approach to the evidence and the writing disciplines that we have explained throughout this book will enable experts to produce expert reports that are more accurate and precise and also more understandable for the lawyers and the court.

The benefit to medical experts who master these disciplines is that a well-written and well-structured report is essential to the overriding objective of the court – 'to deal with cases justly' - and is the best possible illustration of the skills of the expert. A well-written report is also an essential aid to providing effective and high-quality oral evidence in court and withstanding rigorous cross-examination with the minimum of stress.

Producing high–quality reports is also an excellent way to build a good reputation amongst the lawyers who will ultimately enable the expert to build a successful medico-legal practice.

Key-Point Summary

1. High-quality report presentation is an important aspect of the report, enabling the lawyers and the court to use the report more easily and efficiently.

2. The required structure of an expert report separates the factual basis from the opinions expressed by the expert - the factual basis should not contain opinion evidence.

3. Standard report templates are offered as a guide to help experts to present their evidence clearly and concisely; however, experts should always consider whether a particular case requires a template to be adapted to communicate the evidence more clearly.

4. All language used in a medical expert report needs to be accurate and precise, and expressed appropriately for a non-medically qualified readership.

5. Experts need to take particular care to be accurate and precise when using descriptive language and modal auxiliary verbs.

6. Every opinion must be expressed with reference to the civil standard of proof and the appropriate legal test.

Developing Your Medico-Legal Mind (10)

Based on your understanding of expert evidence in the civil courts, answer the following questions:

1. What is the difference between the 'effects' of an injury and its 'consequences'?

2. What are the functions of a personal injury report? What additional functions does medical expert evidence have in disease and illness claims and in clinical negligence claims?

3. How could the following expert evidence be expressed more appropriately?

    'His body habitus prevented palpation of the abdominal aortic, femoral, popliteal or posterior pulses.'

4. What phrases can be used to express the civil standard of proof?

5. What phrases enable clear opinions to be expressed on the causation of injuries?

6. What issues arise for the lawyers in the evidence as written below? How could the evidence be improved to deal with these issues?

    'I have no doubt he was vulnerable at the time of the accident to developing psychological difficulties. It is my view that a substantial subtraction needs to be made from the overall picture to take account of the non-accident related issues. I am unable to put a percentage on the appropriate level of subtraction but I do feel able to say that these non-accident related issues represent at least half of the psychological picture.'

7. What issues arise in the expert's summary of the following entries in medical records?

    'The GP noted on 1.4.09 'Back better; return to work from Monday'. I am therefore of the opinion that the effects of the accident had ceased by the end of March 2009 and that the subsequent complaints of low back pain during the summer of 2009 were unrelated to the accident but the result of the previously asymptomatic spinal degenerative disease.'

8. How could the following expression of opinion be more clearly expressed?

   'It is my view that this lady appears to present with a moderate depressive illness which appears to have been present from the time of the accident. She would be likely to benefit from receiving 12 x 1 hour sessions of CBT. I feel that the psychological difficulties described can be attributed to the index event.'

9. Using the report checklist in Appendix 2, analyse one of your own expert reports to assess what aspects of your evidential writing skills can be improved.

Appendices

1(a)	Personal Injury Report Template – Physical Injuries
1(b)	Personal Injury Report Template –Psychological/Psychiatric Injuries
1(c)	Personal Injury Report Template – Industrial Disease
1(d)	Clinical Negligence Report Template
2	Report Checklist
3	CPR Part 35
4	Practice Direction to Part 35
5	Protocol for the Instruction of Experts to give Evidence in Civil Claims
6	GMC Guidance – Acting as an Expert Witness
7	Example of a Schedule of Loss

Appendix 1

Appendix 1(a)

Personal Injury Report Template (Physical Injuries)

1. **Introduction**
   - Author
   - Instructions
   - Background to the dispute (as necessary)
   - Sources of information
   - Methodology
   - Structure of the report

2. **History of the Accident and Recovery Period** (from the claimant)
   - Incident/accident details and subsequent events
   - Injuries/symptoms/effects following the accident
   - Initial treatment and progression of injuries/symptoms/effects
   - Subsequent treatment and progression of injuries/symptoms/effects
   - Consequences of injuries (from accident to present)

3. **Presenting Condition** (from the claimant)
   - Present injuries/symptoms/effects
   - Present treatment
   - Past medical history

4. **Medical History** (from medical records)
   - Relevant medical history

5. **Examination**
   - Details of examination and findings

6. **Opinion and Prognosis**
   - Summary of examination findings
   - Opinion as to present condition (if not already defined by examination findings)
   - Causation of injuries
   - Relevant pre-existing conditions (if any)
   - Prognosis of injuries
   - Future treatment (if relevant)

7. **Consequences of Injuries**
   - Opinion on the consequences resulting from physical injuries/symptoms/effects

8. **Summary of Conclusions**
   - List of conclusions
   - Declaration and Statement of Truth
   - Sign and Date

Explanatory notes on this template are provided below.

Appendix 1(b)

Personal Injury Report Template: (Psychiatric/Psychological Injuries)

1. **Introduction**
   - Author
   - Instructions
   - Background to the dispute (as necessary)
   - Sources of information
   - Methodology
   - Structure of the report

2. **History of the Accident and Recovery Period** (from claimant)
   - Incident/accident details and subsequent events
   - Injuries/symptoms/effects following the accident
   - Initial treatment and progression of injuries/symptoms/effects
   - Subsequent treatment and progression of injuries/symptoms/effects
   - Consequences of injuries (from accident to present)

3. **Presenting Condition** (from claimant)
   - Present symptoms/effects
   - Present treatment
   - Psychiatric history

4. **Psychiatric/Psychological History** (from medical records)
   - Relevant psychiatric history
     - Personal
     - Family
     - Marital
     - Drugs/Alcohol
     - Employment
     - Personality

5. **Mental State Examination**
   - Details of mental-state examination and findings

6. **Opinion and Prognosis**
   - Summary of mental state examination findings
   - Opinion as to present condition: ICD or DSM-IV classification (if not already defined by examination findings)
   - Causation of injuries
   - Relevant pre-existing conditions (if any)
   - Prognosis
   - Future treatment

7. **Consequences of Injuries**
   - Opinion on the consequences arising from psychiatric/psychological condition/symptoms/effects

8. **Summary of Conclusions**
   - List of conclusions
   - Declaration and Statement of Truth
   - Sign and Date

Explanatory notes on this template are provided below.

Appendix 1(c)

Industrial Disease Report Template

1. **Introduction**
   - Author
   - Instructions
   - Background to the dispute (as necessary)
   - Sources of information
   - Methodology
   - Structure of the report

2. **Employment History** (from employment records)
   - Positions held, when, and type of work
   - Type(s) and degree of exposure and history of exposure
   - Systems of work and safety precautions taken

3. **Medical History** (from medical/occupational health records)
   - Relevant medical history from:
     - Occupational health nursing notes
     - Occupational physician records
     - GP and hospital records
     - Previous medical reports

4. **Presenting Condition** (from claimant)
   - Present conditions/symptoms/effects
   - Present treatment
   - Past medical history
     • Treatment and progression of condition/symptoms/effects
     • Consequences arising from presenting condition

5. **Examination**
   - Details of examination and findings

6. **Opinion and Prognosis**
   - Summary of examination findings
   - Opinion as to present condition (if not already defined by examination findings)
   - Causation of injuries ('but for'/'material contribution')
   - Relevant pre-existing conditions (if any)
   - Prognosis
   - Future treatment (if relevant)

7. **Consequences of Injuries**
   - Opinion on the consequences resulting from condition/symptoms/effects

8. **Summary of Conclusions**
   - List of conclusions
   - Declaration and Statement of Truth
     - Sign and Date

Explanatory notes on this template are provided below.

Notes: Personal Injury Report Templates (1a-c)

The following notes are primarily based on the personal injury template for physical injuries (1a), with the vast majority of these notes applying equally to psychiatric/psychological template (1b) and the industrial disease template (1c).

Additional notes specific to templates (1b) and (1c) are included at the end of the notes on the personal injury template (1a).

1. Introduction

The Introduction establishes the expertise of the author and the issues he/she has been instructed to address in the report.

Author

• Write 2 or 3 paragraphs that establish the expert's qualifications and relevant experience.

Instructions

- Set out the substance of all material instructions from the solicitor or where the instructions to the expert are only briefly stated by the solicitor, set out the expert's understanding of his/her instructions.

Background to the Dispute

- Particularly in more complex cases, it is helpful for the expert to begin by briefly summarising the facts of the case so that the reader understands the basic outline of the issues in dispute.

Sources of Information

- List the information made available to the expert. This may include GP and hospital records, scans, X-rays, witness statements and photographs. If there is an extensive list of sources, it is preferable to place this list in an appendix with a cross-reference in the main text.

- Give the dates of documents or in the case of medical records, the range of dates. This ensures that should the case reach court months or even years later, the specific documents that the expert has seen when producing the report can be identified.

- Where the expert is instructed specifically to report without having had sight of the medical records, this should be clearly stated so that the basis of the report is clear.

Methodology

- For a typical personal injury report (car accident/slip and trip), there is no particular demand from the lawyers for a detailed methodology section, as the process is familiar. However, the expert should set out the basic approach adopted.

- More technically demanding investigations will require that a Methodology section/sub-section be included, either in the Introduction section or in complex cases requiring detailed investigations, as Section 2 of the report.

Structure of the Report

- Set out the structure of the report as a list of sections.

2. History of the Accident and Recovery Period

In this section, give details of the history taken from the claimant, reporting those facts relevant to the medical issues and quoting the claimant's own words where relevant.

Incident/accident details and subsequent events

- Report only on accident details relevant to medical issues (e.g. in a car accident case, experts would be likely to record the type and severity of the collision, whether the claimant was wearing a seat belt, whether the car had headrests fitted, whether the claimant was able to brace before the collision).

- Give details of any immediate or subsequent medical treatment (e.g. did the claimant get out of the car unaided and was he/she taken to casualty).

Injuries/symptoms/effects following the accident

- Include details of the claimant's injuries, symptoms and the effects immediately following and for the first several days following the accident.

Initial treatment and progression of injuries/symptoms/effects

- Include the claimant's account of any initial treatment and the progression of injuries/symptoms/effects.

Subsequent treatment and progression of injuries/symptoms/effects

- Where treatment is extended over several weeks or months, give the claimant's account of the treatment received and the progress made.

Consequences of injuries (from accident to present)

- Give details of all claimed consequential loss since the accident to the date of the examination.

3. Presenting Condition

In this section, give details of the present complaints of the claimant, reporting those facts relevant to the medical issues and quoting the claimant's own words where relevant.

Present injuries/symptoms/effects

- Give details of the claimant's account of present medical complaints and the claimed restrictions arising from these complaints.

Present treatment

- Give details of the claimant's account of present treatment (both conventional and alternative modalities, as necessary).

Past medical history

- Give details of the claimant's account of his/her medical history.

- Give details of the claimant's explanation of any inconsistencies in his/her medical history which arise from a comparison with the claimant's medical records.

4. Medical History

In this section, include relevant details from the claimant's medical records. Where the expert is instructed not to read the claimant's medical records, make clear this instruction here as well as in the instructions received sub-section in the Introduction section.

Relevant medical history

- Identify relevant medical issues in the records.[1]

- Check that the copy of the records you have been sent is complete.

5. Examination

In this section, the information can be written technically and without detailed explanation, as any issue that needs to be explained will be dealt with fully in the Opinion section that follows. However, brief explanatory notes will generally assist the reader to understand medical aspects of the report and therefore, where this explanation can be provided without overwhelming the reader with too much technical information, it is good practice to do so.

---

1   The expert should receive from the instructing solicitor (or agency) medical notes that have been sorted into chronological order. If these records are received unsorted, the expert should contact the instructing solicitor to negotiate a fee for sorting the records. Any fee agreed for sorting the records should be in addition to the fee for writing the report. The terms of business agreed between the expert and the solicitor or agency at the outset of the relationship should also set out the expert's terms in respect of sorting medical notes to avoid any misunderstandings.

Details of examination and findings

- Report fully on the examination as this is direct evidence and is essential to the opinion expressed.

- Report NAD findings to establish that the test or assessment was actually carried out.

- Report findings on examination that are not consistent or are in some way surprising or out of the ordinary.

6. Opinion and Prognosis

This is the most important section of the report from the lawyers' perspective and requires the expert to give clearly stated opinions supported by reasons/reasoning.

Summary of examination findings

- List the injuries to be addressed based on the examination findings and analysis of the records.

Opinion as to present condition

- If not already defined by examination findings, give opinion as to the injuries the claimant has suffered as a result of the accident.

- Address each injury in turn making clear the relevant facts and the reasoning based on those facts.

- The expert may have been instructed not to examine the medical records. Having examined the claimant, if the expert considers that a review of the medical records is necessary or would be helpful, this should be stated.

Causation of injuries

- Give clear opinion on what caused the injury.

- Support all opinion with reasons.

- Give opinion on what the claimant's medical situation would have been without the accident ('but for').

Relevant pre-existing conditions (if any)

- Where the claimant has a pre-existing condition, explain how the progression of this condition would have affected the claimant and contrast this with the situation since the accident and for the future.

Prognosis of injuries

- Give a prognosis for each injury (or all the injuries together) dealing with deterioration/improvement with the likelihood of this occurring and over what time period.

Future treatment (if relevant)

- Give opinion on any future medical treatment that the claimant may need, what is the likelihood (as a percentage) of needing the treatment and when is it likely to be needed.

- Give opinion on any treatment that may improve the claimant's medical situation.

- Where the expert knows the cost of such treatment if carried out privately, this can usefully be included.

7. Consequences of Injuries

Opinion on the consequences resulting from injuries/symptoms/effects

- Use mundane language to describe the restrictions that the claimant faces in his/her activities of daily living.

- Avoid using percentages when describing what difference the injuries have made to the claimant's level of restriction.

- Do not stray into giving evidence beyond the area of expertise.

8. Summary of Conclusions

List of conclusions

- List the conclusions reached in sections 6 and 7. Where specific questions from the solicitor have been addressed, these can be set out in italics with the relevant conclusion set out beneath.

Declaration and Statement of Truth

- Make sure the Expert's Declaration and Statement of Truth comply with PD 35.

<u>Sign and Date</u>

- It is unnecessary to sign every page of expert evidence in civil claims

Psychiatric/Psychological Reports

- Psychiatric/psychological reports are commonly criticised by lawyers for being too long for the complexity of the issues being addressed. There are two reasons for this criticism:

    1. irrelevant information is included in the report; and

    2. relevant information is included, but its relevance to the expert's reasoning in forming an opinion is not explained in the report.

- A psychiatric/psychological injury is often an integral part of the physical injuries a claimant has suffered. It is important that the psychiatric or psychological expert does not misquote a claimant who is discussing physical injuries, as there is a danger of creating inconsistencies in the evidence and therefore further opportunities for dispute between the parties.

- Wherever possible, the expert should read relevant reports on physical injuries prior to conducting the mental state examination.

- In the Opinion section, it is extremely helpful to set out the details of the relevant DSM-IV or ICD-10 classifications, as the court is unlikely to be familiar with the specific features of and distinctions between different classifications.

- As with a report on physical injuries, it is essential that the report covers the likely situation in the absence of the accident ('but for') and specifically, in the case of long term conditions, whether other events in the claimant's life would, at some future time, have brought on the condition that is the subject of the dispute or some other condition. The likely onset and impact of any condition that would have been likely to develop in any event should be contrasted with the situation since the accident.

Industrial Disease Reports

- The employment history should be presented as a chronology. It is extremely important to be as accurate as possible when constructing this chronology as periods of exposure and when these occurred are fundamental to the opinions that will be expressed in the report. The history may also be a focus for challenge should the matter come to court.

- The type and degree of exposure should be detailed for each job and details should be given of the occupational health and safety precautions that were in place at the time of the exposure.

- Given the volume of records that are often available in such cases, it makes sense to set out the medical history after the employment history. The claimant's account of his/her medical history can be included as part of the Presenting Condition section.

- Causation may need to be addressed using the 'but for' test or the 'material contribution' test (or both) depending upon the solicitor's instructions and the facts of the case. If unsure, the expert should discuss the matter with the instructing solicitor.

Appendix 1(d)

Clinical Negligence Report Template

1. **Introduction**
   - Author
   - Instructions
   - Background to the dispute
   - Overview of medical issues (as necessary)
   - Sources of information
   - Methodology
   - Structure of the report

2. **Chronology of Events**
   - Factual account of events from records/witness statements
   - Explanations of technical matters (as required)

3. **Past Medical History**
   - Overview of claimant's PMH with details of relevant history

4. **Opinion**
   - Breach of Duty
   - Causation

5. **Summary of Conclusions**
   - List of conclusions
   - Declaration and Statement of Truth
   - Sign and Date

Notes: Clinical Negligence Report Template

See also notes to the templates above.

1. Introduction

Clinical negligence disputes are generally more complex than personal injury cases, in terms of the facts of the case, conflicts in the evidence, the technical issues to be addressed and the range of medical opinion on the matters to be decided. Ensuring that the report adequately explains the medical issues in the evidence is of great importance.

Instructions Received

- Make clear whether the report will deal with liability (breach of duty), causation or both of these aspects of the claim.

- In some instances, the expert will deal with condition and prognosis as well as liability and causation. If so, it is important that the liability and causation report is separate from the condition and prognosis report. The condition and prognosis report should follow the Personal Injury Report template.

Overview of Medical Issues

- It is often extremely helpful for the expert to introduce the medical issues that are central to the issues in the case. This should be a non-contentious explanation of these issues, drawing attention to the medical issues that need to be considered when deciding the issues in dispute.

- As a rough guide, 3 to 5 paragraphs will often be sufficient to give an introduction to the key medical issues. However, if a longer explanation is required, it may be useful to add this explanation as an appendix, giving a cross-reference in the main text.

Sources of information

- Information supplied to the expert is often extensive – if so, use an appendix to set out sources of information. It is also important to note any information that has not been supplied to the expert (e.g. missing pages of notes at important moments in the treatment process).

2. Chronology of Events

Provide a narrative (accessible to lawyers) of the treatment history, referenced to the sources of information from which it has been derived.

- Quote verbatim any important entries in the clinical record and explain what each entry means.

- Use sub-headings to indicate the date and time that the specific events occurred.

- Explain technical issues but avoid giving opinion on these issues when setting out the chronology. Such opinions should be given in the Opinion section of the report

3. Past Medical History

- The past medical history in a clinical negligence report may need to be more detailed than in a personal injury report. This is because an underlying health condition is often the reason that the claimant was receiving medical treatment in the first instance.

- An underlying health issue may be an important component of the causation question.

- As in personal injury reports, the expert should still focus on the relevant medical history and summarise very briefly (or exclude) non-relevant medical issues.

- Make sure that medical records are quoted accurately.

- Where the past medical history will help to make clear the treatment process the claimant was undergoing, it may be clearer to place the Past Medical History section before the Chronology of Events section.

4. Opinion and Prognosis

- Opinion on breach of duty will be based on the test in *Bolam* or, in rare cases, the test in *Bolitho*. Essentially, the analysis breaks down into the following stages:
    1. What would a reasonably competent clinician have done (or not done) in these circumstances?
    2. What did the clinician do or omit to do?
    3. Is there a range of professional opinion within which a responsible body of clinicians would have acted (or omitted

to act) in the same manner?

4.   (and in cases where *Bolitho* is relevant) Can the treatment decisions made be logically supported in the light of the benefits and risks inherent in those decisions?

- Opinion on causation, unless otherwise instructed, will apply the 'but for' test. When dealing with the actions or inactions of the clinicians involved in the claimant's care, the analysis breaks down into three stages:

  1.   What did the clinician do or omit to do?
  2.   What damage resulted from this action or inaction?
  3.   Had the clinician acted differently, what would the outcome have been and what difference would this have made?

5. Summary of Conclusions

See notes for the Personal Injury Report template above.

Appendix 2

Medico-Legal Report Checklist

Presentation of the Report

- ☐ Header: case name/reference; report author; speciality

- ☐ Footer: report date; page number

- ☐ Margins: 3cm

- ☐ Text: 11-13pt (depending on font)

- ☐ Spacing: Double or 1.5 line spacing

- ☐ Headings: **Section**, Main, *Subheadings* (headings should be easy to differentiate and consistently presented)

- ☐ Numbering: two level system - 1.1, 1.2, 1.3 / 2.1, 2.2, 2.3 etc.

Title Page

- ☐ Title of action and reference no.

- ☐ Title of report (Medical Report on Mr J Smith)

- ☐ Author (speciality)

- ☐ Date (of examination or report, or both)

- ☐ Claimant's contact details

- ☐ Instructions received from: (solicitor)

- ☐ Expert's contact details (include medico-legal practice contact hours)

Contents Page

- ☐ Section headings and page numbers

Body of the Report

Introduction

☐ CV appropriate for case (usually 2-3 paragraphs, with an appended CV as necessary)

☐ Include substance of all material instructions

☐ Refers to 'CPR Part 35 report' or 'report for the court'

☐ Include a background to the dispute (as necessary)

☐ Include sources of information

☐ Include outline methodology

Factual Basis

☐ Present factual basis clearly

☐ Define technical terms in a bracket or footnote

☐ Include appropriate level of technical explanation

☐ Maintain a clear separation of fact and opinion in report structure/template

☐ Reference sources of factual information

☐ Quantify descriptive language (where available, use scales of description - either set out in the report or the appendices)

Opinion

☐ Summary of injuries (Condition and Prognosis reports only)

☐ Give clear diagnosis of injury

☐ Express each opinion in a structured manner (Long-Form/Short-Form)

☐ Deal with causation fully (as appropriate) addressing the 'but for' situation

☐ Apply the standard of proof and appropriate legal tests, using the correct phrases

☐ Support all opinions with reasons/reasoning

☐ Give prognosis: likelihood of deterioration/recovery, giving a range of probabilities/time period

☐   Address consequences by dealing with restrictions appropriate and
attributable to the injuries, symptoms and effects

<u>Summary of Conclusions</u>

☐   Summarise all conclusions

☐   Address all relevant issues (with reference to the solicitor's instructions)

☐   Ensure the Expert's Declaration and Statement of Truth comply with PD35

☐   Sign and date report

Appendix 3

CPR Part 35 Experts and Assessors (as amended by 53rd update)

Duty to restrict expert evidence

35.1

Expert evidence shall be restricted to that which is reasonably required to resolve the proceedings.

Interpretation and definitions

35.2

(1) A reference to an 'expert' in this Part is a reference to a person who has been instructed to give or prepare expert evidence for the purpose of proceedings.

(2) 'Single joint expert' means an expert instructed to prepare a report for the court on behalf of two or more of the parties (including the claimant) to the proceedings.

Experts – overriding duty to the court

35.3

(1) It is the duty of experts to help the court on matters within their expertise.

(2) This duty overrides any obligation to the person from whom experts have received instructions or by whom they are paid.

Court's power to restrict expert evidence

35.4

(1) No party may call an expert or put in evidence an expert's report without the court's permission.

(2) When parties apply for permission they must identify –

(a) the field in which expert evidence is required; and

(b) where practicable, the name of the proposed expert.

(3) If permission is granted it shall be in relation only to the expert named or the field identified under paragraph (2).

(3A) Where a claim has been allocated to the small claims track or the fast track, if permission is given for expert evidence, it will normally be given for evidence from only one expert on a particular issue.

Note: Paragraph 7 of Practice Direction 35 sets out some of the circumstances the court will consider when deciding whether expert evidence should be given by a single joint expert.

(4) The court may limit the amount of a party's expert's fees and expenses that may be recovered from any other party.

General requirement for expert evidence to be given in a written report

35.5

(1) Expert evidence is to be given in a written report unless the court directs otherwise.

(2) If a claim is on the small claims track or the fast track, the court will not direct an expert to attend a hearing unless it is necessary to do so in the interests of justice.

Written questions to experts

35.6

(1) A party may put written questions about an expert's report (which must be proportionate) to –

    (a) an expert instructed by another party; or

    (b) a single joint expert appointed under rule 35.7.

(2) Written questions under paragraph (1) –

    (a) may be put once only;

    (b) must be put within 28 days of service of the expert's report; and

    (c) must be for the purpose only of clarification of the report,

        unless in any case –

        (i) the court gives permission; or

        (ii) the other party agrees.

(3) An expert's answers to questions put in accordance with paragraph (1) shall be treated as part of the expert's report.

(4) Where –

    (a) a party has put a written question to an expert instructed by another party; and

    (b) the expert does not answer that question,

    the court may make one or both of the following orders in relation to the party who instructed the expert –

        (i) that the party may not rely on the evidence of that expert; or

        (ii) that the party may not recover the fees and expenses of that expert from any other party.

Court's power to direct that evidence is to be given by a single joint expert

35.7

(1) Where two or more parties wish to submit expert evidence on a particular issue, the court may direct that the evidence on that issue is to be given by a single joint expert.

(2) Where the parties who wish to submit the evidence ('the relevant parties') cannot agree who should be the single joint expert, the court may –

    (a) select the expert from a list prepared or identified by the relevant parties; or

    (b) direct that the expert be selected in such other manner as the court may direct.

Instructions to a single joint expert

35.8

(1) Where the court gives a direction under rule 35.7 for a single joint expert to be used, any relevant party may give instructions to the expert.

(2) When a party gives instructions to the expert that party must, at the same time, send a copy to the other relevant parties.

(3) The court may give directions about –

    (a) the payment of the expert's fees and expenses; and

(b) any inspection, examination or experiments which the expert wishes to carry out.

(4) The court may, before an expert is instructed –

(a) limit the amount that can be paid by way of fees and expenses to the expert; and

(b) direct that some or all of the relevant parties pay that amount into court.

(5) Unless the court otherwise directs, the relevant parties are jointly and severally liable(GL) for the payment of the expert's fees and expenses.

Power of court to direct a party to provide information

35.9

Where a party has access to information which is not reasonably available to another party, the court may direct the party who has access to the information to –

(a) prepare and file a document recording the information; and

(b) serve a copy of that document on the other party.

Contents of report

35.10

(1) An expert's report must comply with the requirements set out in Practice Direction 35.

(2) At the end of an expert's report there must be a statement that the expert understands and has complied with their duty to the court.

(3) The expert's report must state the substance of all material instructions, whether written or oral, on the basis of which the report was written.

(4) The instructions referred to in paragraph (3) shall not be privileged(GL) against disclosure but the court will not, in relation to those instructions –

(a) order disclosure of any specific document; or

(b) permit any questioning in court, other than by the party who instructed the expert, unless it is satisfied that there are reasonable grounds to consider the statement of instructions given under paragraph (3) to be inaccurate or incomplete.

Use by one party of expert's report disclosed by another

35.11

Where a party has disclosed an expert's report, any party may use that expert's report as evidence at the trial.

Discussions between experts

35.12

(1) The court may, at any stage, direct a discussion between experts for the purpose of requiring the experts to –

    (a) identify and discuss the expert issues in the proceedings; and

    (b) where possible, reach an agreed opinion on those issues.

(2) The court may specify the issues which the experts must discuss.

(3) The court may direct that following a discussion between the experts they must prepare a statement for the court setting out those issues on which –

    (a) they agree; and

    (b) they disagree, with a summary of their reasons for disagreeing.

(4) The content of the discussion between the experts shall not be referred to at the trial unless the parties agree.

(5) Where experts reach agreement on an issue during their discussions, the agreement shall not bind the parties unless the parties expressly agree to be bound by the agreement.

Consequence of failure to disclose expert's report

35.13

A party who fails to disclose an expert's report may not use the report at the trial or call the expert to give evidence orally unless the court gives permission.

Expert's right to ask court for directions

35.14

(1) Experts may file written requests for directions for the purpose of assisting them in carrying out their functions.

(2) Experts must, unless the court orders otherwise, provide copies of the proposed requests for directions under paragraph (1) –

   (a) to the party instructing them, at least 7 days before they file the requests; and

   (b) to all other parties, at least 4 days before they file them.

(3) The court, when it gives directions, may also direct that a party be served with a copy of the directions.

Assessors

35.15

(1) This rule applies where the court appoints one or more persons under section 70 of the Senior Courts Act 1981 or section 63 of the County Courts Act 1984 as an assessor.

(2) An assessor will assist the court in dealing with a matter in which the assessor has skill and experience.

(3) An assessor will take such part in the proceedings as the court may direct and in particular the court may direct an assessor to –

   (a) prepare a report for the court on any matter at issue in the proceedings; and

   (b) attend the whole or any part of the trial to advise the court on any such matter.

(4) If an assessor prepares a report for the court before the trial has begun –

   (a) the court will send a copy to each of the parties; and

   (b) the parties may use it at trial.

(5) The remuneration to be paid to an assessor is to be determined by the court and will form part of the costs of the proceedings.

(6) The court may order any party to deposit in the court office a specified sum in respect of an assessor's fees and, where it does so, the assessor will not be asked to act until the sum has been deposited.

(7) Paragraphs (5) and (6) do not apply where the remuneration of the assessor is to be paid out of money provided by Parliament.

Appendix 4

Practice Direction to Part 35 (as amended by 53rd update)

Introduction

1

Part 35 is intended to limit the use of oral expert evidence to that which is reasonably required. In addition, where possible, matters requiring expert evidence should be dealt with by only one expert. Experts and those instructing them are expected to have regard to the guidance contained in the Protocol for the Instruction of Experts to give Evidence in Civil Claims annexed to this practice direction. (Further guidance on experts is contained in Annex C to the Practice Direction (Pre-Action Conduct)).

Expert Evidence – General Requirements

2.1

Expert evidence should be the independent product of the expert uninfluenced by the pressures of litigation.

2.2

Experts should assist the court by providing objective, unbiased opinions on matters within their expertise, and should not assume the role of an advocate.

2.3

Experts should consider all material facts, including those which might detract from their opinions.

2.4

Experts should make it clear –

    (a) when a question or issue falls outside their expertise; and

    (b) when they are not able to reach a definite opinion, for example because they have insufficient information.

2.5

If, after producing a report, an expert's view changes on any material matter, such change of view should be communicated to all the parties without delay, and when appropriate to the court.

Form and Content of an Expert's Report

3.1

An expert's report should be addressed to the court and not to the party from whom the expert has received instructions.

3.2

An expert's report must:

(1) give details of the expert's qualifications;

(2) give details of any literature or other material which has been relied on in making the report;

(3) contain a statement setting out the substance of all facts and instructions which are material to the opinions expressed in the report or upon which those opinions are based;

(4) make clear which of the facts stated in the report are within the expert's own knowledge;

(5) say who carried out any examination, measurement, test or experiment which the expert has used for the report, give the qualifications of that person, and say whether or not the test or experiment has been carried out under the expert's supervision;

(6) where there is a range of opinion on the matters dealt with in the report –

   (a) summarise the range of opinions; and

   (b) give reasons for the expert's own opinion;

(7) contain a summary of the conclusions reached;

(8) if the expert is not able to give an opinion without qualification, state the qualification; and

(9) contain a statement that the expert –

   (a) understands their duty to the court, and has complied with that duty; and

    (b) is aware of the requirements of Part 35, this practice direction and the Protocol for Instruction of Experts to give Evidence in Civil Claims.

3.3

An expert's report must be verified by a statement of truth in the following form –

I confirm that I have made clear which facts and matters referred to in this report are within my own knowledge and which are not. Those that are within my own knowledge I confirm to be true. The opinions I have expressed represent my true and complete professional opinions on the matters to which they refer.

Note: Part 22 deals with statements of truth. Rule 32.14 sets out the consequences of verifying a document containing a false statement without an honest belief in its truth.

Information

4

Under rule 35.9 the court may direct a party with access to information, which is not reasonably available to another party to serve on that other party a document, which records the information. The document served must include sufficient details of all the facts, tests, experiments and assumptions which underlie any part of the information to enable the party on whom it is served to make, or to obtain, a proper interpretation of the information and an assessment of its significance.

Instructions

5

Cross-examination of experts on the contents of their instructions will not be allowed unless the court permits it (or unless the party who gave the instructions consents). Before it gives permission the court must be satisfied that there are reasonable grounds to consider that the statement in the report of the substance of the instructions is inaccurate or incomplete. If the court is so satisfied, it will allow the cross-examination where it appears to be in the interests of justice.

Questions to Experts

6.1

Where a party sends a written question or questions under rule 35.6 direct to an expert, a copy of the questions must, at the same time, be sent to the other party or parties.

6.2

The party or parties instructing the expert must pay any fees charged by that expert for answering questions put under rule 35.6. This does not affect any decision of the court as to the party who is ultimately to bear the expert's fees.

Single joint expert

7

When considering whether to give permission for the parties to rely on expert evidence and whether that evidence should be from a single joint expert the court will take into account all the circumstances in particular, whether:

(a) it is proportionate to have separate experts for each party on a particular issue with reference to –

    (i) the amount in dispute;

    (ii) the importance to the parties; and

    (iii) the complexity of the issue;

(b) the instruction of a single joint expert is likely to assist the parties and the court to resolve the issue more speedily and in a more cost-effective way than separately instructed experts;

(c) expert evidence is to be given on the issue of liability, causation or quantum;

(d) the expert evidence falls within a substantially established area of knowledge which is unlikely to be in dispute or there is likely to be a range of expert opinion;

(e) a party has already instructed an expert on the issue in question and whether or not that was done in compliance with any practice direction or relevant pre-action protocol;

(f) questions put in accordance with rule 35.6 are likely to remove the need for the other party to instruct an expert if one party has already instructed an expert;

(g) questions put to a single joint expert may not conclusively deal with all issues that may require testing prior to trial;

(h) a conference may be required with the legal representatives, experts and other witnesses which may make instruction of a single joint expert impractical; and

(i) a claim to privilege(GL) makes the instruction of any expert as a single joint expert inappropriate.

Orders

8

Where an order requires an act to be done by an expert, or otherwise affects an expert, the party instructing that expert must serve a copy of the order on the expert. The claimant must serve the order on a single joint expert.

Discussions between experts

9.1

Unless directed by the court discussions between experts are not mandatory. Parties must consider, with their experts, at an early stage, whether there is likely to be any useful purpose in holding an experts' discussion and if so when.

9.2

The purpose of discussions between experts is not for experts to settle cases but to agree and narrow issues and in particular to identify:

(i)   the extent of the agreement between them;

(ii) the points of and short reasons for any disagreement;

(iii) action, if any, which may be taken to resolve any outstanding points of disagreement; and

(iv) any further material issues not raised and the extent to which these issues are agreed.

9.3

Where the experts are to meet, the parties must discuss and if possible agree whether an agenda is necessary, and if so attempt to agree one that helps the experts to focus on the issues which need to be discussed. The agenda must not be in the form of leading questions or hostile in tone.

9.4

Unless ordered by the court, or agreed by all parties, and the experts, neither the parties nor their legal representatives may attend experts discussions.

9.5

If the legal representatives do attend –

    (i) they should not normally intervene in the discussion, except to answer questions put to them by the experts or to advise on the law; and

    (ii) the experts may if they so wish hold part of their discussions in the absence of the legal representatives.

9.6

A statement must be prepared by the experts dealing with paragraphs 9.2(i) - (iv) above. Individual copies of the statements must be signed by the experts at the conclusion of the discussion, or as soon thereafter as practicable, and in any event within 7 days. Copies of the statements must be provided to the parties no later than 14 days after signing.

9.7

Experts must give their own opinions to assist the court and do not require the authority of the parties to sign a joint statement.

9.8

If an expert significantly alters an opinion, the joint statement must include a note or addendum by that expert explaining the change of opinion.

Assessors

10.1

An assessor may be appointed to assist the court under rule 35.15. Not less than 21 days before making any such appointment, the court will notify each party in writing of the name of the proposed assessor, of the matter in respect of which the assistance of the assessor will be sought and of the qualifications of the assessor to give that assistance.

10.2

Where any person has been proposed for appointment as an assessor, any party may object to that person either personally or in respect of that person's qualification.

10.3

Any such objection must be made in writing and filed with the court within 7 days of receipt of the notification referred to in paragraph 10.1 and will be taken into account by the court in deciding whether or not to make the appointment.

10.4

Copies of any report prepared by the assessor will be sent to each of the parties but the assessor will not give oral evidence or be open to cross-examination or questioning.

Appendix 5

Protocol for the Instruction of Experts to give Evidence in Civil Claims

1. Introduction

Expert witnesses perform a vital role in civil litigation. It is essential that both those who instruct experts and experts themselves are given clear guidance as to what they are expected to do in civil proceedings. The purpose of this Protocol is to provide such guidance. It has been drafted by the Civil Justice Council and reflects the rules and practice directions current [in June 2005], replacing the Code of Guidance on Expert Evidence. The authors of the Protocol wish to acknowledge the valuable assistance they obtained by drawing on earlier documents produced by the Academy of Experts and the Expert Witness Institute, as well as suggestions made by the Clinical Dispute Forum. The Protocol has been approved by the Master of the Rolls.

2. Aims of Protocol

2.1   This Protocol offers guidance to experts and to those instructing them in the interpretation of and compliance with Part 35 of the Civil Procedure Rules (CPR 35) and its associated Practice Direction (PD 35) and to further the objectives of the Civil Procedure Rules in general. It is intended to assist in the interpretation of those provisions in the interests of good practice but it does not replace them. It sets out standards for the use of experts and the conduct of experts and those who instruct them. The existence of this Protocol does not remove the need for experts and those who instruct them to be familiar with CPR35 and PD35.

2.2   Experts and those who instruct them should also bear in mind para 1.4 of the Practice Direction on Protocols which contains the following objectives, namely to:

    (a) encourage the exchange of early and full information about the expert issues involved in a prospective legal claim;

    (b) enable the parties to avoid or reduce the scope of litigation by agreeing the whole or part of an expert issue before commencement of proceedings; and

    (c) support the efficient management of proceedings where litigation cannot be avoided.

3. Application

3.1   This Protocol applies to any steps taken for the purpose of civil proceedings by experts or those who instruct them on or after 5th September 2005.

3.2   It applies to all experts who are, or who may be, governed by CPR Part 35 and to those who instruct them. Experts are governed by Part 35 if they are or have been instructed to give or prepare evidence for the purpose of civil proceedings in a court in England and Wales (CPR 35.2).

3.3   Experts, and those instructing them, should be aware that some cases may be "specialist proceedings" (CPR 49) where there are modifications to the Civil Procedure Rules. Proceedings may also be governed by other Protocols. Further, some courts have published their own Guides which supplement the Civil Procedure

Rules for proceedings in those courts. They contain provisions affecting expert evidence. Expert witnesses and those instructing them should be familiar with them when they are relevant.

3.4   Courts may take into account any failure to comply with this Protocol when making orders in relation to costs, interest, time limits, the stay of proceedings and whether to order a party to pay a sum of money into court.

Limitation

3.5   If, as a result of complying with any part of this Protocol, claims would or might be time barred under any provision in the Limitation Act 1980, or any other legislation that imposes a time limit for the bringing an action, claimants may commence proceedings without complying with this Protocol. In such circumstances, claimants who commence proceedings without complying with all, or any part, of this Protocol must apply, giving notice to all other parties, to the court for directions as to the timetable and form of procedure to be adopted, at the same time as they request the court to issue proceedings. The court may consider whether to order a stay of the whole or part of the proceedings pending compliance with this Protocol and may make orders in relation to costs.

4. Duties of experts

4.1   Experts always owe a duty to exercise reasonable skill and care to those instructing them, and to comply with any relevant professional code of ethics. However when they are instructed to give or prepare evidence for the purpose of civil proceedings in England and Wales they have an overriding duty to help the court on matters within their expertise (CPR 35.3). This duty overrides any obligation to the person instructing or paying them. Experts must not serve the exclusive interest of those who retain them.

4.2   Experts should be aware of the overriding objective that courts deal with cases justly. This includes dealing with cases proportionately, expeditiously and fairly (CPR 1.1). Experts are under an obligation to assist the court so as to enable them to deal with cases in accordance with the overriding objective. However the overriding objective does not impose on experts any duty to act as mediators between the parties or require them to trespass on the role of the court in deciding facts.

4.3   Experts should provide opinions which are independent, regardless of the pressures of litigation. In this context, a useful test of 'independence' is that the expert would express the same opinion if given the same instructions by an opposing party. Experts should not take it upon themselves to promote the point of view of the party instructing them or engage in the role of advocates.

4.4   Experts should confine their opinions to matters which are material to the disputes between the parties and provide opinions only in relation to matters which lie within their expertise. Experts should indicate without delay where particular questions or issues fall outside their expertise.

4.5   Experts should take into account all material facts before them at the time that they give their opinion. Their reports should set out those facts and any literature or any other material on which they have relied in forming their opinions. They should indicate if an opinion is provisional, or qualified, or where they consider that further information is required or if, for any other reason, they are not satisfied that an opinion can be expressed finally and without qualification.

4.6   Experts should inform those instructing them without delay of any change in their opinions on any material matter and the reason for it.

4.7   Experts should be aware that any failure by them to comply with the Civil Procedure Rules or court orders or any excessive delay for which they are responsible may result in the parties who instructed them being penalised in costs and even, in extreme cases, being debarred from placing the experts' evidence before the court. In *Phillips v Symes*[1] Peter Smith J held that courts may also make orders for costs (under section 51 of the Supreme Court Act 1981) directly against expert witnesses who by their evidence cause significant expense to be incurred, and do so in flagrant and reckless disregard of their duties to the Court.

5. Conduct of Experts instructed only to advise

5.1   Part 35 only applies where experts are instructed to give opinions which are relied on for the purposes of court proceedings. Advice which the parties do not intend to adduce in litigation is likely to be confidential; the Protocol does not apply in these circumstances.[2,3]

5.2   The same applies where, after the commencement of proceedings, experts are instructed only to advise (e.g. to comment upon a single joint expert's report) and not to give or prepare evidence for use in the proceedings.

5.3   However this Protocol does apply if experts who were formerly instructed only to advise are later instructed to give or prepare evidence for the purpose of civil proceedings.

6. The Need for Experts

6.1   Those intending to instruct experts to give or prepare evidence for the purpose of civil proceedings should consider whether expert evidence is appropriate, taking account of the principles set out in CPR Parts 1 and 35, and in particular whether:
   (a) it is relevant to a matter which is in dispute between the parties.
   (b) it is reasonably required to resolve the proceedings (CPR 35.1);
   (c) the expert has expertise relevant to the issue on which an opinion is sought;
   (d) the expert has the experience, expertise and training appropriate to the value, complexity and importance of the case; and whether
   (e) these objects can be achieved by the appointment of a single joint expert (see section 17 below).

6.2   Although the court's permission is not generally required to instruct an expert, the court's permission is required before experts can be called to give evidence or their evidence can be put in (CPR 35.4).

7. The appointment of experts

7.1   Before experts are formally instructed or the court's permission to appoint named experts is sought, the following should be established:
   (a) that they have the appropriate expertise and experience;
   (b) that they are familiar with the general duties of an expert;

---

1   *Phillips v Symes* [2004] EWHC 2330 (Ch)

2   *Carlson v Townsend* [2001] 1 WLR 2415

3   *Jackson v Marley Davenport* [2004] 1 WLR 2926

(c) that they can produce a report, deal with questions and have discussions with other experts within a reasonable time and at a cost proportionate to the matters in issue;

(d) a description of the work required;

(e) whether they are available to attend the trial, if attendance is required; and

(f) there is no potential conflict of interest.

7.2 Terms of appointment should be agreed at the outset and should normally include:

(a) the capacity in which the expert is to be appointed (e.g. party appointed expert, single joint expert or expert advisor);

(b) the services required of the expert (e.g. provision of expert's report, answering questions in writing, attendance at meetings and attendance at court);

(c) time for delivery of the report;

(d) the basis of the expert's charges (either daily or hourly rates and an estimate of the time likely to be required, or a total fee for the services);

(e) travelling expenses and disbursements;

(f) cancellation charges;

(g) any fees for attending court;

(h) time for making the payment;

(i) whether fees are to be paid by a third party; and

(j) if a party is publicly funded, whether or not the expert's charges will be subject to assessment by a costs officer.

7.3 As to the appointment of single joint experts, see section 17 below.

7.4 When necessary, arrangements should be made for dealing with questions to experts and discussions between experts, including any directions given by the court, and provision should be made for the cost of this work.

7.5 Experts should be informed regularly about deadlines for all matters concerning them. Those instructing experts should promptly send them copies of all court orders and directions which may affect the preparation of their reports or any other matters concerning their obligations.

Conditional and Contingency Fees

7.6 Payments contingent upon the nature of the expert evidence given in legal proceedings, or upon the outcome of a case, must not be offered or accepted. To do so would contravene experts' overriding duty to the court and compromise their duty of independence.

7.7 Agreement to delay payment of experts' fees until after the conclusion of cases is permissible as long as the amount of the fee does not depend on the outcome of the case.

8. Instructions

8.1 Those instructing experts should ensure that they give clear instructions, including the following:

(a) basic information, such as names, addresses, telephone numbers, dates of birth and dates of incidents;

(b) the nature and extent of the expertise which is called for;

(c) the purpose of requesting the advice or report, a description of the matter(s) to be investigated, the principal known issues and the identity of all parties;

(d) the statement(s) of case (if any), those documents which form part of standard disclosure and witness statements which are relevant to the advice or report;

(e) where proceedings have not been started, whether proceedings are being contemplated and, if so, whether the expert is asked only for advice;

(f) an outline programme, consistent with good case management and the expert's availability, for the completion and delivery of each stage of the expert's work; and

(g) where proceedings have been started, the dates of any hearings (including any Case Management Conferences and/or Pre-Trial Reviews), the name of the court, the claim number and the track to which the claim has been allocated.

8.2 Experts who do not receive clear instructions should request clarification and may indicate that they are not prepared to act unless and until such clear instructions are received.

8.3 As to the instruction of single joint experts, see section 17 below.

9. Experts' Acceptance of Instructions

9.1 Experts should confirm without delay whether or not they accept instructions. They should also inform those instructing them (whether on initial instruction or at any later stage) without delay if:

(a) instructions are not acceptable because, for example, they require work that falls outside their expertise, impose unrealistic deadlines, or are insufficiently clear;

(b) they consider that instructions are or have become insufficient to complete the work;

(c) they become aware that they may not be able to fulfil any of the terms of appointment;

(d) the instructions and/or work have, for any reason, placed them in conflict with their duties as an expert; or

(e) they are not satisfied that they can comply with any orders that have been made.

9.2 Experts must neither express an opinion outside the scope of their field of expertise, nor accept any instructions to do so.

10. Withdrawal

10.1 Where experts' instructions remain incompatible with their duties, whether through incompleteness, a conflict between their duty to the court and their instructions, or for any other substantial and significant reason, they may consider withdrawing from the case. However, experts should not withdraw without first discussing the position fully with those who instruct them and considering carefully whether it would be more appropriate to make a written request for directions from the court. If experts do withdraw, they must give formal written notice to those instructing them.

11. Experts' Right to ask Court for Directions

11.1 Experts may request directions from the court to assist them in carrying out their functions as experts. Experts should normally discuss such matters with those who instruct them before making any such request. Unless the court otherwise orders, any proposed request for directions should be copied to the party instructing the expert at least seven days before filing any request to the court, and to all other parties at least four days before filing it. (CPR 35.14).

11.2   Requests to the court for directions should be made by letter, containing:
  (a) the title of the claim;
  (b) the claim number of the case;
  (c) the name of the expert;
  (d) full details of why directions are sought; and
  (e) copies of any relevant documentation.

12. Power of the Court to Direct a Party to Provide Information

12.1   If experts consider that those instructing them have not provided information which they require, they may, after discussion with those instructing them and giving notice, write to the court to seek directions (CPR 35.14).

12.2   Experts and those who instruct them should also be aware of CPR 35.9. This provides that where one party has access to information which is not readily available to the other party, the court may direct the party who has access to the information to prepare, file and copy to the other party a document recording the information. If experts require such information which has not been disclosed, they should discuss the position with those instructing them without delay, so that a request for the information can be made, and, if not forthcoming, an application can be made to the court. Unless a document appears to be essential, experts should assess the cost and time involved in the production of a document and whether its provision would be proportionate in the context of the case.

13. Contents of Experts' Reports

13.1   The content and extent of experts' reports should be governed by the scope of their instructions and general obligations, the contents of CPR 35 and PD35 and their overriding duty to the court.

13.2   In preparing reports, experts should maintain professional objectivity and impartiality at all times.

13.3   PD 35, para 2 provides that experts' reports should be addressed to the court and gives detailed directions about the form and content of such reports. All experts and those who instruct them should ensure that they are familiar with these requirements.

13.4   Model forms of Experts' Reports are available from bodies such as the Academy of Experts or the Expert Witness Institute.

13.5   Experts' reports must contain statements that they—
  (i) understand their duty to the court and have complied and will continue to comply with it; and
  (ii) are aware of the requirements of Part 35 and Practice Direction 35, this protocol and the practice direction on pre-action conduct.
       Experts' reports must also be verified by a statement of truth. The form of the statement of truth is as follows—
       " I confirm that I have made clear which facts and matters referred to in this report are within my own knowledge and which are not. Those that are within my own knowledge I confirm to be true. The opinions I have expressed represent my true and complete professional opinions on the matters to which they refer."
       This wording is mandatory and must not be modified.

Qualifications

13.6   The details of experts' qualifications to be given in reports should be commensurate with the nature and complexity of the case. It may be sufficient merely to state academic and professional qualifications. However, where highly specialised expertise is called for, experts should include the detail of particular training and/or experience that qualifies them to provide that highly specialised evidence.

Tests

13.7   Where tests of a scientific or technical nature have been carried out, experts should state:
(a) the methodology used; and
(b) by whom the tests were undertaken and under whose supervision,summarising their respective qualifications and experience.

Reliance on the work of others

13.8   Where experts rely in their reports on literature or other material and cite the opinions of others without having verified them, they must give details of those opinions relied on. It is likely to assist the court if the qualifications of the originator(s) are also stated.

Facts

13.9   When addressing questions of fact and opinion, experts should keep the two separate and discrete.
13.10   Experts must state those facts (whether assumed or otherwise) upon which their opinions are based. They must distinguish clearly between those facts which experts know to be true and those facts which they assume.
13.11   Where there are material facts in dispute experts should express separate opinions on each hypothesis put forward. They should not express a view in favour of one or other disputed version of the facts unless, as a result of particular expertise and experience, they consider one set of facts as being improbable or less probable, in which case they may express that view, and should give reasons for holding it.

Range of opinion

13.12   If the mandatory summary of the range of opinion is based on published sources, experts should explain those sources and, where appropriate, state the qualifications of the originator(s) of the opinions from which they differ, particularly if such opinions represent a well-established school of thought.
13.13   Where there is no available source for the range of opinion, experts may need to express opinions on what they believe to be the range which other experts would arrive at if asked. In those circumstances, experts should make it clear that the range that they summarise is based on their own judgement and explain the basis of that judgement.

Conclusions

13.14 A summary of conclusions is mandatory. The summary should be at the end of the report after all the reasoning. There may be cases, however, where the benefit to the court is heightened by placing a short summary at the beginning of the report whilst giving the full conclusions at the end. For example, it can assist with the comprehension of the analysis and with the absorption of the detailed facts if the court is told at the outset of the direction in which the report's logic will flow in cases involving highly complex matters which fall outside the general knowledge of the court.

Basis of report: material instructions

13.15 The mandatory statement of the substance of all material instructions should not be incomplete or otherwise tend to mislead. The imperative is transparency. The term "instructions" includes all material which solicitors place in front of experts in order to gain advice. The omission from the statement of 'off-the-record' oral instructions is not permitted. Courts may allow cross-examination about the instructions if there are reasonable grounds to consider that the statement may be inaccurate or incomplete.

14. After receipt of experts' reports

14.1 Following the receipt of experts' reports, those instructing them should advise the experts as soon as reasonably practicable whether, and if so when, the report will be disclosed to other parties; and, if so disclosed, the date of actual disclosure.

14.2 If experts' reports are to be relied upon, and if experts are to give oral evidence, those instructing them should give the experts the opportunity to consider and comment upon other reports within their area of expertise and which deal with relevant issues at the earliest opportunity.

14.3 Those instructing experts should keep experts informed of the progress of cases, including amendments to statements of case relevant to experts' opinion.

14.4 If those instructing experts become aware of material changes in circumstances or that relevant information within their control was not previously provided to experts, they should without delay instruct experts to review, and if necessary, update the contents of their reports.

15. Amendment of reports

15.1 It may become necessary for experts to amend their reports:
(a) as a result of an exchange of questions and answers;
(b) following agreements reached at meetings between experts; or
(c) where further evidence or documentation is disclosed.

15.2 Experts should not be asked to, and should not, amend, expand or alter any parts of reports in a manner which distorts their true opinion, but may be invited to amend or expand reports to ensure accuracy, internal consistency, completeness and relevance to the issues and clarity. Although experts should generally follow the recommendations of solicitors with regard to the form of reports, they should form their own independent views as to the opinions and contents expressed in their reports and exclude any suggestions which do not accord with their views.

15.3   Where experts change their opinion following a meeting of experts, a simple signed and dated addendum or memorandum to that effect is generally sufficient. In some cases, however, the benefit to the court of having an amended report may justify the cost of making the amendment.

15.4   Where experts significantly alter their opinion, as a result of new evidence or because evidence on which they relied has become unreliable, or for any other reason, they should amend their reports to reflect that fact. Amended reports should include reasons for amendments. In such circumstances those instructing experts should inform other parties as soon as possible of any change of opinion.

15.5   When experts intend to amend their reports, they should inform those instructing them without delay and give reasons. They should provide the amended version (or an addendum or memorandum) clearly marked as such as quickly as possible.

16. Written Questions to Experts

16.1   The procedure for putting written questions to experts (CPR 35.6) is intended to facilitate the clarification of opinions and issues after experts' reports have been served. Experts have a duty to provide answers to questions properly put. Where they fail to do so, the court may impose sanctions against the party instructing the expert, and, if, there is continued non-compliance, debar a party from relying on the report. Experts should copy their answers to those instructing them.

16.2   Experts' answers to questions automatically become part of their reports. They are covered by the statement of truth and form part of the expert evidence.

16.3   Where experts believe that questions put are not properly directed to the clarification of the report, or are disproportionate, or have been asked out of time, they should discuss the questions with those instructing them and, if appropriate, those asking the questions. Attempts should be made to resolve such problems without the need for an application to the court for directions.

Written requests for directions in relation to questions

16.4   If those instructing experts do not apply to the court in respect of questions, but experts still believe that questions are improper or out of time, experts may file written requests with the court for directions to assist in carrying out their functions as experts (CPR 35.14). See Section 11 above.

17. Single Joint Experts

17.1   CPR 35 and PD35 deal extensively with the instruction and use of joint experts by the parties and the powers of the court to order their use (see CPR 35.7 and 35.8, PD35, para 5).

17.2   The Civil Procedure Rules encourage the use of joint experts. Wherever possible a joint report should be obtained. Consideration should therefore be given by all parties to the appointment of single joint experts in all cases where a court might direct such an appointment. Single joint experts are the norm in cases allocated to the small claims track and the fast track.

17.3   Where, in the early stages of a dispute, examinations, investigations, tests, site inspections, experiments, preparation of photographs, plans or other similar preliminary expert tasks are necessary, consideration should be given to the instruction of a single joint expert, especially where such matters are not, at that stage, expected to be contentious as between the parties. The objective of such an appointment should be to agree or to narrow issues.

17.4 Experts who have previously advised a party (whether in the same case or otherwise) should only be proposed as single joint experts if other parties are given all relevant information about the previous involvement.

17.5 The appointment of a single joint expert does not prevent parties from instructing their own experts to advise (but the costs of such expert advisers may not be recoverable in the case).

Joint instructions

17.6 The parties should try to agree joint instructions to single joint experts, but, in default of agreement, each party may give instructions. In particular, all parties should try to agree what documents should be included with instructions and what assumptions single joint experts should make.

17.7 Where the parties fail to agree joint instructions, they should try to agree where the areas of disagreement lie and their instructions should make this clear. If separate instructions are given, they should be copied at the same time to the other instructing parties.

17.8 Where experts are instructed by two or more parties, the terms of appointment should, unless the court has directed otherwise, or the parties have agreed otherwise, include:

(a) a statement that all the instructing parties are jointly and severally liable to pay the experts' fees and, accordingly, that experts' invoices should be sent simultaneously to all instructing parties or their solicitors (as appropriate); and

(b) a statement as to whether any order has been made limiting the amount of experts' fees and expenses (CPR 35.8(4)(a)).

17.9 Where instructions have not been received by the expert from one or more of the instructing parties the expert should give notice (normally at least 7 days) of a deadline to all instructing parties for the receipt by the expert of such instructions. Unless the instructions are received within the deadline the expert may begin work. In the event that instructions are received after the deadline but before the signing off of the report the expert should consider whether it is practicable to comply with those instructions without adversely affecting the timetable set for delivery of the report and in such a manner as to comply with the proportionality principle. An expert who decides to issue a report without taking into account instructions received after the deadline should inform the parties who may apply to the court for directions. In either event the report must show clearly that the expert did not receive instructions within the deadline, or, as the case may be, at all.

Conduct of the single joint expert

17.10 Single joint experts should keep all instructing parties informed of any material steps that they may be taking by, for example, copying all correspondence to those instructing them.

17.11 Single joint experts are Part 35 experts and so have an overriding duty to the court. They are the parties' appointed experts and therefore owe an equal duty to all parties. They should maintain independence, impartiality and transparency at all times.

17.12 Single joint experts should not attend any meeting or conference which is not a joint one, unless all the parties have agreed in writing or the court has directed that such a meeting may be held[4] and who is to pay the experts' fees for the meeting.

17.13 Single joint experts may request directions from the court - see Section 11 above.

17.14 Single joint experts should serve their reports simultaneously on all instructing parties. They should provide a single report even though they may have received instructions which contain areas of conflicting fact or allegation. If conflicting instructions lead to different opinions (for example, because the instructions require experts to make different assumptions of fact), reports may need to contain more than one set of opinions on any issue. It is for the court to determine the facts.

Cross-examination

17.15 Single joint experts do not normally give oral evidence at trial but if they do, all parties may cross-examine them. In general written questions (CPR 35.6) should be put to single joint experts before requests are made for them to attend court for the purpose of cross-examination.[5]

18. Discussions between Experts

18.1 The court has powers to direct discussions between experts for the purposes set out in the Rules (CPR 35.12). Parties may also agree that discussions take place between their experts.

18.2 Where single joint experts have been instructed but parties have, with the permission of the court, instructed their own additional Part 35 experts, there may, if the court so orders or the parties agree, be discussions between the single joint experts and the additional Part 35 experts. Such discussions should be confined to those matters within the remit of the additional Part 35 experts or as ordered by the court.

18.3 The purpose of discussions between experts should be, wherever possible, to:
   (a) identify and discuss the expert issues in the proceedings;
   (b) reach agreed opinions on those issues, and, if that is not possible, to narrow the issues in the case;
   (c) identify those issues on which they agree and disagree and summarise their reasons for disagreement on any issue; and
   (d) identify what action, if any, may be taken to resolve any of the outstanding issues between the parties.

Arrangements for discussions between experts

18.4 Arrangements for discussions between experts should be proportionate to the value of cases. In small claims and fast-track cases there should not normally be meetings between experts. Where discussion is justified in such cases, telephone discussion or an exchange of letters should, in the interests of proportionality, usually suffice. In multi-track cases, discussion may be face to face, but the practicalities or the proportionality principle may require discussions to be by telephone or video

---

4   *Peet v Mid Kent Area Healthcare NHS Trust* [2002] 1 WLR 210

5   *Daniels v Walker* [2000] 1 WLR 1382

conference.

18.5 The parties, their lawyers and experts should co-operate to produce the agenda for any discussion between experts, although primary responsibility for preparation of the agenda should normally lie with the parties' solicitors.

18.6 The agenda should indicate what matters have been agreed and summarise concisely those which are in issue. It is often helpful for it to include questions to be answered by the experts. If agreement cannot be reached promptly or a party is unrepresented, the court may give directions for the drawing up of the agenda. The agenda should be circulated to experts and those instructing them to allow sufficient time for the experts to prepare for the discussion.

18.7 Those instructing experts must not instruct experts to avoid reaching agreement (or to defer doing so) on any matter within the experts' competence. Experts are not permitted to accept such instructions.

18.8 The parties' lawyers may only be present at discussions between experts if all the parties agree or the court so orders. If lawyers do attend, they should not normally intervene except to answer questions put to them by the experts or to advise about the law.[6]

18.9 The content of discussions between experts should not be referred to at trial unless the parties agree (CPR 35.12(4)). It is good practice for any such agreement to be in writing.

18.10 At the conclusion of any discussion between experts, a statement should be prepared setting out:
(a) a list of issues that have been agreed, including, in each instance, the basis of agreement;
(b) a list of issues that have not been agreed, including, in each instance, the basis of disagreement;
(c) a list of any further issues that have arisen that were not included in the original agenda for discussion;
(d) a record of further action, if any, to be taken or recommended, including as appropriate the holding of further discussions between experts.

18.11 The statement should be agreed and signed by all the parties to the discussion as soon as may be practicable.

18.12 Agreements between experts during discussions do not bind the parties unless the parties expressly agree to be bound by the agreement (CPR 35.12(5)). However, in view of the overriding objective, parties should give careful consideration before refusing to be bound by such an agreement and be able to explain their refusal should it become relevant to the issue of costs.

19. Attendance of Experts at Court

19.1 Experts instructed in cases have an obligation to attend court if called upon to do so and accordingly should ensure that those instructing them are always aware of their dates to be avoided and take all reasonable steps to be available.

19.2 Those instructing experts should:
(a) ascertain the availability of experts before trial dates are fixed;
(b) keep experts updated with timetables (including the dates and times experts are to attend) and the location of the court;

---

6   *Hubbard v Lambeth, Southwark and Lewisham HA* [2001] EWCA 1455

(c) give consideration, where appropriate, to experts giving evidence via a video-link.

(d) inform experts immediately if trial dates are vacated.

19.3 Experts should normally attend court without the need for the service of witness summonses, but on occasion they may be served to require attendance (CPR 34). The use of witness summonses does not affect the contractual or other obligations of the parties to pay experts' fees.

Appendix 6

General Medical Council Guidance

Acting as an expert witness - guidance for doctors

1. Our core guidance Good Medical Practice sets out the principles which underpin good care. When doctors act as expert witnesses, they take on a different role from that of a doctor providing treatment or advice to patients. The principles set out in Good Medical Practice also apply to doctors working as expert witnesses.

2. In paragraphs 63-67 of Good Medical Practice we say

   - You must be honest and trustworthy when writing reports and when completing or signing forms, reports and other documents.

   - You must always be honest about your experience, qualifications and position, particularly when applying for posts.

   - You must do your best to make sure that any documents you write or sign are not false or misleading. This means that you must take reasonable steps to verify the information in the documents, and that you must not deliberately leave out relevant information.

   - If you have agreed to prepare a report, complete or sign a document or provide evidence, you must do so without unreasonable delay.

   - If you are asked to give evidence or act as a witness in litigation or formal inquiries, you must be honest in all your spoken and written statements. You must make clear the limits of your knowledge or competence.

3. This guidance explains how the principles set out in Good Medical Practice apply to the work of the medical expert witness. It also lists other sources of information and advice. If you have concerns arising from an appointment as a medical expert witness, you should consider seeking advice from the GMC, your medical defence body or professional association.

4. Serious or persistent failure to follow this guidance will put your registration at risk.

The role of the expert witness

5.   The role of an expert witness is to assist the court on specialist or technical matters within their expertise[1]. The expert's duty to the court overrides any obligation to the person who is instructing or paying them[2]. This means that you have a duty to act independently and not be influenced by the party who retains you.

Giving expert advice and evidence

6.   You must ensure that you understand exactly what questions you are being asked to answer. If your instructions are unclear, inadequate or conflicting, you should seek clarification from those instructing you. If you cannot obtain sufficiently clear instructions, you should not provide expert advice or opinion.

7.   When giving evidence or writing reports, you must restrict your statements to areas in which you have relevant knowledge or direct experience. You should be aware of the standards and nature of practice at the time of the incident under proceedings.

8.   You must only deal with matters, and express opinions, that fall within the limits of your professional competence[3]. If a particular question or issue falls outside your area of expertise, you should make this clear. In the event that you are ordered by the court to answer a question, regardless of your expertise, you should answer to the best of your ability but make clear that you consider the matter to be outside your competence.

9.   You must give a balanced opinion, and be able to state the facts or assumptions on which it is based. If there is a range of opinion on the question upon which you have been asked to comment, you should summarise the range of opinion and explain how you arrived at your own view. If you do not have enough information on which to reach a conclusion on a particular point, or your opinion is otherwise qualified, you must make this clear[4].

10. You must make sure that any report that you write, or evidence that you give, is accurate and is not misleading. This means that you must take reasonable steps to verify any information you provide, and you must not deliberately leave out relevant information.

---

1   Doctors are not necessarily expert witnesses. They may also be witnesses of fact (testifying about events that they themselves have observed) or professional witnesses (giving evidence regarding a particular patient that they have treated).

2   Civil Procedure Rules Part 35.3, Criminal Justice Procedure Rules Part 33.2, Rule 156 of the draft Family Procedure Rules

3   The same principle applies where doctors act in other roles, for example as an advisor in a case.

4   See judgment of Cresswell J in The "Ikarian Reefer" [1993] FSR 563

11. Where you are asked to give advice or opinion about an individual without the opportunity to consult with or examine them, you should explain any limitations that this may place on your advice or opinion, and be able to justify the decision to proceed on such a basis.

12. Your advice and evidence will be relied upon for decision-making purposes by people who do not come from a medical background. Wherever it is possible to do so without being misleading, you should use language and terminology that will be readily understood by those for whom you are providing expert advice or opinion. You should explain any abbreviations and medical or other technical terminology that you use.

13. If, at any stage, you change your view on any material matter, you have a duty to ensure that those instructing you, the opposing party and the judge are made aware of this without delay. Usually you need only inform your instructing solicitor who will communicate with the other parties. If the solicitor fails to disclose your change of view, you should inform the court. If you are unsure what to do, you should seek legal advice.

14. You must be honest, trustworthy, objective and impartial. You must not allow your views about any individual's age, colour, culture, disability, ethnic or national origin, gender, lifestyle, marital or parental status, race, religion or beliefs, sex, sexual orientation or social or economic status to prejudice the evidence or advice that you give.

Keeping up to date

15. You must keep up to date in your specialist area of practice. You must also ensure that you understand, and adhere to, the laws and codes of practice that affect your work as an expert witness. In particular, you should make sure that you understand

  * how to construct a court-compliant report

  * how to give oral evidence

  * the specific framework of law and procedure within which you are working

Information security and disclosure

16. You must take all reasonable steps to access all relevant evidence materials and maintain their integrity and security whilst in your possession.

17. If you have reason to believe that appropriate consent for disclosure of information has not been obtained (from the patient or client, or from any third party to whom their medical records refer) you should return the information to the person instructing you and seek clarification.

18. You should not disclose confidential information other than to the parties to proceedings, unless

    • the subject consents (and there are no other restrictions or prohibitions on disclosure)

    • you are obliged to do so by law

    • you are ordered to do so by a court or tribunal

    • your overriding duty to the court and the administration of justice demands that you disclose information

Conflicts of interest

19. If there is any matter that gives rise to a potential conflict of interest, such as any prior involvement with one of the parties, or a personal interest, you must follow the guidance on disclosure in paragraph 13. You may continue to act as an expert witness only if the court decides that the conflict is not material to the case.

July 2008

Appendix 7 - Schedule of Loss (Example)

C.T. -V- EVER-SO-QUICK DELIVERIES LTD

SCHEDULE OF LOSS

Date of birth of Claimant   15th February 1965
Date of accident   1st April 2008
Calculation date   1st April 2010

SUMMARY

PAST LOSSES

1	LOSS OF EARNINGS	8,180.97
2	CARE AND ASSISTANCE	10,276.71
3	COST OF MEDICAL TREATMENT	15,525.00
4	MEDICAL EQUIPMENT	205.99
5	LOSS OF INCOME AS FOOTBALL REFEREE	936.00
6	INTEREST	1,148.58

TOTAL OF PAST LOSSES AND INTEREST   36,273.25

FUTURE LOSSES

7	LOSS OF EARNINGS/EARNINGS CAPACITY	65,000.00
8	LOSS OF PROFIT FROM HOME IMPROVEMENTS	To be assessed
9	CARE AND ASSISTANCE	41,785.22
10	FUTURE EQUIPMENT AND TREATMENT COSTS	3,044.70
11	LOSS OF INCOME AS FOOTBALL REFEREE 2199.60	

Plus damages for pain, suffering and loss of amenity   To be assessed

See medical reports of Mr Sawbones, Consultant Orthopaedic
and Spinal Surgeon, dated 1st April 2009 and 28th February 2010

PAST LOSSES

1   **LOSS OF EARNINGS**

The Claimant is employed as a maintenance
electrician by Pan-World Call Centre on a

short term contract. Prior to the accident
his average weekly net wage was -   261.70

The Claimant was off work for an initial
period of 3 months and then following the
discectomy on 30th June 2009 for 6 months.

The Claimant has arranged his work so
that he can avoid all but the lightest of
work and has managed to remain at
work since the operation.

1)   **Period 1st April to 30th June 2008**
       Paid   275.00
       At pre accident rate would have earned   3,402.10
       Loss for period   3,127.10

2)   **Period 30th June 2009 to 29th**
       December 2009
       Paid   1,750.33
       At pre-accident rate   6,804.20
       Loss for period   5,053.87

       TOTAL LOSS OF EARNINGS   8,180.97

2   CARE AND ASSISTANCE

       All care and assistance is claimed at the
       aggregate rates for National Joint
       Council pay rates Spinal Point 8
       discounted by 25% to reflect the
       gratuitous nature of the care and
       assistance provided, an hourly rate of -   6.73 per hour

1)   The Claimant spent 4 days in hospital.
       His wife visited each day to provide
       support and comfort, and to provide
       some care needs when hospital staff
       were too busy to care for the Claimant.

       His wife spent an average of 5 hours
       per day providing this care for the
       Claimant

       5 hours x 4 days =   134.60

2)   For 3 weeks after discharge from

hospital the Claimant was in great pain and dependant on his wife to provide him with all his needs, including drinks and food and assisting him with washing and toilet needs, and providing him with support and comfort.

His wife spent an average of 6 hours per day providing this care for the Claimant

6 hours x 3 weeks x 7 days =   847.98

3)   The Claimant gradually became more independent until in July he was able to return to work on light duties and no longer had care needs. His wife's care and assistance during that period reduced. Care is claimed on the basis of an average of 3 hours per day throughout the period of 9 weeks

3 hours x 9 weeks x 7 days =   1,271.97

4)   The Claimant has been unable to carry out any domestic or household tasks since the accident. Prior to the accident he used to carry out all vacuum cleaning and heavy cleaning tasks, maintain the garden and do the weekly supermarket shop. These tasks are now performed by his wife

These tasks are assessed at 5 hours per week

5 hours x 104 =   3,499.60

5)   Following the operation the Claimant required a great deal of assistance. This was provided for by his wife and is assessed as being 12 hours per day for 4 weeks, 6 hours per day for 4 weeks and 2 hours per day for 12 weeks

(12 hours x 4 weeks x 7 days) +
(6 hours x 4 weeks x 7 days) +
(2 hours x 12 weeks x 7 days) =   4,522.56

	TOTAL CARE AND ASSISTANCE		10,276.71

3   COST OF MEDICAL TREATMENT

1)	Cost of discectomy operation	15,000.00	
2)	Cost of post-operative physiotherapy		
	15 sessions at £35	525.00	
	TOTAL COST OF MEDICAL TREATMENT		15,525.00

4   MEDICAL EQUIPMENT

1)	Support belts	75.00	
2)	Heat pads	21.00	
3)	TENS machine	19.99	
4)	Batteries for TENS machine @£5 per month - to date 18 months	90.00	
	TOTAL COST OF EQUIPMENT		205.99

5   LOSS OF INCOME AS FOOTBALL REFEREE

The Claimant was a Football Association referee class 5, and regularly refereed matches at weekends, for which he received a payment of £30 per match. A claim is made on the basis of 1 match every other week from September to May (39 weeks) and allowing for tax at 20%

Period 1st April 2008 to 1st April 2010

78/2 matches = 39 x £30 x 0.8 =	936.00	
TOTAL NET LOSS OF INCOME AS REFEREE		936.00

6   INTEREST

Interest is claimed at one half the Special Account rate from 1st April 2008 to the date at which this schedule is calculated namely 1st April 2010

namely at 3.27%
on losses to date, namely 35,124.67

TOTAL INTEREST 1,148.58

TOTAL OF PAST LOSSES AND INTEREST 36,273.25

FUTURE LOSSES

Age of Claimant at calculation date 45
Life time multiplier (Ogden Table 1) 23.88
Multiplier for loss of earnings to age 6
(Ogden Table 9) 15.19

7 **LOSS OF EARNINGS/EARNINGS CAPACITY**

The Claimant is not suffering any loss
of earnings at present. However he is at
risk of having to take periods of time
off because of the continuing back
symptoms. He has sustained an
impairment of his earning capacity and
is at risk of suffering loss of earnings.
Ogden 6 calculation:
Annual net earnings - 13,608.40

1) Multiplier not disabled, in employment,
no qualifications
Adjustment Table A 0.86
Apply to multiplier to age 65 15.19
Adjusted multiplier 13.06
Apply to net earnings 177,725.70

2) Multiplier disabled, in employment, no
qualifications
Adjustment Table B 0.55
Apply to multiplier to age 65 15.19
Adjusted multiplier 8.35
Apply to net earnings 113,630.14

Probable future loss of earnings
(Ogden 6) 64,095.56

Therefore a reasonable sum to
compensate the Claimant for his risk of
unemployment in the future as a result
of the effect of his injury on him would

be of the order of -   65,000.00

8   LOSS OF PROFIT FROM HOME IMPROVEMENTS

The Claimant had bought, done up and
sold houses in which he lived for over
10 years. He bought his current home in
September 2006 and had carried out
some improvements. However because
of the accident and the continuing
symptoms the Claimant is unable to
carry out the works of re-wiring,
re-plumbing, improvements and
decorating which he had planned and
which the house required. He will have
to employ labour to carry out this work
for him. The Claimant claims the cost
of such labour. Full particulars will be
provided in due course.

The Claimant has lost the opportunity
to make profits on future properties
which he would have purchased and
done up for sale. The Claimant is
obtaining accountancy evidence to
demonstrate the likely profit he would
have made on each such property.   To be assessed

9   **CARE AND ASSISTANCE**

Continuing at 5 hours per week - see
2(3) above - value per year -   1,749.80
Multiplier (life time)   23.88

TOTAL VALUE   41,785.22

10   **FUTURE EQUIPMENT AND TREATMENT COSTS**

1)   Batteries for TENS machine @ £5 per
month - per year   60.00
Multiplier (life time)   23.88

Total value   1,432.80

2)   Physiotherapy - allow 3 sessions per
year during periods of exacerbation @

£45 each - per year	135.00
Multiplier (say 50% of life time)	11.94
Total value	1,611.90

TOTAL VALUE	3,044.70

11   LOSS OF INCOME AS FOOTBALL REFEREE

The Claimant would have continued to act as referee until aged 50 on 15th February 2015.	
Annual net loss = 39/2 x £30 x 0.8 =	468.00
Period of loss 5 years - multiplier (Ogden Table 28)	4.70

TOTAL VALUE	2,199.60

Dated 1st April 2010

Statement of Truth

[I believe] [The claimant believes] that the facts stated in this schedule are true.

I am duly authorised by the Claimant to sign this statement

Full name

Signed

Sue Quickly & Co
Claims House
Nowin Nofee Boulevard
Goldchester
Solicitors for the Claimant

Index

Acceleration		*See Causation*
Breach of Duty		
	Definition	2.2.1
	Statutory duty	2.2.1
	Terms of contract	2.2.1
Burden of Proof		
	Claimant need to prove case	5.1
Case Management		
	Court control of expert evidence	3.7.1
	Court management of cases	3.1.1, 3.2.2
	Limitations on recoverable fees of experts	3.7.1
	Tracks	3.5.1
Causation		
	Acceleration / Exacerbation	6.4
	…Differences in valuation	6.4.1
	Breaking the chain of causation (novus actus interveniens)	7.8
	Consequences of injuries	6.6
	…Additional housing, mobility or transportation needs	6.6.9
	…Care and assistance	6.6.5
	…Current employment	6.6.6
	…Future employment and 'Ogden 6'	6.6.7
	…Life expectancy	6.6.8
	…Medical or therapeutic treatment	6.6.4
	…Pain and suffering, and loss of amenity	6.6.3
	…Restrictions on activities of daily living	6.6.10
	…Restrictions on domestic, recreational, social and sporting activities	6.6.11
	…Test for consequential loss	6.6.1
	Criticism of medical treatment in a personal injury claim	7.9
	Definition of causation	2.2.3, 6.1
	'Egg-Shell Skull' principle	6.2.2
	Exaggeration and malingering	7.4, 7.4.1, 7.4.2
	Factual basis (causation issues)	6.1
	…Factual evidence (sources of)	4.2.4
	…Observations of claimant outside the medical examination	7.4.4

...Observations of claimant within the medical examination	7.4.5
...Opinion on likely factual situation	See Clinical Negligence - Resolving Conflicting Opinion on Factual Issues
...Signs and Symptoms	6.1
Factual disputes	See Civil Procedure Rules See Medical Expert Reports – Factual Basis of the Evidence
Failure to treat	See Clinical Negligence
Giving opinion on causation	6.2, 6.2.1
...Causation graphs	6.2.1
...Competing causes of injury	6.1.1
...Criticism of medical treatment in personal injury claims	7.9
...Difficulties in diagnosis ('difficult opinions')	7.1
...Injuries, Symptoms, Effects, Consequences	6.1
Material contribution	6.1.2
...in Clinical Negligence claims	8.7
...in complex factual situations	6.3.1
...in Industrial Disease claims	6.3
Material contribution and apportionment of damages	6.3.2
...Culpable and non-culpable exposure	6.3.3
...Divisible and non-divisible conditions	6.3.2
Multiple Accident Claims	7.7
...Writing opinion on	See Medical Expert Reports - Opinion
Use of percentages	6.2.3
...Use of percentages (legal questions to experts)	6.2.4

Civil Litigation / Civil Claims

Adversarial litigation process	2.3
Clinical negligence marketplace	9.1
Commercial realities	1.5
Defending a claim	2.2
Heads of claim	2.6, 6.6.2
Motivation of claimants to litigate	2.1
Proceedings (commencement of)	3.5
...Claim Form	3.5
...Particulars of Claim	3.5
...Schedule of Loss	3.5
...Schedule (Counter)	3.5

...*Statement of Case* 3.5

Proving a claim 2.2

Purpose of a claim for damages 2.1

Right to recover damages 2.2

Valuation of a Claim 2.7

...*Supporting the claim with evidence* 2.7

Civil Procedure
Rules (CPR)

Introduction to CPR 3.1

Court orders 4.6.1

CPR (structure of rules) 3.2

Directions from the court (seeking) 4.6.2

Duty to co-operate with court process 4.1.6

Expert's Declaration 4.2.14

Factual basis of the evidence *See Medical Expert Reports*

Factual disputes (Protocol) 4.2.7 *See also Medical Expert Reports - Factual Basis of the Evidence*

Form of expert evidence 4.1.9

Instructions 4.2.1

Joint discussion (Meeting of experts) 4.7

...*Agenda for the meeting* 4.7.2

...*Objectives of meeting* 4.7.1

...*People present at meeting* 4.7.3

...*Providing explanations for changes in opinion* 4.7.1

...*Status of the discussion* 4.7.5

Medical literature (reliance on) 4.2.3

Opinion evidence 4.2.9

...*Qualified opinion* 4.2.11

...*Range of opinion* 4.2.12

'Overriding Objective' 3.2.1

Part 35 4.1.3

Part 36 offers 2.8.1

Practice Directions 3.2

Pre-Action Protocols (PAPs) 3.3

...*for Disease and Illness claims* 3.3.3

...*for Personal Injury Claims* 3.3.2

...*for Resolution of Clinical Disputes* 3.3.1

...*Low Value Personal Injury Claims in Road Traffic Accidents* 3.4

Proportionality 3.2.1

Restrictions on expert evidence 4.1.8

Single Joint Expert *See Expert Witness*

Statement of Truth 4.2.15

Summary of Conclusions *See Medical Expert*

		Reports
	Written questions to experts	4.4
Claimant		
	Expert's relationship with	1.2
	Giving medical history	4.2.8
	Incident/Accident details	4.2.5
Clinical Negligence		
	Bolam test	8.1.1
	...*Applying the Bolam test*	8.1.1
	...*Decision of the court*	8.1.1
	Bolitho test	8.6
	Consent and failure to warn	8.3, 8.3.1
	Difficulties in reporting in clinical negligence cases	9.3
	...*Bias*	9.3.1
	...*Complex medical issues*	9.3.5
	...*Establishing the factual basis*	9.3.2
	...*Factual disputes*	9.3.3
	...*Series of events*	9.3.4
	Failure to treat	8.4
	Level of skill required	8.2
	...*Novices*	8.2.1
	...*Specialists*	8.2.2
	Material Contribution in clinical negligence	*See Causation*
	Reporting in clinical negligence cases	9.2
	...*Chronologies*	*See Medical Expert Reports – Report Templates*
	...*Report structures (linear/modular)*	*See Medical Expert Reports*
	...*Report summaries*	*See Medical Expert Reports - Summary of Conclusions*
	...*Report template*	Appendix 1d
	Resolving conflicting opinion on factual issues	8.5
	Resolving conflicting opinion standard of care	8.6
Consequences of Injuries		*See Causation*
Costs of Litigation		
	100% Recovery Principle	2.5
	After the Event insurance 'ATE insurance'	2.8.1
	Before the Event insurance 'BTE insurance'	2.8.1
	Conditional Fee Agreements 'CFAs'	2.8.1

Damages

Damages (Categories of)	2.6
...Non-Pecuniary Loss (General Damages / Generals)	2.6.1
...Pecuniary Loss (Special Damages / Specials)	2.6.2
...Court's assessment as 'more than minimal'	2.2.2
Death	2.6.3
Difficult cases	
...in diagnosis of injury	7.1
...in linking claimed injury to cause	7.2
Liability for costs	2.8
Provisional damages	2.6.4
Types of claim for damages (Heads of Claim)	2.6
Valuation of claim	2.7
...Non-Pecuniary Loss	2.7.1
...Pecuniary Loss/Future Pecuniary Loss	2.7.2, 2.7.3

'Egg-Shell Skull' Principle *See Causation*

Evidential Skills

Imperative for developing	1.5.1

Exacerbation *See Causation - Acceleration / Exacerbation*

Exaggeration *See Causation - Exaggeration and Malingering*

Expert Witness

Expert's role	1.2
...Duties	4.1, 4.1.5, 4.1.6
...GMC Guidance	4.1.2
...Ikarian Reefer Principles	4.1.3
...Narrowing issues in dispute	4.1.4
Investigating claims	4.1.7
Independence	4.1.5
...Side letters	4.2.15
Jointly selected experts	3.3.2
Meeting of experts	*See Civil Procedure Rules - Joint Discussions*
Qualifications	4.2.2
Single joint expert	3.7.1, 4.5
...Comparison with jointly selected experts	4.5.1
Written questions	4.4

Factual Disputes   *See Civil Procedure Rules*

Fatal Accidents Act Claims
     Death of claimant caused by the accident   2.6.3

'Foot-Wearing'
     Explanation of origin   Authors' Note

Future Risk   *See Prognosis and Future Risk - Assessing the Future*

Law Reform Act Claims
     Death of claimant   2.6.3

Legal Professionals (roles)
     Barristers   3.8.2
     Judges   3.8.3
     ...Approach to conflicting expert evidence   3.9
     Para-legals / Claims Handlers   3.8.1
     Solicitors   3.8.1

Life Expectancy
     Consequences of reduced life expectancy   *See Causation – Consequences of Injuries*
     Court approach to deciding life expectancy   *See Prognosis and Future Risk*

Malingering   *See Causation - Exaggeration and Malingering*

Material Contribution   *See Causation*

Medical Expert Reports
     Amendments to   4.3
     ...Changes of opinion   4.3
     Comparison with medical reports   1.3.3
     Definition   1.3
     Dissatisfaction with   1.4
     ...Common problems for lawyers using   1.4.2
     ...Consequences arising from substandard reporting   1.4.1

Factual basis of the evidence	4.2.4
...Differentiation of factual sources	10.2.3
...Disputes between claimant's account and medical records	4.2.8
...Examination findings	4.2.6
...Facts and opinion	4.2.10
...Factual disputes	4.2.7, 7.3, 9.3.3
...Incident/Accident details	4.2.5
...Signs and symptoms	See Causation - Factual Basis
Functions of expert reports	1.3.1
Opinion (Expressing)	10.4
...Long-form / Short-form	10.4.1, 10.4.2
...Standard phrases (Standard of proof and legal tests)	10.3
...Writing opinion in multi-incident/accident cases	7.7.2
'Owning' an opinion	10.4
Presentation of the report	10.1
Report Structures	10.2
...Linear	10.2.1
...Modular	10.2.2
Report Templates	10.2.3, Appendix 1a-d
...Approach to presenting factual information	10.2.3
...Chronologies	10.2.4
...Concise account of events	10.2.4
Summary of Conclusions	4.2.13
Writing Skills (Importance of)	1.3.2
Writing Skills (Techniques)	10.3
...Accuracy and precision in language (technical/descriptive)	10.3.3
...Modal auxiliary verbs	10.3.4
...Technical Explanations	10.3.2
...Writing for the court	10.3.1
'Medico-legal Mind'	
Explanation of	1.1
Negligence (Legal Principle)	
Clinical negligence (Bolam test)	See Clinical Negligence
Contributory negligence	2.2.4
...and seat belts	7.6
Definition of negligence	2.2.1
Novus Actus Interveniens	See Causation - Breaking the Chain of Causation

'Ogden 6'

See Causation -
Consequences of Injuries

Prognosis and
Future Risk

Assessing the future   6.5
...*Clinician's approach to the future*   6.5.3
...*Use of dates*   6.5.2
...*Use of percentages*   6.5.1, 6.5.4
Life Expectancy   5.3, 6.5.5, 6.6.8

Proof

Applying the civil standard of proof   5.3
...*Life expectancy*   *See Prognosis and Future*
                                            Risk

Civil standard of proof   2.4, 5.1
Decision-making (in professional life)   5.1.1
Decision-making (in civil litigation)   5.2
Establishing proof   5.4

Seat Belts

See Negligence -
Contributory Negligence

Surveillance
Evidence

Reviewing foootage   7.5

Tracks

See Case Management

Waddell's Signs

Reporting on   7.4.5

Lightning Source UK Ltd.
Milton Keynes UK
177751UK00001B/40/P